AN INTRODUCTION TO

QUALITATIVE ANALYSIS

T. R. HOGNESS
Professor of Chemistry, University of Chicago

WARREN C. JOHNSON
Professor of Chemistry, Dean, Division of the Physical Sciences, University of Chicago

HENRY HOLT AND COMPANY
NEW YORK

PREFACE

In writing the original edition of *Qualitative Analysis and Chemical Equilibrium*, we had three principal objectives in mind: (1) to present a good course in qualitative analysis, a course which immediately followed one in general chemistry; (2) to include a review, in perhaps a different presentation, of some of the more salient facts and principles that were taught in the course in general or introductory chemistry; and (3) to provide a transitional introduction, in very simple terms, to the subject of physical chemistry or, rather, to the fundamental concepts upon which the fuller science of chemistry is based.

With each new edition we modified slightly the analytical procedures. These modifications came in large part from suggestions by interested teachers who were using our text for their courses. We also enlarged on the review aspects and introduced new sections or chapters on the more fundamental aspects of the science.

With some teachers this expanding textbook presented a problem. They could not find the time in the curriculum to present adequately all the text material. As the result of a survey, our publishers have found that there is a definite demand for a shorter textbook and have asked us to prepare one. This textbook, *An Introduction to Qualitative Analysis*, is the result. It is a condensation of our *Qualitative Analysis and Chemical Equilibrium*. It is not meant to replace the older text. Both will be available to suit the needs of different curricula.

In making this condensation, it became necessary to omit some material which had been introduced to meet our second and third objectives and which now appears in some of the more modern textbooks in general chemistry. However, all the principles that pertain to qualitative analysis — particularly chemical equilibrium — have been retained. The analytical schemes have been left intact, with the exception that the analyses of a very few of the less common negative ions have been omitted.

This textbook, together with an appropriate one in General Chemistry, should meet all the requirements for a full first-year course in college chemistry.

T. R. H.
W. C. J.

The University of Chicago
Feb. 20, 1957

CONTENTS

PART I

PART II

PART
I

CHAPTER *1*

Water
and Electrolytes

In this Introduction to Qualitative Analysis and Chemical Equilibrium we shall be concerned very little with the physical methods of analysis — as, for example, the use of the spectroscope. Rather, we shall emphasize the chemical approach to the subject, an approach which has to do with chemical reactions in water solution. Therefore, it is appropriate that we have a reasonably good knowledge of the environment in which the chemically reacting substances exist, namely, water.

Water, while it is the most commonly known of all chemical substances, is somewhat unique. It is different from other common liquids in that it is a highly polar substance. It is because of this unique property that water plays such an important role in all the chemical processes of life. To better understand the background of our subject let us consider those properties of pure water which make it different. Following this first discussion on pure water we shall consider the properties of solutions.

Polarity of Molecules. Suppose that two large sheets of metal are connected electrically with a battery B, a switch and a current-measuring instrument as shown in Figure 1.1. When the switch S is closed, the plate connected to the negative pole of the battery becomes negatively charged and the plate connected to the positive pole of the battery positively charged. Just at the moment the switch is closed the small current charging the plates will flow through and be measured by the current-measuring instrument. The positive charges

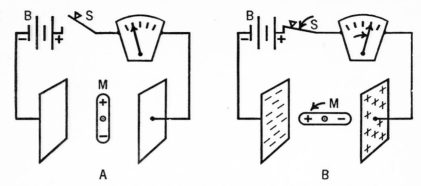

FIG. 1.1   Action of electric field on polar molecule.

on the one plate attract the negative charges of the other and vice versa, and this attraction builds up the charge-holding ability or capacity of the two plates.   If the size of the plates is increased, it is obvious that the two plates will hold a greater electric charge, that is, the capacity will be increased.

The nearer two oppositely charged objects are to each other the greater is the attractive force between them.   If the two plates are moved closer together the attractive force which holds the charge on the surface of each plate becomes greater and the two plates therefore have a greater capacity.   One might argue that as the charge increases on each of the plates the attractive force will also increase, resulting in an accumulatively greater capacity.   There is an opposing force, however, which stops this accumulative effect.   Like charges *on the same plate* repel each other and this repulsive force, which is greater as the charge on each plate is increased, prevents any indefinite accumulation of charge on any one plate.   Such an arrangement of plates is known as a condenser.

Suppose that a bar *M* which can pivot about its center and which has one end positively charged and one end negatively charged is placed between the two plates.   When the plates are now charged the bar will be found to tilt in such a position that the positive end will move toward the negative plate (Figure 1.1B).   Such a bar will increase the electrical capacity of the two plates, for this action of the bar will have the effect of putting the two plates closer together. The positive end of the bar will produce an attractive effect on the negative plate; and the negative end, an attractive effect on the positive plate.

Many molecules are like the bar shown in Figure 1.1. They have positive and negative ends and when placed between two such charged plates tend to line up as does the bar. This alignment increases the electrical capacity of the plates as measured by the current-measuring instrument.

The ratio of the electrical capacity of the condenser when some substance is placed between its plates to the electrical capacity when there is a vacuum between these same plates is known as the ***dielectric constant*** of the substance.

$$\frac{\text{capacity with substance}}{\text{capacity in vacuum}} = \text{dielectric constant}$$

The greater the separation of the positive and negative charges in a molecule, the greater will be the turning effect on the molecule in the condenser, and therefore the greater will be the capacity of the condenser and the greater the dielectric constant of the substance. In Figure 1.2, the molecule B has a greater turning effect than molecule A. Since a greater separation of charge produces a greater torque or electrical leverage, molecule B can be more easily turned than molecule A. Therefore B has a greater dielectric constant than A. The dielectric constant is then a measure of the separation of the charges in a molecule.

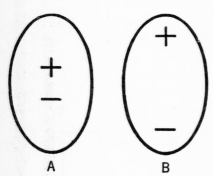

FIG. 1.2 Schematic representation of two polar molecules. B more polar than A.

Not all the molecules placed between the plates of a condenser are turned at right angles to the plates as shown in the case of the charged bar (Figure 1.1). The thermal agitation of the molecules prevents perfect alignment. We can deduce that the lower the temperature the less will be the thermal agitation and the greater will be the alignment. The dielectric constant of a polar molecule should therefore decrease with increasing temperature. This conclusion is completely verified by experiment.

Polar and Non-Polar Substances. Those substances which have a large dielectric constant, that is, a large separation in the charges, are known as polar substances and those which have little or no separation in charges as non-polar substances. Water is a polar substance and methane, CH_4, and hexane, C_6H_{14}, a constituent of gasoline, are non-polar substances. We shall have more to say regarding such substances at a later time.

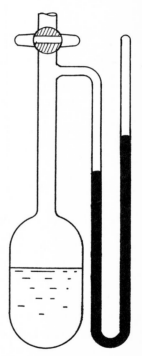

Vapor Pressure and the Boiling Point. Suppose that a pure liquid is confined in a closed vessel and all extraneous gases such as air are removed from the space above the liquid. (See Figure 1.3). Then it is found that at a given, definite temperature there will be a definite gas pressure due to the evaporated molecules of the liquid. An equilibrium is established between the liquid and the gas, such that the rate of gas molecules entering the liquid is the same as that of molecules of liquid leaving it to enter the gas phase. This pressure can be measured by some suitable device such as a manometer shown in Figure 1.3, and it is known as the vapor pressure of the liquid for that temperature. Thus, the vapor pressure of water at 25° C is 25.76 mm. of mercury.

FIG. 1.3 Schematic diagram of apparatus for determining vapor pressure.

When a liquid is heated in an open vessel such as a beaker, vapor is constantly passing off into the air above it. However, when the temperature of the liquid gets sufficiently high so that its vapor pressure equals the pressure of the air above it, the liquid boils. This boiling temperature evidently will depend upon the barometric pressure. The *normal boiling point* of the liquid is defined as the temperature at which the liquid boils when the barometric pressure is 760 mm. of mercury. In other words, the *normal boiling point* is the temperature at which the vapor pressure of the liquid is 760 mm. of mercury.

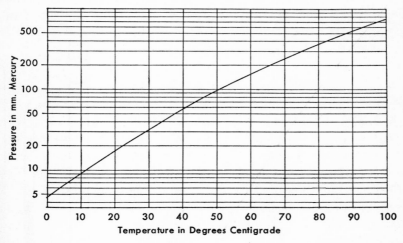

FIG. 1.4 The vapor pressure of water as a function of the temperature.

By plotting the vapor pressure of a liquid against the temperature one obtains a curve such as is illustrated in Figure 1.4.

We might expect that the boiling points of non-polar liquids, for which the attractive forces between the molecules are very similar, would depend upon the molecular weight of the compound in such a way that the greater the molecular weight, the higher the boiling point. The heavier molecules move more slowly at any given temperature; therefore, a higher temperature is required for them to escape from the liquid. If we compare the non-polar hydrocarbons as shown in Table 1, we find this to be the case.

If the forces holding water molecules together were the same as those for the hydrocarbons shown in Table 1, then,

TABLE 1

RELATIONSHIP BETWEEN MOLECULAR WEIGHT
AND BOILING POINT

Compound	Molecular Weight	Boiling Point, ° C
Methane, CH_4	16	−161.8
Ethane, C_2H_6	30	−88.6
Propane, C_3H_8	44	−42.1
Butane, C_4H_{10}	58	−0.5
Pentane, C_5H_{12}	72	36.1
Hexane, C_6H_{14}	86	68.7

since its molecular weight approximates that of methane, we might expect its boiling point to be essentially the same. However, the boiling point of water is 100° C; 261.5° higher than that of methane. Ammonia (NH_3) has a molecular weight of 17. It is also a polar liquid but not as polar as water. Its boiling point is −33.4° C. These facts show the great effects which can be produced by unequal distribution of electric charges within the molecule. Similar effects due to polarity will be encountered when we study the problem of solubility.

The Problem of Solubility. Some substances are soluble in each other in all proportions, while some are only so slightly soluble that we say they are insoluble. This difference in solubility of various substances in the same or different solvents has been a subject of the greatest concern for the chemist. It is a problem which is so complex that its quantitative solution offers great difficulties, yet the fundamental principles involved are not at all out of our reach.

Let us consider two liquids which are practically insoluble in each other. There are a great many systems of pairs of liquids which conform to this condition of low mutual solubility, but as a specific example we shall choose water and carbon tetrachloride. The water molecules are polar and those of carbon tetrachloride are non-polar. By virtue of their polarity, the water molecules have a greater tendency to adhere to each other (the positive end of one adhering to the negative end of another) than to molecules of carbon tetrachloride. As a result of the attractive forces of the water molecules for each other, any molecules of carbon tetrachloride which happen to be mixed with the water molecules are squeezed out. Due to thermal agitation, a few water molecules will probably break through the water surface in contact with carbon tetrachloride and wander off into this medium. For this reason, we cannot say that water and carbon tetrachloride are absolutely immiscible (absolutely insoluble in each other). The water molecules prefer each other to the molecules of carbon tetrachloride as neighbors. Likewise the molecules of carbon tetrachloride prefer each other. The polar dissimilarity of these two types of molecules, in a general way, accounts for the insolubility of water and carbon tetrachloride in each other.

Let us next consider a solution of two substances the molecules of both of which are polar. Water and ordinary alcohol are two such substances. The water molecules are somewhat more polar than the alcohol molecules. In this case the water molecules do not have any very great tendency to prefer each other as neighbors and the same is true of the alcohol molecules. The water molecules adhere to the alcohol molecules almost as strongly as they do to each other. Now there is no tendency for the water molecules to squeeze the alcohol molecules out of solution, nor do the alcohol molecules have this tendency toward water molecules. The result is that water and alcohol are soluble in each other in all proportions.

Non-polar substances are also soluble in each other, for there is no great tendency for the like molecules to prefer each other as neighbors; hence no "squeezing-out" effect.

No new considerations need be introduced in the problem of the solubility of solids in liquids. The attractive forces of the particles for each other in the crystal, in general, are very great; nevertheless there will be competition between the crystal and the solvent for the particles of the solid. The stronger the crystal forces operating between the atoms or particles of the solid and the greater the "squeezing-out" tendency of the solvent, the less soluble will be the solid in question.

It is possible to arrange substances in a series or table in order of the attractive forces operating between the molecules. An example of such a series is given in the following table. The non-polar substances appear at the top of the table and the polar substances at the bottom. Two substances lying close together in the series are very soluble in each other; those far apart are relatively insoluble in each other.

TABLE 2

RELATIVE ATTRACTIVE FORCES BETWEEN MOLECULES

Hexane
Carbon tetrachloride
Benzene
Toluene
Chloroform
Naphthalene
Anthracene
Nitrobenzene
Pyridine
Carbon bisulfide
Acetone
Acetic acid
Ethyl alcohol
Methyl alcohol
Water

POLAR — NON-POLAR

Some organic molecules are so complicated in structure that parts of the molecule may be regarded as polar and other parts as non-polar. With such substances the problem of solubility is necessarily a much more complex one.

The compound, $CH_3CH_2CH_2CH_2CH_2CH_2CH_2CH_2OH$, octyl alcohol, for example, consists of a long chain of carbon atoms, to one end of which is attached an OH radical. This OH end of the molecule is polar and the other end is non-polar. When placed in contact with water, only one end of the molecule is squeezed out of solution and the other end remains in contact with the water. The result is that the octyl alcohol molecule is squeezed to the surface of the water, with one end out of solution. Such phenomena are common and are of great interest in the study of surface chemistry.

There is one type of solution, electrolytic solution, which we have not yet considered and to which we shall later largely confine our attention. Before going on with the problems of solubility pertaining to such solutions, we must first deal with some of their properties.

Conductance of Electricity by Solutions. We shall compare the conductance of electricity by solutions of different substances. Such a comparison will allow us to divide practically all substances into two general classes, **electrolytes** and **non-electrolytes**. The conductance of any substance is the inverse of the resistance offered by the substance to the passage of the electric current, that is, $C = 1/R$, where C and R represent the conductance and resistance, respectively. Conductance, like resistance, is determined by measuring the electric current passing through the substance when a definite voltage is applied between the two terminals of the containing cell. For a given voltage the amount of current is proportional to the conductance, that is, a solution having twice the conductance of another will allow twice as much current to pass through it for the same applied voltage.

In order to compare the conductances of solutions it is necessary that we consider the same number of equivalents of solute in each case. What we really wish to know is the *conductance per equivalent weight of solute.*

Consider a conductance cell of the type illustrated in Figure 1.5. The cell itself is constructed of some non-conductor such as glass. The two electrodes A and B consist of metal strips which fit closely between the sides of the cell. The top is open. G is a current-measuring instrument such as an ammeter or a galvanometer and should be very sensitive if we wish to measure very small currents. For very rough measurements a light bulb may be used instead of the ammeter. If a conducting solution is placed in this box and a voltage applied to the electrodes, any current which passes from A to B must pass through the solution. If a sugar solution is placed in this cell together with any additional amount of water, the mixture shows no appreciable conductance. The same is true of solutions of alcohol, ether, glycerine and many similar substances. On the other hand, if sodium chloride in water is placed in this cell, the solution is a very good conductor of electricity. Solutions of many solutes such as HCl, H_2SO_4, NaOH, and K_2SO_4 show a high conductance, while only a relatively small number of compounds give solutions which are slightly conducting.

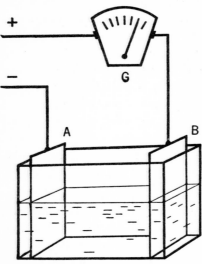

FIG. 1.5 Conductance cell and measuring instrument.

The great majority of solutions fall into one of two distinct classes, very good conductors and non-conductors. Substances the solutions of which are good conductors of electricity are called ***electrolytes,*** and substances that are non-conductors in solution, ***non-electrolytes.*** The difference in conductance shown by electrolytes and non-electrolytes is not merely a difference of degree. It is a *difference of kind.* If we were to classify all substances according to ability to conduct an electric current, we should find a great number which show practically no conductance; almost all the rest show high conductance, with only a relatively few substances falling between these two classes. Were the difference between non-electrolytes and electrolytes one of degree rather than one of kind, we should expect most substances to show about the same conductance, with only a relatively few displaying very high conductance, and a very few, almost no conductance. Such would be the case if we were to consider the density rather than conductance of these same substances. The density of most substances lies between 2 and 5 grams per milliliter (or cubic centimeter). Very few substances have densities less than 0.6 gram per milliliter, and very few, greater than 18 grams per milliliter.

The difference of kind between strong and weak electrolytes suggests that there is a fundamental difference between the molecular structures of these two classes of substances. At a later time we shall show that our concept of molecular structure adequately explains this difference.

Variation of Conductance with Concentration. If 1 mole (gram formula weight) of an electrolyte such as sodium chloride is placed in the cell (Figure 1.5) together with 1 liter of water (the cell is not filled), a definite conductance will be observed. Upon the addition of more water, the solution will be diluted but the same amount of sodium chloride will remain between the plates. However, it is observed that the conductance is increased. The fact that the conductance increases with dilution may at first sight seem to be an anomaly, since by dilution the concentration decreases, but it must be borne in mind that we are not considering the conductance of a solution with a fixed cross section. As water is added to the cell the surface of the electrode exposed to the solution increases, as does the cross section of the conducting solution.

The conductance of an electrolyte increases with increasing dilution as shown in Figure 1.6. As the solution is diluted the concentration decreases (from right to left along the horizontal axis). After considering the next section on "The Lowering of the Freezing Point" we shall give an explanation of this phenomenon.

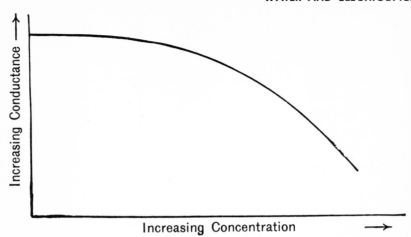

FIG. 1.6   Change in conductance with concentration.

The Lowering of the Freezing Point.   The freezing point of water is lowered by the addition of a solute.   The difference between electrolytes and non-electrolytes in this respect is well demonstrated in Table 3.   The second column of the table gives the concentration of the solute in question in terms of moles or gram formula weights per liter of water, while the third column lists the freezing point lowering, i.e., freezing point of solution in degrees below 0° C.

We see that for non-electrolytes 0.1 mole of any substance dissolved in 1 liter of water lowers the freezing point about 0.186° C, and 0.2 mole per liter has twice this effect.   It is to be observed that there is some variation in the effects of different solutes, but this variation is a relatively small one (methyl alcohol 0.181° C).   The conclusion we can immediately draw is that the total number of moles per liter or the total number of molecules per liter of non-electrolytes is the principal determining factor in the lowering of the freezing point.   The kind of molecule has little or no effect.   If electrolytes behaved like non-electrolytes in solution, we should expect that their freezing point lowerings would be the same.   More specifically, if sodium chloride in solution consisted of molecules, each of which contained one atom of sodium and one atom of chlorine, a gram formula weight would be the same as a mole and we

TABLE 3

FREEZING POINT LOWERING OF SOLUTIONS OF
SUBSTANCES IN WATER

Substance (Non-electrolytes)	Concentration (Moles per liter)	Freezing Point Lowering
Glycerine	0.1	0.187
Glycerine	0.2	0.374
Ethyl alcohol	0.1	0.183
Methyl alcohol	0.1	0.181
Methyl alcohol	0.2	0.362
Dextrose	0.1	0.186
Dextrose	0.2	0.374
Cane Sugar	0.1	0.188
Hydrogen peroxide	0.1	0.184
Sugar 0.05 ⎱ Glycerine 0.05 ⎰	0.1	0.187
Average of a large number of non-electrolytes	0.1	0.186
Electrolytes		
HCl	0.1	0.352
KNO_3	0.1	0.331
KCl	0.1	0.345
NaCl	0.1	0.348
Na_2SO_4	0.1	0.434
$CaCl_2$	0.1	0.494
$NiCl_2$	0.1	0.538

should expect that the lowering of the freezing point would be the same·as for non-electrolytes. Instead the lowering of the freezing point for HCl, KNO_3, KCl, and NaCl is almost twice that for non-electrolytes; and for Na_2SO_4, $CaCl_2$, and $NiCl_2$ more' than twice and almost three times that of non-electrolytes. Again we see a difference in kind between electrolytes and non-electrolytes.

Interpretation of the Foregoing Facts by the Theory of Ionization. Our problem is to interpret the fact that electrolytes give a greater lowering of the freezing point — almost two and sometimes three times as great as that of non-electrolytes. In a general way, we already know the answer — the theory of ionization — yet let us follow the logic of the argument to determine what the assumptions are and to judge the justification of any conclusions we may draw. In order to explain the fact that the lowering of the freezing point of some electrolytes like NaCl is almost twice that for non-electrolytes, we assume that the electrolyte is present in the solution as ions, not as molecules. If sodium chloride existed in solution as uncharged molecules of NaCl we should expect a lowering of the freezing point of 0.186° per 0.1 formula weight. Twice this lowering would mean twice as many particles, which effect could be explained only by the presence of sodium and chlorine particles existing separately in solution. Since a solution of sodium chloride is a good conductor we also assume that the particles are charged; one kind to be positively charged and one kind negatively charged.

In a general way the explanation seems to be a satisfactory one. However, we may ask why the lowering of the freezing point of sodium chloride and similar substances is not more nearly twice that of non-electrolytes. There are two possible ways of explaining this latter fact. Let us consider a 0.1 molal solution (0.1 formula weight per 1000 grams of water — refer to page 17) of sodium chloride as an example. For this solution the freezing point lowering is 0.348° C. If all the sodium chloride existed as Na^+ and Cl^- ions we would expect the freezing point lowering to be $2 \times 0.186°$ or 0.372° C, *if ions behaved exactly like neutral particles or molecules in solution.* If ions behaved like molecules in solution we can calculate that about 13 percent of the Na^+ and Cl^- ions are united in the form of uncharged NaCl molecules, i.e., 87 percent of all the sodium chloride in a 0.1 M solution is in the form of ions and 13 percent in the form of molecules.

How does this explanation apply to the experimental results

of conductance? If the assumption that only part of the sodium chloride (87 percent) is in the form of ions is valid, then we should expect that at very great dilutions all or almost all of the sodium chloride would be in the ionic form, for at great dilutions the ions would be relatively far apart and would not have the same chance of combining with each other to form molecules. The molar or equivalent conductance would therefore increase with increasing dilution, as it does. If further we assume that ions move with the same velocity in dilute as in the more concentrated solutions, then the conductance of a 0.1 M sodium chloride solution should be 87 percent of that of an exceedingly dilute one. As a matter of fact the conductance is about 90 percent that of the very dilute solution. The agreement between experiment and prediction, in this case, is not perfect but good enough to have led chemists to this view, which they retained over thirty years. Today the idea of partial ionization of *strong* electrolytes is no longer considered tenable in spite of the reasonable agreement referred to above. Chemists now regard practically *all* the sodium chloride in 0.1 M solution to be present as ions, not to the extent of 87 percent or 90 percent, but *100 percent as ions*. How then are we to explain the fact that the lowering of the freezing point is not $2 \times 0.186°$ instead of $0.348°$ and how are we to explain the increased conductance of sodium chloride with increasing dilution?

Let us first get a picture of what we mean by the sodium ion or chloride ion in solution. The sodium ion is designated by the symbol Na^+ and from this it might be inferred that we believe that the sodium ion exists alone and unattached to other molecules in the solution. Evidence from conductance experiments tells us, however, that the sodium ion has several molecules of water quite firmly attached to it. The number is somewhat variable and is dependent upon the concentration of the sodium chloride and upon the temperature of the solution. From what we said previously regarding the polarity of water molecules we might expect such a process to take place. We might expect that the negative ends of the water molecules would be attached to the positive sodium ion and form a blanket around it. Such a condition is illustrated in Figure 1.7. The same concept is held for the negative chloride ion and in general for all ions.

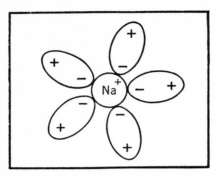

FIG. 1.7   Concept of the hydrated Na$^+$ ion.

Let us now examine closely the assumptions made in drawing conclusions regarding the partial ionization of sodium chloride to determine, if possible, the weak point of the argument. Two assumptions were implicitly made: (1) that charged particles (ions) behave like neutral molecules in lowering the freezing point of water and (2) that ions under the influence of an electric field move with the same velocity in the dilute as in the more concentrated solutions. Contrary to the first assumption we might expect that ions in solution with their greater attractions for the polar molecules of water would not behave exactly like neutral molecules. The second assumption does not seem reasonable, since a positive ion will certainly be hindered in its movement toward the negative electrode by the proximity of negative ions. The negative ions will act as a "drag" upon the positive ions and vice versa, tending to retard them. For this reason alone we should expect the conductance of concentrated solutions to be less than that of dilute solutions.

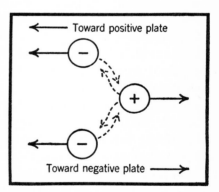

FIG. 1.8   The attractive force between the ions prevents easy flow.

The concept of ionic conductance and the effect of the close proximity of oppositely charged ions is illustrated in Figure 1.8. The attractive force between positively and negatively charged particles tends to keep them near each other and to prevent the easy flow of these ions when they are placed between the two charged plates of a conductance cell. The nearer the particles are to each other (the more concentrated the solution), the greater is this hindrance to flow, or the greater the "drag-effect" becomes.

We can assume that the lowering of the conductance with increasing concentration is entirely due to this "drag-effect" and that the molecules are completely dissociated. Evidence which we cannot present here has further strengthened this view until it has become almost universally accepted by chemists. Therefore we shall consider most strong electrolytes to exist in solution entirely in the form of ions.

Of all the common acids that we encounter in the laboratory, H_2SO_4, HNO_3, and HCl are 100 percent ionized (strong). All other common acids are partially ionized (weak). The hydroxides of the alkali and alkaline earth metals are strong bases. All salts are strong electrolytes with the exception of the halides of zinc, cadmium, and mercury and a few of the salts of lead.

There are other arguments which support the theory of ionization, as it was first proposed by the Swedish chemist, Arrhenius. These include the transfer of matter by electricity in solutions of electrolytes, Faraday's Law which was used to assign the number of charges on each ion, and the common color of the same ion in solutions of different salts. A consideration of these phenomena may be found in almost any textbook of general chemistry.

The Solubility of Electrolytes in Water. In considering the solubility of electrolytes we must first regard the substances in solution to be in the form of ions and not molecules. Experiment supports the view that in the crystal form the electrolyte also exists as positive and negative ions regularly arranged with respect to each other. The sodium chloride crystal, for example, is built up of sodium ions and chloride ions, alternately spaced in such a way that each sodium ion is surrounded by six negative chloride ions and each chloride ion by six positive sodium ions. The difference in state between the ions in the crystal and those in solution is the close regular packing in the crystal and the hydration as well as random distribution of the ions in solution. The process of solution of sodium chloride is given in Figure 1.9. The positive

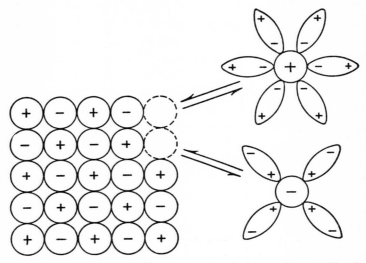

FIG. 1.9 Schematic view of the process of solution and crystallization of sodium chloride.

sodium ions leave the crystal and become surrounded by the polar water molecules, and the same is true of the negative chloride ions. The ions are said to be hydrated. The same number of chloride ions as of sodium ions enters the solution but nowhere is it necessary to assume that the sodium and chloride ions leave the crystal as molecules. The same picture would apply to the reverse process, that of precipitation.

Whether any electrolyte is soluble or only slightly soluble will depend upon the nature of the competition for its ions. If the forces of attraction of the ions for each other are great in the crystal, the solubility will necessarily be less, but if the tendency of the water molecules to hold the ions is great, the solubility will be increased. To say that a substance is very soluble means, according to our concept, that the crystal forces are small and that the attractive forces of the water molecules for the ions are great. Hydrated ions may be regarded as having some similarity to water molecules, since they have water molecules attached to them.

Weak Electrolytes. Inasmuch as any strong electrolyte is to be regarded as completely ionized, its conductance in water solution will be equal to the sum of the conductances of its individual ions. For example, the conductance of a solution of sodium chloride is equal to the conductance due to the Na^+ ion plus the conductance due to the Cl^- ion. If in very dilute solution all ions were to move independently of each other and with the same velocity when subjected to the same conditions, it would follow that the equivalent conductance values of all electrolytes would be identical. Since the conductance values are not the same for all electrolytes of the same type we must conclude that some ions travel faster than others. Thus it might be expected that the light and small H^+ ion would travel faster than the heavy and large Cs^+ ion.

In very dilute solutions we might expect that the "drag-effect" would be inappreciably small and that, when subjected to the same electric field (same voltage per centimeter length of cell), each ion would move with a definite velocity which is independent of the nature of the ion with which it is associated. For example, the chloride ion would move with the same velocity in a dilute solution of potassium chloride as it would in a dilute solution of sodium chloride. In other words, the conductance contributed by the chloride ion is the same in both solutions.

However, in solutions of potassium chloride and sodium chloride the sodium ion would not travel with the same velocity as the potassium ion, nor would either of these ions necessarily travel with the same velocity as the negative chloride ion. At first sight it may be confusing to have a condition in which positive and negative ions travel with different velocities. One might argue that positive or negative ions would accumulate at one end of the conductance cell. It must be borne in mind that reactions take place at the electrodes which will offset to a large extent any such accumulation and keep the number of positive and negative charges practically the same in all parts of the cell.

Let us assume that in dilute solution the ions are independent of each other in their current-carrying capacities, and follow the method of determining the conductance of nitric acid from the conductance values of solutions of sodium nitrate, sodium chloride, and hydrochloric acid. Let us imagine that we are using a cell such as that described on page 10 and that in all of the experiments we impose the same potential between the two electrodes. Under these conditions the current carried by any electrolyte is proportional to its conductance. We shall designate the current carried by one equivalent of any substance as Λ. Since sodium nitrate is completely ionized, the current carried by this substance is equal to the current carried by the sodium ion plus the current carried by the nitrate ion.

$$\Lambda(\text{NaNO}_3 \text{ soln.}) = \Lambda(\text{Na}^+) + \Lambda(\text{NO}_3^-) \qquad (1)$$
$$\Lambda(\text{HCl soln.}) = \Lambda(\text{H}^+) + \Lambda(\text{Cl}^-) \qquad (2)$$

By adding these two equations we obtain the conductance of a solution containing one equivalent each of sodium nitrate and of hydrochloric acid. The total conductance is the sum of the conductances of all four ions.

$$\Lambda(\text{NaNO}_3 + \text{HCl soln.})$$
$$= \Lambda(\text{Na}^+) + \Lambda(\text{H}^+) + \Lambda(\text{NO}_3^-) + \Lambda(\text{Cl}^-) \qquad (3)$$

If we could remove the sodium and chloride ions from this solution, a solution of nitric acid would be left. However, it is not necessary to remove these ions to obtain the conductance of a solution containing H^+ and NO_3^- ions. Since the conductance of a solution of sodium chloride is

$$\Lambda(\text{NaCl soln.}) = \Lambda(\text{Na}^+) + \Lambda(\text{Cl}^-) \qquad (4)$$

we need only subtract equation (4) from equation (3) to obtain the desired result, $\Lambda(H^+) + \Lambda(NO_3^-)$, which is equal to the conductance of a dilute solution of nitric acid. Making this calculation quantitatively, we find that the value so calculated for the conductance of a nitric acid solution agrees with that obtained experimentally. Thus we have evidence that our assumption regarding the independent movement or current-carrying capacity of the ions is a reasonably valid one when applied to dilute solutions.

In the same way we can calculate the conductance that a solution of acetic acid (HAc) would have if it were a strong electrolyte. This is the sum of the conductances of the hydrogen and acetate ions, which we can determine in the following manner:

$$\Lambda(\text{NaAc soln.}) = \Lambda(Na^+) + \Lambda(Ac^-) \qquad (5)$$
$$\Lambda(\text{HCl soln.}) = \Lambda(H^+) + \Lambda(Cl^-) \qquad (6)$$
$$\Lambda(\text{NaCl soln.}) = \Lambda(Na^+) + \Lambda(Cl^-) \qquad (7)$$

Adding equations (5) and (6) and subtracting (7) we obtain

$$(5) + (6) - (7) = \Lambda(H^+) + \Lambda(Ac^-) \qquad (8)$$

The value so calculated would be the conductance of a dilute acetic acid solution *if acetic acid were completely ionized.*

Comparing the value for the conductance of an acetic acid solution, as calculated above, with that determined experimentally for a 0.1 M solution, we find that the experimentally determined conductance is only about 1 percent of the value calculated. The value of the conductance of a 0.1 M sodium chloride solution is about 90 percent that for a very dilute solution. This fact we explained by the "drag-effect" due to the attractions of the positive and negative ions for each other. With acetic acid, however, the ratio of the conductance of a 0.1 M solution to that of a very dilute solution is of another order of magnitude (1 percent) and we cannot explain this in the same way. We must now assume that acetic acid exists in solution chiefly as acetic acid molecules and that only about 1 percent of these molecules is dissociated into hydrogen and acetate ions. There are quite a number of substances, particularly organic acids and bases, which are only partially ionized. Such substances are known as **weak electrolytes** and are intermediate between non-electrolytes and strong electrolytes. While such substances are not as numerous, by any means, as either the **strong electrolytes** (sodium chloride type) or as the non-electrolytes, they are nevertheless a very important class of substances with which we shall be very much concerned.*

The Use of Ionic Equations. If a solution of sodium hydroxide is neutralized by one of hydrochloric acid the resulting solution will be one of sodium chloride. The hydroxide ion, OH^-, of the sodium hydroxide solution reacts with the hydrogen ion of the hydrochloric acid solution to produce water; no reaction takes place between the sodium and the chloride ions. If the equation we are to use to represent the change taking place in this reaction is to include only those substances which disappear and those which are formed, we may express the above change by

$$H^+ + OH^- = H_2O \qquad (9)$$

Some prefer to express this change as

$$HCl + NaOH = NaCl + H_2O \qquad (10)$$

or if the substances involved are to be expressed as ions,

$$H^+ + Cl^- + Na^+ + OH^- = Na^+ + Cl^- + H_2O \qquad (11)$$

In the last equation the ions Na^+ and Cl^- appear on both sides and may be cancelled to give equation (9).

Equation (9) does not give information as to what particular kind of solutions were used, since the neutralization of solutions of potassium hydroxide and nitric acid would be ex-

---

* The terms **strong** and **weak** must not be confused with **dilute** and **concentrated**. A strong electrolyte is completely or almost completely ionized in solution, while a weak electrolyte is ionized to only a small extent. A concentrated solution is one which contains a relatively large amount of solute per unit volume, regardless of whether the solute is strong, weak or a non-electrolyte. A dilute solution contains a relatively small amount of the solute.

pressed by the same equation. On the other hand, the use of the simple equation (9) includes only those substances that enter into the reaction and gives the information that strong electrolytes are involved. *This equation also tells us that the substances involved are in solution.* If gaseous hydrogen chloride were to react with solid sodium hydroxide to give steam and solid sodium chloride, the equation for the reaction would be more properly expressed by (10). Furthermore, when we come to deal with equilibria and the corresponding equilibrium constants for chemical reactions, we shall find that equations such as (10) and (11) have to be interpreted in terms of ionic equations such as (9). Ionic equations are conventional, as well as expressions of the net result of ionic reactions, and we shall use such equations whenever ions are involved in the reactions.

Some chemists prefer to indicate the hydration of the ions in the equation for the reaction, then to consider these reactions from a somewhat different point of view (a point of view which we shall consider more fully in a later chapter). This school would indicate the H^+ ion as H_3O^+ (the hydronium ion), i.e., the H^+ ion as attached to one molecule of water. Under this system equation (9) would be written as

$$H_3O^+ + OH^- = 2H_2O \qquad (12)$$

For the most part we shall not follow this system but rather indicate the formulae of the ions in their simplest forms, always bearing in mind that the ions are all hydrated.

The equation for the neutralization of a solution of acetic acid (HAc) by a solution of sodium hydroxide, we write as

$$HAc + OH^- = H_2O + Ac^- \qquad (13)$$

Here we write acetic acid as HAc and not as H^+ for in this case most of the acetic acid in solution is in the form of molecules and not in the form of ions. It is the molecules of acetic acid which ultimately disappear in the reaction, so it is necessary to designate them as such and to include them in the equation.

defined as the number of gram-molecular-weights or gram-formula-weights of solute dissolved in 1000 grams of water. In qualitative analysis we shall have no need to use solutions the concentrations of which are defined in this way.

Molar Solutions. The **molar** concentration of a solution is defined as the number of gram-molecular-weights (**moles**) or gram-formula-weights dissolved in 1 liter of *solution*, i.e., in enough water to produce 1 liter of solution. Thus, a 2 molar solution of NaCl may be prepared by adding enough water to 116.92 (2 × 58.46) grams of NaCl so that the final volume is exactly 1 liter. The **molarity** (moles per liter) of this solution is 2 moles NaCl per liter or 2 M NaCl. A 2 M NaCl solution could also be prepared by adding enough water to 11.692 grams of NaCl to make 100 ml. (0.1 liter) of solution.

The concentration of a solution bears no relation to the amount of solution. If the concentration of a solution is designated as 2 M then every drop, every milliliter, every liter or even every barrel of that solution has the same concentration, 2 M.

The number of moles of a solute contained in a given amount of solution is never equal to the molarity of that solution unless the volume should happen to be exactly 1 liter. The number of moles of a solute contained in any solution is equal to the molarity multiplied by the volume of the solution expressed in liters. In 1 ml. of a 2 M NaCl solution there is present .001 × 2 moles or .002 moles of NaCl. It is to be observed that a 2 M solution may also be defined as one which contains 2 *millimoles* per *milliliter* (a millimole is .001 mole and a milliliter is .001 liter).

$$\frac{.002 \text{ mole}}{.001 \text{ liter}} = \frac{2 \text{ moles}}{1 \text{ liter}} = 2 \; M$$

In this text the concentrations of solutions will always be expressed in terms of molarity.

Normal Solutions. The concentration of a solution is said to be 1 normal (1 N) when enough water is added to 1 gram-equivalent-weight of the solute to make 1 liter of the solution.

Concentrations expressed in terms of normality are very convenient in quantitative volumetric analysis, but use of normal rather than molar solutions offers no decided advantage in this course. We shall therefore not be concerned with this method for expressing concentration.

Examples of Problems

Example 1.

How many grams of KBr will be needed to make 150 ml. of a 2 *M* solution?

1 mole (formula weight) KBr = 39.1 + 79.9 = 119.0 g.

2 moles KBr = 2 × 119.0 = 238.0 g.

1 liter of a 2 *M* KBr solution contains 238.0 g.

1 ml. of a 2 *M* KBr solution contains 0.238 g.

150 ml. contains 150 × 0.238 = 35.7 g.

Therefore, if enough water is added to 35.7 g. KBr to make 150 ml. a 2 *M* solution will be obtained.

Example 2.

It is desired to make a 0.1 *M* solution by adding water to 5 g. of $AgNO_3$. What must be the final volume of the solution after all the water is added?

1 mole $AgNO_3$ = 107.9 + 14.0 + 3 × 16 = 169.9 g.

A 0.1 *M* $AgNO_3$ solution contains 16.99 g. per liter or .01699 g. per ml.

5 g. $AgNO_3$ furnishes enough for $\dfrac{5}{.01699}$ or 294 ml.

Example 3.

How many ml. of water must be added to 5 ml. of 12 *M* HCl solution to make a 3 *M* HCl solution?

NOTE: *In all dilution problems we shall assume that the final volume is equal to the volume of the initial solution plus the volume of the water added; i.e., that the volume occupied by all molecules or ions is the same in solutions of all concentrations.*

In 1 ml. of a 3 *M* solution there are $\frac{3}{12}$ or $\frac{1}{4}$ as many molecules as there are in 1 ml. of a 12 *M* solution. Therefore, enough water must be added to the 12 *M* solution to make its final volume 4 times as great as it was originally. In this problem the final volume must be

4×5 ml. or 20 ml. Therefore 15 ml. of water must be added. In brief, the final volume must be 5×12 ml.

The amount of water added is $5 \times \dfrac{12 - 3}{3} = 15$ ml. In general, the volume of water added equals the *initial volume of solution* multiplied by $\dfrac{C_2 - C_1}{C_1}$ where C_2 is the larger concentration and C_1 the smaller.

Example 4.

How many ml. of a 2 M HCl solution is necessary to neutralize 3 ml. of a 0.5 M NaOH solution?

1 mole HCl neutralizes 1 mole NaOH.

The same number of moles of HCl are required as there are moles of NaOH in 3 ml. of a 0.5 M NaOH solution.

If the HCl solution were 0.5 M, instead of 2 M, equal volumes of each would be required. But the HCl is 2 M or 4 times as concentrated as the NaOH therefore less is required. Specifically, $\frac{1}{4}$ as much would be required as would be the case if the HCl were 0.5 M.

Number of ml. of HCl required $= 3 \times \dfrac{0.5}{2} = 0.75$ ml.

Example 5.

How many ml. of 6 M H_2SO_4 would be required to neutralize 100 ml. of 3 M NaOH?

Since the H_2SO_4 contains 2 replaceable H atoms (H^+ ions) and NaOH contains only 1 replaceable OH radical (OH^- ion), one-half as many moles H_2SO_4 are required as the number of moles of NaOH contained in 100 ml. of 3 M NaOH.

If the H_2SO_4 were 1.5 M, instead of 6 M, 100 ml. would be required, but with 6 M H_2SO_4 the amount required would be $100 \times \dfrac{1.5}{6} = 25$ ml.

Example 6.

What is the molarity of a H_2SO_4 solution which contains 33.33 percent H_2SO_4 by weight and which has a density of 1.25?

One liter of the solution weighs 1000×1.25 or 1250 g.

The number of grams of H_2SO_4 in one liter is 0.3333×1250 or 417 g.

One mole of H_2SO_4 is 98.1 g. The number of moles in one liter is $\dfrac{417}{98.1} = 4.25$ moles per liter. The solution is therefore 4.25 M.

Questions and Problems

1. What is the dielectric constant of any given substance?
2. How does a polar molecule differ from a non-polar one?
3. Taking into account the thermal agitation of molecules, explain why the dielectric constant for a given substance is lower the higher the temperature of the substance.
4. Does a molecule of solid sodium chloride consist of one ion of sodium and one of chlorine? Explain.
5. Explain why two liquids, one of which consists of polar molecules and one of non-polar molecules, are immiscible in each other.
6. What is the molarity of a solution which contains 5 g. HCl in 100 ml. of solution?
7. How many moles of NaOH are contained in 200 ml. of a 0.5 M solution?
8. How many grams of H_2SO_4 are there in 40 ml. of a 0.1 M H_2SO_4 solution? (H=1, S=32, O=16)
9. If 27 ml. of water is added to 35 ml. of a 0.1 M solution of any substance, what is the molarity of the final solution?
10. (a) How many moles are 5.85 g. of NaCl? (Use 23.0 as the atomic weight of sodium and 35.5 as the atomic weight of chlorine.)
    (b) If this amount of NaCl is dissolved to make one liter of solution, what is the molarity of the solution?
    (c) If this amount of NaCl is dissolved to make 500 ml. of solution, what is its molarity?
11. How many grams of solute are contained in each of the following solutions?
    (a) 250 ml. of 0.1 M $MnCl_2$ solution
    (b) 500 ml. of 5 M H_2SO_4 solution
    (c) 25 ml. of 2 M Na_2CO_3 solution
    (d) 12 ml. of 0.1 M $AgNO_3$ solution
    (e) 125 ml. of 0.5 M $BaCl_2$ solution
    (Assume the solute to have the formula indicated in each problem, i.e., unhydrated. See inside front cover for atomic weights — use only first figure beyond decimal point.)
12. If, in each of the following cases, it is desired to make a 0.1 M solution, what must be the final volume of the solution after the addition of water?

(a) 10 g. NaCl, (b) 20 g. AgNO₃, (c) 10 g. HgCl₂, (d) 10 g. Na₂SO₄·10H₂O, (e) 1 g. CuSO₄·5H₂O

13. How many ml. of water must be added to each of the following solutions to give the desired concentration?
    (a) 10 ml. 6 M HCl to give a 2 M solution
    (b) 25 ml. 2 M H₂SO₄ to give a 0.1 M solution
    (c) 6 ml. 0.1 M AgNO₃ to give a .01 M solution
    (d) 35 ml. 1.5 M H₂SO₄ to give a 0.3 M solution
    (e) 2 ml. 0.3 M NaCl to give a 0.25 M solution

14. How many ml. of 0.1 M AgNO₃ solution and how many ml. of water must be mixed to give 250 ml. of .03 M AgNO₃ solution?

15. How many ml. of 0.1 M HCl solution is required to neutralize 25 ml. of 0.3 M NaOH solution?

16. How many ml. of 0.1 M H₂SO₄ solution is required to neutralize 25 ml. of a 0.3 M KOH solution?

17. How many ml. of a 1.5 M HCl solution is required to neutralize 75 ml. of a 0.2 M NaOH solution?

18. How many ml. of a 0.1 M HNO₃ solution is necessary to neutralize 15 drops of a 1 M NaOH solution? (Assume that 20 drops equals 1 ml.)

19. What is the molarity of each of the following solutions?
    (a) 93.1 percent H₂SO₄ by weight (Density is 1.835)
    (b) 32.3 percent HNO₃ by weight (Density is 1.200)
    (c) 40.0 percent HCl by weight (Density is 1.200)
    (d) 16.0 percent NaOH by weight (Density is 1.180)

The following review problems cover material not treated in this text. If necessary the student should refer to any general chemistry text for help.

20. A flask is filled with NH₃ gas at 76 cm. pressure and at 25° C. After a catalyst has been placed in the flask it is sealed. The flask is then heated and the NH₃ is completely converted into H₂ and N₂ in accordance with the equation

$$2NH_3 = 3H_2 + N_2$$

What is the total pressure of the mixed gases after the flask has again been cooled to 25° C?

21. What percent of lead is there in each of the following oxides: (a) PbO, (b) PbO₂, (c) Pb₂O₃, and (d) Pb₃O₄?

22. Ten grams of $CuSO_4 \cdot 5H_2O$ is heated to drive off the water of crystallization. After dehydration what is the weight of the anhydrous $CuSO_4$?

23. One hundred grams of iron combine with 30.1 liters of oxygen, measured at standard conditions, to form a solid oxide. What is the formula of the oxide?

24. Lead oxide decomposes to form oxygen in accordance with the following equation

$$2PbO_2 = 2PbO + O_2$$

How many grams of PbO_2 are necessary to give 22.4 liters of O_2, measured at standard conditions?

25. How many grams of oxygen will combine with 10 g. of magnesium to form MgO?

26. Assuming that a certain iron ore were pure Fe_2O_3 calculate the maximum number of pounds of iron that could be obtained from one ton of this ore.

27. 1.000 g. of copper is placed in a crucible covered with sulfur and heated out of contact with air. A reaction takes place between the copper and the sulfur. After the reaction is complete the excess sulfur is burned off as SO_2. The residue in the crucible now weighs 1.253 g. How many atoms of copper combine with one atom of sulfur? What is the formula for the sulfide of copper?

28. An oxide of chromium contains 68.4 percent chromium and 31.6 percent oxygen. What is its formula?

29. The chloride of a certain metal contains 64.1 percent of chlorine. What is the equivalent weight of the metal?

30. A 68.0 weight percent solution of sulfuric acid has a specific gravity of 1.587. What is the molarity of this solution?

31. What volume of the solution in question 30 would be necessary to make 1 liter of a 0.1 M solution?

32. What volume of 0.1 M HCl would be necessary to precipitate all the silver from a solution containing 1.00 g. of $AgNO_3$? (Assume that all the silver in solution will be precipitated as AgCl.)

33. Beginning with 0.1 M solutions of $AgNO_3$, $Pb(NO_3)_2$ and $Hg_2(NO_3)_2$, how many ml. of each must be added to enough water to make 1 liter of a solution which is .02 M with respect to each of the ions, Ag^+, Pb^{++}, and Hg_2^{++}?

34. (Optional) The lift of any given airplane is proportional to $\frac{\rho V^2}{M}$ where ρ is the density of the air, V is the velocity of the airplane, and M is the total weight of the plane. Suppose that a given airplane must go 200 miles per hour to lift 100,000 pounds when the temperature of the air is 0° C and the barometric pressure is 760 mm. Suppose now that this same plane takes off when the barometric pressure is 750 mm. and the temperature is 38° C (100° F).

(a) Assume the load M to the same, using Boyle's and Gay-Lussac's laws, calculate what the take-off speed will have to be.

(b) Assume the take-off speed to be the same, i.e., 200 miles per hour (the maximum the airfield will permit), with what load can the airplane now take off?

35. (Optional) Can an airplane take off with a greater or smaller maximum load on a humid day as compared with a dry day, the temperature and barometric pressure being the same on the two days?

36. What is the difference between an electrolyte and a non-electrolyte?

37. By what reasoning can we come to the conclusion that there is a sharp difference between electrolytes and non-electrolytes (e.g., a difference of kind)?

38. Is the equivalent conductance (conductance of 1 gram formula weight) of sodium chloride in solution increased or decreased if the solution is diluted with water?

39. What is the average lowering of the freezing point of water if 0.1 mole per liter of a non-electrolyte is added to it?

40. What would be the freezing point of a solution which contains .05 mole of sugar, .05 mole of glycerine and .05 mole of alcohol, all in 1 liter of the same solution?

41. Explain why a dilute solution of sodium chloride has a greater conductance (per formula weight of NaCl) than does a more concentrated solution.

42. Do ions in solution behave like neutral molecules in their effect on the lowering of the freezing point?

43. Is a sodium chloride solution regarded as containing both sodium chloride molecules and the ions Na^+ and Cl^-? Explain.

44. What is the distinction between a strong acid and a concentrated one? Name three strong acids.

45. Give a schematic picture of the process taking place when solid sodium chloride dissolves in water.

46. Give an example of a weak electrolyte.

47. The equivalent conductance of a .01 molar solution of $NaNO_3$ at 25° C is 99 reciprocal ohms; that for a .01 molar solution of HCl, 391 reciprocal ohms; and for a .01 molar solution of NaCl it is 107 reciprocal ohms. Calculate the equivalent conductance of a .01 molar solution of HNO_3 and compare with the experimental value of 384 reciprocal ohms.

CHAPTER 2

Oxidation
and Reduction

All chemical reactions may be classified into two types: those which involve oxidation and reduction and those which do not. The reactions of the latter type consist of exchanges of atoms or groups of atoms without any change in the valence states of any of the reactants or, in terms of the electronic concept of matter, without any transfer of electrons. Familiar examples of reactions in water solution which do not involve any change in the valence state are:

$$Ag^+ + Cl^- = AgCl(solid) \tag{1}$$
$$Ba^{++} + SO_4^{--} = BaSO_4(solid) \tag{2}$$
$$SO_3^{--} + 2H^+ = SO_2 + H_2O \tag{3}$$
$$Cu^{++} + H_2S = CuS(solid) + 2H^+ \tag{4}$$

In each of these reactions the valence states of the atoms or groups comprising the products are the same as those of the reactants. The equations representing these reactions are relatively simple as compared with those of the oxidation-reduction type.

Since we shall encounter oxidation-reduction equations so often in our later work it is essential that we have a clear understanding of this type of reaction at the outset. We must be certain that we fully understand the balancing of oxidation-reduction equations to the extent that the balancing of any equation whatsoever will never baffle us. Once the principles of equation balancing are mastered there will never be any need to remember any equation in all its details. We shall, also, in this chapter introduce the concept of *valence number,* sometimes known as *oxidation number,* a direct consequence of our previous discussion.

Balancing of Oxidation-Reduction Equations

To understand clearly oxidation-reduction processes it is essential to obtain a thorough working knowledge of a systematic scheme for balancing equations.

As an example of an oxidation-reduction reaction we shall choose the reaction of ferrous ion with chlorine in water solution.

$$2Fe^{++} + Cl_2 = 2Fe^{+++} + 2Cl^{-*} \tag{5}$$

It is apparent that the condition of the iron and of the chlorine in the reactants is entirely different from that in the products. In the reactants the ferrous ion carries two positive charges while in the product the ferric ion bears three positive charges. Likewise, molecular chlorine is a reactant but the only product containing chlorine is the chloride ion. Both reactants have changed their valence states. In the course of the reaction the iron becomes more positive and the chlorine more negative. The valence number of the iron in equation (5) changes from +2 to +3, whereas that of the chlorine changes from 0 to −1. Thus, the ferrous ion loses one electron in the reaction while the chlorine atom gains one electron (the chlorine molecule accordingly gains two electrons). Substances which lose electrons are *reducing agents,* while those which gain electrons are known as *oxidizing agents.* *The oxidizing agent oxidizes the reducing agent and the reducing agent reduces the oxidizing agent.* In the reaction under discussion the ferrous ion is the reducing agent and it is oxidized to the ferric ion since it loses an electron. On the other hand, the chlorine in the zero state

---

* In writing equations for oxidation-reduction reactions we shall continue to omit those substances which do not contribute in any way to the progress of the reaction. For example, in equation (5), if a solution of ferrous sulfate were the reactant employed, we would omit the sulfate ion (SO_4^{--}) from both sides of the equation.

is the oxidizing agent and it is reduced to the chloride ion since it gains an electron. Every oxidation process is simultaneously accompanied by a reduction process; the two processes are associated with each other and cannot act independently. The total number of electrons gained by an oxidizing agent in a given reaction must equal the total number of electrons lost by the corresponding reducing agent. It is through this concept that we shall balance equations of the oxidation-reduction type.

The Valence Number. Before we balance equation (5) on the basis indicated above let us consider parenthetically what is meant by a change in valence state or valence number. In some cases the valence number of an atom in a molecule is equal to the charge that the atom will acquire when the molecule dissociates in water to produce ions. Thus, the valence number of iron in ferrous chloride is +2, the same as the charge on the ferrous ion (Fe^{++}) in solution. In other cases, however, the valence number of an atom in a molecule is assigned in a more arbitrary manner; its value does not correspond to the charge on any known ion of that element. The valence number of carbon in methane (CH_4) is −4. A carbon ion with four negative charges is not known. In assigning a valence of −4 to carbon in methane, we have quite arbitrarily assumed a valence number of +1 for hydrogen. Acids dissociate to give the hydrogen ion, H^+, which bears a +1 charge. Likewise, water to a smaller extent dissociates to give hydrogen ions as one of the products. Methane, to the best of our knowledge, does not dissociate in solution to give hydrogen ions, yet in considering the valence number of the molecule we recall the concept that hydrogen atoms have a tendency to lose one electron and produce hydrogen ions. To be consistent we therefore assign a +1 valence number to hydrogen in methane. In fact, in all compounds containing hydrogen this same valence number for the hydrogen atom is arbitrarily assumed and the valence numbers of other atoms are assigned accordingly.*

* An exception to this statement is found in the case of the hydrogen compounds (hydrides) of the strongly electropositive elements such as LiH, NaH, CaH_2, etc. In these compounds the valence number is evidently −1.

The valence number of the oxygen atom in the water molecule is -2 and since the state of oxidation of the oxygen atom in water is the same as it is in oxides, it is assumed that the valence number of oxygen in all oxygen compounds, with the exception of the peroxides, is -2. In hydrogen peroxide, as well as in all peroxides, each oxygen atom must have a valence number of -1 if the valence number of each hydrogen atom is to be retained as $+1$.

In assigning the valence number of any atom, the only principle to be observed is that the algebraic sum of the valence numbers of all atoms in the molecule under consideration must equal zero in the case of neutral molecules, or must have the same value as the charge in the case of an ion. The following examples will serve to illustrate this point.

Substance	*Atoms*	*Valence Number per Atom*		*Total Charge*
Water	2 hydrogen	$+1$		$+2$
	1 oxygen	-2		-2
			Net charge	0
Sulfuric Acid	2 hydrogen	$+1$		$+2$
	4 oxygen	-2		-8
	1 sulfur	$+6$		$+6$
			Net charge	0
Ammonium ion	4 hydrogen	$+1$		$+4$
(NH_4^+)	1 nitrogen	-3		-3
			Net charge	$+1$

In the last case the net charge of $+1$ is the same as the charge on the ion.

In some cases there may be two atoms of the same element but in different valence states in one and the same molecule. For the purpose of balancing equations, either the algebraic sum or the average valence number is used. For example, consider the valence state of carbon in ethyl chloride,

$$\begin{array}{c} \text{H}\quad\text{H} \\ |\quad\;\; | \\ \text{H--C--C--Cl} \\ |\quad\;\; | \\ \text{H}\quad\text{H} \end{array}$$

From the structural formula it is apparent that one carbon atom has a valence number of −3 and the other carbon atom a valence number of −1. The sum of the valence numbers of these two carbon atoms is −4. This result could also be determined from the empirical formula, C_2H_5Cl. The algebraic sum of the valence numbers of all the atoms must equal zero. Thus, five hydrogen atoms give +5; one chlorine atom, −1; and the two carbon atoms must give −4 to give an algebraic sum equal to zero. Obviously the average valence number of the carbon atoms is −2 and for purposes of balancing equations this value should be used.

Atoms in the elementary state have a valence number of zero. Thus elementary copper, zinc, sodium, chlorine, hydrogen, oxygen, etc., possess atoms which as such function in reactions with a valence number of zero. In order that an atom have a positive or a negative valence number the atom must be in the form of an ion or in molecular combination.

Returning to the example of the oxidation of ferrous ion by chlorine, we may balance the equation on the basis of an equality in the number of electrons lost and gained. Writing the unbalanced equation

$$Fe^{++} + Cl_2 = Fe^{+++} + Cl^- \qquad (6)$$

we see that when one ferrous ion changes to a ferric ion the process involves a loss of one electron, and when one chlorine atom in the zero valence state changes to a chloride ion, the process involves the gain of one electron. From an electronic standpoint the equation would be balanced if chlorine existed as a single atom and not as Cl_2, but since we know that elementary chlorine under ordinary conditions of temperature exists in the molecular form, as two atoms to the molecule, we must maintain it in this condition in our equation. The two chlorine atoms are held together in the molecule through a sharing of electrons, in other words, as a non-polar binding. This condition places each chlorine atom in the zero state of valence. Since two atoms of chlorine would necessarily gain a total of two electrons, and since one ferrous ion loses only one electron, equation (6) is not balanced. It may be balanced electronically, as illustrated in the following equation in which the change in valence numbers is indicated.

$$\overset{+2}{Fe^{++}} + \overset{0}{Cl_2} = \overset{+3}{Fe^{+++}} + \overset{-1}{Cl^-} \quad (7)$$

$$\underbrace{|\ 2 \times 1\ e^-\ \text{lost}\ |}_{\underbrace{2\ e^-\ \text{gained per molecule}}}$$

For an electronic balance the gain of two electrons by the two chlorine atoms of the chlorine molecule must be equaled by a loss of two electrons by the ferrous ion. The latter process requires two ferrous ions. In this particular case the complete balancing is relatively simple since no other substances are involved in the reaction aside from the oxidizing and reducing agents and their products. Thus, the completely balanced equation is

$$2Fe^{++} + Cl_2 = 2Fe^{+++} + 2Cl^- \quad (8)$$

In the following sections we shall present examples to illustrate the completion of more complicated equations after they have been balanced from the electronic standpoint only.

Oxidation and Reduction in Acid Solution. Many oxidation-reduction reactions take place with the production or consumption of hydrogen ions and these ions must therefore be included in the balanced equation. Among those substances which act as oxidizing agents in acid solution are included permanganate ion, MnO_4^-, dichromate ion, $Cr_2O_7^{--}$, and nitrate ion, NO_3^-. In the process of oxidation and reduction some or all of the oxygen atoms in these ions react with hydrogen ions to produce water. Thus chloride ion is oxidized by permanganate ion in acid solution to give the products shown in the following equation:

$$\overset{+7}{MnO_4^-} + \overset{-1}{Cl^-} + H^+ = \overset{+2}{Mn^{++}} + \overset{0}{Cl_2} + H_2O \quad (9)$$

The procedure is, (1) assign valence numbers, (2) balance the equation electronically, and (3) make a complete balance. It is evident that the MnO_4^- ion is the oxidizing agent and the Cl^- ion the reducing agent; the MnO_4^- ion is reduced and the Cl^- ion is oxidized. The valence number of the manganese atom in the MnO_4^- ion is +7, while in the Mn^{++} ion it is +2. Evidently a change has taken place which involves a gain of five electrons by the MnO_4^- ion since the valence number of the oxygen is not changed in this reaction. Chloride ion, valence number −1, changes to free chlorine of zero valence number, which process can be accounted for only by a loss of one electron per Cl^- ion. The change in the electrons may now be represented as

$$\overset{+7}{MnO_4^-} + \overset{-1}{Cl^-} + H^+ = \overset{+2}{Mn^{++}} + \overset{0}{Cl_2} + H_2O \qquad (10)$$

5 e^- gained

1 e^- lost

For an electronic balance the same number of electrons must be taken up by the oxidizing agent as is given up by the reducing agent. Therefore five Cl^- ions are required for each MnO_4^- ion to produce an exchange of five electrons, and therefore

$$MnO_4^- + 5Cl^- + ?H^+ = Mn^{++} + \tfrac{5}{2}Cl_2 + ?H_2O \qquad (11)$$

Multiplying both sides of the equation by 2 to remove the fraction $\tfrac{5}{2}$, the equation becomes

$$2MnO_4^- + 10Cl^- + ?H^+ = 2Mn^{++} + 5Cl_2 + ?H_2O \qquad (12)$$

A balance of the hydrogen and oxygen atoms is still lacking. However, it will be observed that all of the oxygen of the oxidizing agent through combination with hydrogen ions is converted into water. Since two molecules of permanganate ion contain eight oxygen atoms, eight molecules of water must be formed. In turn, eight molecules of water require sixteen hydrogen ions and the equation is finally written

$$2MnO_4^- + 10Cl^- + 16H^+ = 2Mn^{++} + 5Cl_2 + 8H_2O \qquad (13)$$

When the permanganate ion acts as an oxidizing agent in acid solution the manganese is always reduced to the manganous ion, Mn^{++}.

Another very satisfactory method for completing the balancing of the equation, after the oxidation-reduction part has been taken care of, is one involving a balance of the ion charges (not necessarily valence numbers) on both sides of the equation. Beginning with equation (12) the coefficients for the hydrogen ions and water molecules may be determined as follows: On the right side of the equation the only charged particles are the two Mn^{++} ions. The total ionic charge on the right is therefore $+4$. The algebraic sum of the charges on the left side must also be $+4$. Neglecting the H^+ ion for the moment, which is not balanced, the total charge on the left side is found to be -12, $(2MnO_4^- + 10Cl^-)$. Sixteen H^+ ions are necessary to make the algebraic sum $+4$, $(-2 - 10 + 16 = +4)$. The sixteen H^+ ions produce eight molecules of water. As a final check on the method the number of oxygen atoms on both sides of the equation must be the same, which is the case for the finally balanced equation (13). This method of final balance is often simpler than the alternative method previously given.

Another strong oxidizing ion in acid solution is the dichromate ion, $Cr_2O_7^{--}$, which in this medium is always reduced to the chromic ion, Cr^{+++}. Thus, iodide ion is oxidized by $Cr_2O_7^{--}$ to I_2:

$$
\begin{array}{ccccccc}
2 \times (+6) & -1 & & 2 \times (+3) & 0 & & \\
Cr_2O_7^{--} & + \ I^- & + \ H^+ & = \ 2Cr^{+++} & + \ I_2 & + \ H_2O & \quad (14)
\end{array}
$$

| $6\ e^-$ gained |
| $1\ e^-$ lost per atom |

The valence number of the chromium atom in the $Cr_2O_7^{--}$ ion is $+6$, but since there are two chromium atoms per ion the total charge is $+12$. When one $Cr_2O_7^{--}$ ion is reduced to two Cr^{+++} ions there is a gain of six electrons, three electrons for each chromium atom, whereas one I^- ion loses one electron in the oxidation to an iodine atom in the iodine molecule. For an electronic balance it is evident that six I^- ions are required to take care of the gain of six electrons by the chromium atoms of the $Cr_2O_7^{--}$ ion; thus

$$Cr_2O_7^{--} + 6I^- + ?H^+ = 2Cr^{+++} + 3I_2 + ?H_2O \qquad (15)$$

The equation is now balanced electronically. Making the final balance by means of the ionic charge method we find a charge of +6 on the right side of the equation due to the two Cr^{+++} ions, and a charge of -8 on the left side ($Cr_2O_7^{--}$ + $6I^-$). To make the algebraic sum of the charges on the left equal that on the right, namely +6, it is necessary to add a charge of +14 to the left side. This is accomplished by using fourteen H^+ ions which form seven molecules of water. The final completely balanced equation is therefore

$$Cr_2O_7^{--} + 6I^- + 14H^+ = 2Cr^{+++} + 3I_2 + 7H_2O \qquad (16)$$

The correctness of the balance is checked by the presence of seven oxygen atoms on each side of the equation.

The alternative method of making the final balance (beginning with equation 15) is somewhat simpler. The seven oxygen atoms on the left are completely converted into water. It is evident that in order for this to take place fourteen H^+ ions must be furnished and seven molecules of water will be formed.

Oxidation-reduction equations can be balanced without the introduction of the concept of electron change. When this is done one merely takes into account the positive or negative change in valence number. For example, in equation (14) the valence number of the chromium atoms in the $Cr_2O_7^{--}$ ion changes from +12 to +6, a net change of -6, in the process of conversion to two Cr^{+++} ions. The valence number of each I^- ion changes from -1 to zero, a net change of +1, in going to free iodine. To make the net positive charge equal the net negative charge six I^- ions are necessary.

We shall now consider an example of the balancing of an oxidation-reduction equation in which the reducing agent contains more than one kind of atom undergoing change in valence number. For this purpose let us choose the reaction of arsenous sulfide with nitric acid in which there is produced arsenic acid, free sulfur, and nitric oxide.

$$\overset{2\times(+3)+3\times(-2)}{As_2S_3} + \overset{+5}{NO_3^-}+H^+ = \overset{2\times(+5)}{2HAsO_3}+\overset{0}{3S}+\overset{+2}{NO}+H_2O$$

$$\underset{10\ e^-\ \text{lost}}{\underline{\qquad\qquad}} \Big|\ \underset{(2\times2)+(3\times2)}{\underline{\qquad\qquad}}\ \Big|$$

$$\underset{3\ e^-\ \text{gained}}{\underline{\qquad\qquad}} \qquad\qquad (17)$$

The valence number of the arsenic atom in As_2S_3 is $+3$ and the valence number of the sulfur in this molecule is -2. Both the arsenic and the sulfur change valence number and the total change for each As_2S_3 molecule is $+10$ as indicated in the above equation. On the other hand, each NO_3^- ion gains three electrons in its conversion to nitric oxide. Thus ten NO_3^- ions and three molecules of As_2S_3 are necessary to produce the same loss as gain in electrons (namely 30).

$$3As_2S_3 + 10NO_3^- + ?H^+ = 6HAsO_3 + 9S + 10NO + ?H_2O \quad (18)$$

Balancing equation (18) by the ion charge method, we find zero charge on the right side of the equation and a charge of -10 on the left (omitting the H^+ ion). Accordingly, ten H^+ ions are necessary to produce a net ionic charge on the left equal to zero. This amount of H^+ ion produces two molecules of water since six H^+ ions are required for the production of six molecules of $HAsO_3$ and the finally balanced equation becomes

$$3As_2S_3 + 10NO_3^- + 10H^+ = 6HAsO_3 + 9S + 10NO + 2H_2O \quad (19)$$

Checking the balancing by the oxygen atom count we find thirty oxygen atoms on each side of the equation.

Oxidation and Reduction in Alkaline Solution. As an example we shall choose the oxidation of chromite ion, CrO_2^-, by hypochlorite ion, ClO^-, in the presence of hydroxide ion, OH^-. The unbalanced equation with the valence numbers indicated is

$$\overset{+3}{CrO_2^-} + \overset{+1}{ClO^-} + OH^- = \overset{+6}{CrO_4^{--}} + \overset{-1}{Cl^-} + H_2O \quad (20)$$

$|2\times3\ e^-\ \text{lost}|$

$|3\times2\ e^-\ \text{gained}$

and the electronic balance is

$$2CrO_2^- + 3ClO^- + ?OH^- = 2CrO_4^{--} + 3Cl^- + ?H_2O \quad (21)$$

Since the algebraic sum of the charges on the ions on the right side of the equation is -7 and that on the left (leaving the OH^- out of consideration for the present) is -5, it is evident that two OH^- ions are required on the left. One molecule of water is formed and the balanced equation is

$$2CrO_2^- + 3ClO^- + 2OH^- = 2CrO_4^{--} + 3Cl^- + H_2O \quad (22)$$

Oxidation-reduction reactions in acid solution often take place with the production (not consumption) of hydrogen ions. In such cases H^+ appears on the right side of the equation. The same is true in alkaline solutions except that here we are concerned with OH^- rather than H^+ ions.

Exercises

Complete and balance the following equations.

(The column on the right indicates the type of solution in which the reaction takes place. H^+ or OH^- may appear on either side of the equation and when neither is necessary the solution is designated as "neutral.")

Reaction	*Solution*
1. $MnO_4^- + Fe^{++} = Mn^{++} + Fe^{+++}$	H^+
2. $MnO_4^- + Sn^{++} = Sn^{++++} + Mn^{++}$	H^+
3. $Cr_2O_7^{--} + Fe^{++} = Fe^{+++} + Cr^{+++}$	H^+
4. $Cr_2O_7^{--} + Sn^{++} = Sn^{++++} + Cr^{+++}$	H^+
5. $CrO_4^{--} + HSnO_2^- = HSnO_3^- + CrO_2^-$	OH^-
6. $H_2S + I_2 = S + I^-$	H^+
7. $S_2O_3^{--} + I_2 = S_4O_6^{--} + I^-$	"neutral"
8. $NO_3^- + Cu = Cu^{++} + NO$	H^+
9. $SO_4^{--} + Cu = Cu^{++} + SO_2$	H^+
10. $NO_3^- + Zn = Zn^{++} + NH_4^+$	H^+

Reaction	*Solution*
11. $H_2SO_3 + Fe^{+++} = Fe^{++} + SO_4^{--}$	H^+
12. $CrO_2^- + ClO^- = Cl^- + CrO_4^{--}$	OH^-
13. $MnO_4^- + H_2C_2O_4 = CO_2 + Mn^{++}$	H^+
14. $H_2SO_3 + I_2 = SO_4^{--} + I^-$	H^+
15. $CeO_2 + Cl^- = Ce^{+++} + Cl_2$	H^+
16. $H_3AsO_4 + I^- = H_3AsO_3 + I_2$	H^+
17. $O_2 + H_2O + I^- = I_2$	OH^-
18. $CH_2O + Ag_2O = Ag + HCO_2^-$	OH^-
19. $CH_2O + Ag(NH_3)_2^+ = Ag + HCO_2^- + NH_3$	OH^-
20. $NO_3^- + Cu = Cu^{++} + NO_2$	H^+
21. $NO_3^- + Ag = Ag^+ + NO_2$	H^+
22. $NO_3^- + Ag = Ag^+ + NO$	H^+
23. $NO_3^- + Fe^{++} = Fe^{+++} + NO$	H^+
24. $NO_3^- + Zn = Zn^{++} + N_2$	H^+
25. $NO_3^- + H_2S = S + NO_2$	H^+
26. $BaO_2 + Cl^- = Cl_2 + Ba^{++}$	H^+
27. $MnO_4^- + Br^- = Br_2 + MnO_2$	H^+
28. $SO_4^{--} + I^- = I_2 + H_2S$	H^+
29. $Cu^{++} + I^- = I_2 + Cu^+$	"neutral"
30. $ClO^- + Mn(OH)_2 = MnO_2 + Cl^-$	"neutral"
31. $Cl_2 = ClO_3^- + Cl^-$	OH^-
32. $Fe^{+++} + H_2S = Fe^{++} + S$	H^+
33. $NO_3^- + Fe = Fe^{+++} + NO$	H^+
34. $ClO^- = ClO_3^- + Cl^-$	"neutral"
35. $PbO_2 + Pb + SO_4^{--} = PbSO_4$	H^+
36. $CN^- + MnO_4^{--} = CNO^- + MnO_2$	OH^-
37. $CN^- + Fe(CN)_6^{---} = CNO^- + Fe(CN)_6^{----}$	OH^-
38. $C_2H_4O + NO_3^- = NO + C_2H_4O_2$	H^+
39. $NO_3^- + Cl^- = NOCl + Cl_2$	H^+
40. $C_2H_3OCl + Cr_2O_7^{--} = Cr^{+++} + CO_2 + Cl^-$	H^+
41. $CHCl_3 + MnO_4^- = Cl_2 + CO_2 + Mn^{++}$	H^+
42. $Fe_3O_4 + MnO_4^- = Fe^{+++} + Mn^{++}$	H^+
43. $SnS + S_2^{--} = SnS_3^{--}$	"neutral"
44. $As_2S_3 + S_2^{--} = AsS_4^{---} + S$	"neutral"
45. $Cu^{++} + CN^- = Cu(CN)_3^{--} + (CN)_2$	"neutral"
46. $Hg_2Cl_2 + NH_3 = Hg(NH_2)Cl + Hg + NH_4^+ + Cl^-$	"neutral"
47. $Ag^+ + AsH_3 = Ag + H_3AsO_3$	H^+
48. $CrO_2^- + H_2O_2 = CrO_4^{--}$	OH^-
49. $Sn^{++} + H_2O_2 = Sn^{++++}$	H^+

CHAPTER 3

Reaction Velocity
and Chemical
Equilibrium

In this chapter we shall be concerned with the problem of determining the extent to which chemical reactions take place and with the ways and means that are employed to control reactions and have them proceed as advantageously as possible. The problem can be stated more concretely by considering some specific example. For this purpose we shall choose the reaction

$$N_2 + 3H_2 = 2NH_3 \tag{1}$$

In which direction does this reaction proceed at some specified temperature and pressure? At 1000° C and at a total pressure of one atmosphere, for example, will nitrogen react with hydrogen to form ammonia or will ammonia at this same temperature and pressure decompose into its constituent elements? From the results of experiment we know that at this temperature and pressure ammonia decomposes to a very large extent (practically completely) into nitrogen and hydrogen. Therefore, at one atmosphere pressure and at 1000° C nitrogen and hydrogen cannot combine appreciably to form ammonia.

At 450° C and one atmosphere pressure about 99.7 percent of the ammonia decomposes but in the absence of a catalyst it is necessary to wait a very long time before the reaction reaches this point. Once this amount of decomposition has taken place, the reaction will proceed no further. This is the limit beyond which the reaction will not go. At 25° C it can be shown that only about 3 percent of the ammonia should decompose if the reaction proceeded rapidly enough. No means are known to the chemist of increasing the velocity of this reaction sufficiently to observe any change under these extreme conditions.

The limit to which any reaction can proceed is one of the important factors in determining its course. But it is apparent that there is another important factor controlling it, that of speed. These two factors, limit and speed, are sometimes confused when the "reactivity" of any substance or group of substances is considered. Reactivity usually refers to the velocity, or speed.

If only 3 percent of ammonia at 25° C and at one atmosphere pressure can decompose, then, conversely, hydrogen and nitrogen should combine at this same temperature and pressure to form ammonia, but this reaction also is not a feasible one because of its slow speed. Nitrogen is said to be nonreactive toward hydrogen in spite of the favorable limit of the reaction.

The subject of chemical equilibrium deals only with the limit or extent to which a reaction can take place. But a clear understanding of this subject demands a clear concept of reaction velocity and the factors which control it.

The Factors Controlling the Speed of a Reaction. Before two or more molecules can react they must collide with each other. But not every collision between reacting molecules is *effective*. In a vessel containing a mixture of hydrogen and oxygen at room temperature, billions of collisions occur each second between the molecules, yet no reaction occurs. Only those collisions which allow the molecules to penetrate deeply into each other result in reaction. This means that only collisions between fast moving molecules or between molecules having large energies with respect to each other will be effective. At room temperature there are not enough effective collisions between hydrogen and oxygen molecules to cause an appreciable number to react. How can the number of effective collisions be increased?

Effect of Temperature. From our knowledge of the kinetic theory of gases and our concept of temperature, it is easy to predict that an increase in the temperature of the reactants will increase the speed of the reaction. By increasing the temperature the velocity of the molecules is increased. Consequently, at a higher temperature there are more effective collisions, and the number of such collisions increases very rapidly as the temperature is raised. Suppose, for example, that each effective collision must involve molecules which have fifty times as much energy with respect to each other as the average energy. In such a case one in every 10^{22} * collisions, as calculated from quantitative kinetic theory considerations, would be effective at 25° C. At 100° C there would be one effective collision in every 10^{17}, an increase of one hundred-thousand-fold in the number of effective collisions. While the *average* energy of the molecules does not increase very rapidly as the temperature is increased, the number of collisions involving large energies does. In the case just considered, we assumed that an effective collision required fifty times the average molecular energy. If the effective collision required only twenty times the average energy, then at 25° C one in every 10^9 collisions would be effective and at 100° C one in about every 10^7. This time the number of effective collisions increases only one hundred times in going from 25° C to 100° C.

For a large proportion of all reactions the speed approximately doubles for every 10° rise in temperature. The process of cooking food involves chemical reactions. Most of these reactions proceed at about 100° C, the boiling point of water, but the cooking process can be hastened by the use of pressure cookers since, by not allowing the steam to escape, the temperature of the water can be increased beyond 100° C. When the vapor pressure of the water in the cooker is 25 lbs. per square inch in excess of that of the atmosphere, the temperature of the water is about 130° C. If the increase in the cooking

* For a discussion of exponential numbers refer to the Appendix.

speed doubles for every 10° rise, the speed at 130° C should be about eight times (2 × 2 × 2) that at 100° C. Conversely, when the cooking is done at high altitudes in open vessels, the speed of the cooking reaction is decreased, for at decreased atmospheric pressure water boils at a lower temperature.

When hydrogen and oxygen are heated to 500° C the reaction to form steam proceeds at a measurable rate. For this reaction the velocity more than doubles with every 10° rise in temperature, and at room temperature its rate is millions of millions of times slower. The combination of hydrogen with oxygen liberates a large amount of heat. If heat is generated faster than it can be removed, the reacting substances are raised to still higher temperatures and the reaction is further accelerated. This acceleration may take place in a fraction of a second and give rise to an explosion.

The burning of fuel such as wood also evolves heat. In this case the reaction does not get out of control but the heat evolved is sufficient to keep the burning material and the air above the *kindling* temperature. This reaction is a self-sustaining one, as are many of the reactions which evolve heat. When heat is absorbed by the reaction, the reaction cannot be self-sustaining. In this case heat must be supplied to the reactants.

Reactions involving ions, such as the neutralization of a strong acid by a strong base (see equation 10, Chapter 1), proceed very rapidly. For such reactions the ions have an attraction for each other and no excess energy is required for contact close enough to give rise to a reaction. Every collision or practically every collision between the ions is an effective one.

Effect of Concentration. By increasing the concentration of all or any of the reacting substances, the velocity of a reaction increases. With increased concentration any one molecule has a greater chance of colliding with another with which it may react. Hydrogen does not react as rapidly with air which is one-fifth oxygen as it does with pure oxygen. Also, a mixture of hydrogen and oxygen at very low pressures reacts more slowly than at high pressures. In fact, a mixture of hydrogen and oxygen does not explode when ignited if the total pressure of the mixture is sufficiently low. In any reaction taking place between two reactants, doubling the concentration of any one reactant doubles the number of total collisions and also doubles the number of effective collisions. Doubling the concentration of both reactants quadruples the number of collisions.

The reaction between gaseous iodine and hydrogen to form gaseous hydrogen iodide may be considered as an example to illustrate the effect of concentration on the speed of the reaction.

$$H_2 + I_2 = 2HI \tag{2}$$

Consider first the reactants under conditions of temperature and concentration (or pressure) which allow a measurable reaction speed. If the hydrogen concentration is now doubled and the concentration of the iodine kept the same, the reaction speed will be doubled, for now each iodine atom will make twice as many collisions with hydrogen atoms, hence twice as many effective collisions. The same result would be obtained by doubling the concentration of iodine and keeping the concentration of the hydrogen the same as it was originally. If now both the concentration of the hydrogen and the concentration of the iodine are doubled, the number of effective collisions will be increased fourfold and the speed of the reaction will be four times as great. This concept will be developed more fully in the latter part of this chapter.

Effect of a Catalyst. The speed of many reactions is increased by the presence of some substance which itself undergoes no permanent chemical change during the reaction. Such a substance is known as a ***catalyst.*** Catalysts may be divided into two general classes: (1) contact catalysts, and (2) those which form intermediate substances which in turn react to regenerate the catalyst. The reaction of sulfur dioxide with oxygen to form sulfur trioxide in the presence of nitric oxide is an example of the latter class. Oxygen does not react with sulfur dioxide with any appreciable speed at 500° C when no other substance is present, yet in the presence of nitric oxide, NO, this reaction proceeds rapidly. The nitric oxide itself combines readily with oxygen and the product formed, NO_2, then reacts with the sulfur dioxide forming sulfur trioxide and regenerating the nitric oxide for further uses as a catalyst. Known catalysts of this type are far fewer than contact catalysts.

Contact catalysts are those which provide a surface upon which the reacting substances may come in contact with each other. The catalyst has the ability to hold (adsorb), a monomolecular layer of one or more of the reactants on its surface. When the reactant is thus adsorbed, the field of force about the adsorbed reacting molecule is so changed that the molecule with which it is to react does not have to penetrate so deeply to cause reaction. More of the collisions are therefore effective, hence the speed of the reaction is increased. Finely divided platinum is used as a catalyst for many reactions, among which are the oxidation of sulfur dioxide to sulfur trioxide (contact process of making sulfuric acid), the addition of hydrogen to unsaturated organic compounds (hydrogenation of cottonseed oil, for example), the oxidation of methanol to formaldehyde ($2CH_3OH + O_2 = 2CH_2O + 2H_2O$), the reaction between nitrogen and hydrogen to form ammonia, the oxidation of carbon monoxide to carbon dioxide, and the reaction between hydrogen and oxygen to form water. Since the function of the platinum is to provide an active surface, the greater the surface area of the catalyst the greater is its effectiveness. The surface of the catalyst is increased by spreading the platinum over some other inert substance such as asbestos. This can be done by soaking asbestos in a solution of a platinum salt and then decomposing the salt by heat. For commercial practice a substitute for platinum is usually sought because of the high cost of the metal.

Heterogeneous and Homogeneous Reactions. All reactions may be classified as either *heterogeneous* or *homogeneous*. Those which take place at some surface are the heterogeneous reactions, examples of which were cited in the last section. In some cases the surface itself may be one of the reactants. The rusting of iron, for example, is a heterogeneous reaction in which the surface of the iron reacts with the oxygen. In this case one of the reactants is a gas and the other a solid. When manganese dioxide is placed in a solution of hydrogen peroxide, the latter substance decomposes to give water and oxygen. The manganese dioxide acts as a catalyst and the reaction is a heterogeneous one. When copper sulfate solution reacts with zinc to give zinc sulfate solution, it is the copper ion in solution which is involved in the reaction with the zinc to give zinc ions and metallic copper. This reaction also is a heterogeneous one.

Reactions which do not take place on a surface or at an interface between two different phases are called homogeneous reactions. In homogeneous reactions all reactants are gases, liquids in the same solution, or solids dissolved in each other. In other words, for homogeneous reactions there is no boundary surface between the reactants nor do the reactants combine with each other on the surface of a catalyst The burning of illuminating gas is an example of a homogeneous reaction. All the reactants, the gas and the oxygen of the air are gaseous (of the same phase) and the reaction does not take place on a surface. However, when this reaction takes place on a Welsbach mantle, the mantle acts as a catalyst and the reaction is then a heterogeneous one. When gaseous hydrogen reacts with gaseous iodine to form gaseous hydrogen iodide (equation 2), the reaction is a homogeneous one since all the constituents are confined to a single phase.

Reactions Involving Ions. When a barium chloride solution is added to a solution of sodium sulfate a precipitate of barium sulfate immediately forms. Barium ions and the sulfate ions must eventually attach themselves to the surface of the crystal in their regular places to form the crystal of barium sulfate. The crystal of barium sulfate grows by deposition on its surface and part of the reaction at least must be heterogeneous.

The formation of the crystal nucleus, that is, the attachment of the first ions to each other, is a different kind of a reaction. Perhaps that part of the reaction is a homogeneous one. The phenomenon of supersaturation attests to the fact that this part of the reaction is different. In a super-saturated solution of sodium thiosulfate, for example, the rate of formation of crystal nuclei is so slow that crystallization cannot set in. If a crystal of solid sodium thiosulfate is added to such a solution, crystallization immediately occurs. In most ionic reactions, however, the rate of formation of crystal nuclei is very fast, as is crystallization once nuclei have been formed.

The neutralization of a solution of sodium hydroxide by a solution of hydrochloric acid is an example of a homogeneous ionic reaction. As was previously stated, this reaction involves the combination of the hydrogen and hydroxide ions to form water and is confined to a single phase. The ionization of any weak acid or weak base in water solution is a homogeneous reaction of the ionic type.

Reversible Reactions. The formation of water by the combination of hydrogen with oxygen has previously been used to illustrate the different factors to be considered in an understanding of reaction velocity. It has been stated that these two elements react with each other almost completely at moderate temperatures. On the other hand, at 2000° C or above, an appreciable amount of steam is broken up into hydrogen and oxygen. Even at room temperature we may assume that some water vapor molecules dissociate into hydrogen and oxygen, but that the rate of dissociation and its extent are so small that the change cannot be detected. All reactions may be regarded as reversible. Often the amount of reversibility is so small that it cannot be determined by any known experimental method, but it would be contrary to our ideas concerning probability to suppose that any chemical reaction is absolutely irreversible. However, when no detectable amount of reversibility is ever observed it is common practice to regard the reaction as "irreversible."

When sodium reacts with water, hydrogen and a solution of sodium hydroxide are produced:

$$2Na + 2H_2O = 2NaOH + H_2 \tag{3}$$

If the reverse process of passing hydrogen into a solution of sodium hydroxide is carried out, no detectable amount of sodium is produced, yet we may not say that not even a single atom of sodium is formed in such a process. If we were to be entirely practical, we would regard such a process as irreversible, yet from the standpoint of equilibrium, the subject we are to consider next, it will be very useful to regard every chemical reaction as having some tendency to reverse itself, however small that tendency may be.

Chemical Equilibrium. The reaction

$$2NH_3 = N_2 + 3H_2 \tag{4}$$

was previously used to show that there is a definite limit beyond which a reaction cannot proceed. At the time the example was given, it was not made apparent why the reaction stopped before completion, but it was by no means implied that the reaction suddenly comes to a standstill. The reason for the definite limit is that the NH_3 is simultaneously being formed and finally a condition is reached in which the two opposing reactions proceed at the same rate. In this state of balance the amounts of NH_3, N_2, and H_2 present in the reaction mixture remain constant.

This condition of equilibrium, which any chemical reaction can attain, can be likened to a horse running on a treadmill which moves faster as the horse increases his speed. When the horse and the treadmill are in equilibrium, the horse is apparently stationary to an observer. If the horse runs faster, he advances a few feet, but the mill also moves faster and again he appears to be stationary, although his stationary position will be in advance of his previous one. In the case in which the reaction just considered is in equilibrium the amount of NH_3, N_2, and H_2 remains constant, yet like the horse and the treadmill the reactions proceed in opposite directions with the same speed. At equilibrium the forward and reverse reactions always proceed at the same rate.

The Law of Mass Action. The Law of Mass Action is a quantitative statement relating the velocity of a reaction to the concentrations of its reactants. To develop the quantitative notions of chemical equilibrium, that is, to understand the Law of Mass Action, we shall consider the hypothetical reaction

$$A + B = C + D \tag{5}$$

In this reaction A molecules react with B molecules to form C and D molecules. For the A and B molecules to react it is necessary that they collide with each other. The number of molecules reacting in a given time will be proportional to the number of collisions between them. If the number of collisions between A and B molecules in one case were twice as great as that in another in a given time, then twice as

many A and B molecules would react. To determine the dependence of the rate of the reaction upon the concentrations of A and B, it is only necessary to determine the manner in which the number of collisions between A and B molecules varies with their respective concentrations. To do this, consider a closed vessel containing only A and B mole-

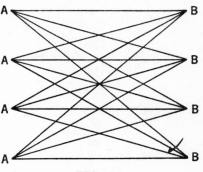

FIG. 3.1

cules and for simplicity, suppose that there are only 4 A molecules and 4 B molecules present in the vessel. Let us determine the chance that any A molecule will collide with a B molecule in a given time. We arbitrarily indicate the chance of collision by drawing lines between A and B molecules (Figure 3.1). Under the conditions we have chosen, the chance that any A molecule will collide with any B molecule is 16 (16 lines). Each A molecule has 4 chances of colliding with a B molecule and since there are 4 A molecules the total chance becomes 4×4 or 16. It is obvious that collisions between like molecules are not to be included since they do not lead to reaction in this case.

Now suppose the concentration of *A* molecules is doubled, that is, there are 8 *A* molecules and 4 *B* molecules in the same container (Figure 3.2). The chance that any *A* molecule will collide with any *B* molecule will now be 32 (4 × 8 lines). The number of *A* molecules in the second case is now twice that in the first and the chance for collision between the *A* and *B*

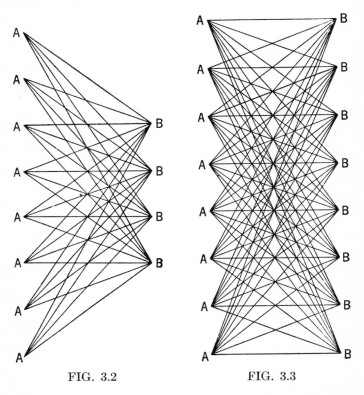

FIG. 3.2   FIG. 3.3

molecules is doubled. With 8 *A* molecules and 8 *B* molecules (Figure 3.3), the chance of collision is 64 (8 × 8 lines). In general, the chance of collision will be equal to $N_a \times N_b$, where N_a and N_b represent the number of *A* and *B* molecules respectively.

In all of the above cases the size of the container was the same, so N_a, expressed in proper units, is the concentration of *A* molecules, and N_b the concentration of *B* molecules. The chance for collision between A and B molecules is then proportional to the *product of the concentrations of A and of B molecules*. But the rate of the reaction is directly proportional to the number of collisions. Therefore, the rate at which A molecules combine with B molecules is also proportional to the *product of the concentrations of A and B.*

$$\text{Rate}_1 \sim (A) \times (B) \tag{6}$$

or
$$\text{Rate}_1 = k_1(A) \times (B) * \tag{7}$$

where (A) and (B) represent the concentrations of A and B respectively, and k_1 is a proportionality constant.

Let us now consider the reverse reaction

$$C + D \rightarrow A + B \tag{8}$$

By the same argument it can be shown that the rate of this reaction is proportional to the product of the concentration of the C molecules and the concentration of the D molecules, that is,

$$\text{Rate}_2 = k_2(C) \times (D) \tag{9}$$

where (C) and (D) now represent the concentrations of C and D molecules, and k_2 is a proportionality constant.

When the system is in equilibrium both the reactions proceed simultaneously,

$$A + B = C + D \tag{10}$$

and the rate in the forward direction is equal to the rate in the backward direction,

$$\text{Rate}_1 = \text{Rate}_2 \tag{11}$$

or
$$k_1(A) \times (B) = k_2(C) \times (D) \tag{12}$$

and
$$\frac{k_1}{k_2} = \frac{(C) \times (D)}{(A) \times (B)} \tag{13}$$

Since k_1 and k_2 are both constants, the ratio $\dfrac{k_1}{k_2}$ is also a constant.

$$\frac{(C) \times (D)}{(A) \times (B)} = K_{eq} \tag{14}$$

---

* See discussion of proportion and proportionality constants in the Appendix.

K_{eq} is known as the equilibrium constant for the reaction. This expression means that the concentrations of all four substances are so related that if the concentration of any one is changed, the concentrations of the others must vary through a chemical reaction in such a way as to make the value of the expression $\dfrac{(C) \times (D)}{(A) \times (B)}$ the same as it was originally.

Let us now consider another hypothetical case in which we have two molecules of the same kind reacting with each other, for example,

$$2A \rightarrow C + D \qquad (15)$$

Two molecules of A react with each other to form one molecule of C and one of D. This time we shall determine the chance of collision between any two A molecules. Suppose there are 6 A molecules in the enclosed vessel. Counting the chances as was done in the previous case we find that there are 15 ($5 + 4 + 3 + 2 + 1$ lines, Figure 3.4), that is, the first molecule to be considered has 5 chances of collision, the next molecule has 4 chances (not counting the same chance twice), the third molecule, 3 chances, etc.

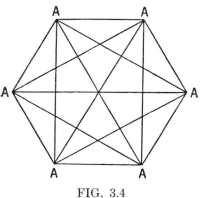

FIG. 3.4

If we double the number of A molecules (now 12), we find that the chance is 66 ($11 + 10 + 9 + 8 + 7 + 6 + 5 + 4 + 3 + 2 + 1$ lines). In general, for N molecules the chance of collision will be $(N - 1) + (N - 2) + (N - 3) + \cdots + 1$. The mathematical formula for determining the sum of such a series of combinations is

$$\frac{(N - 1) N}{2} \qquad (16)$$

Therefore, the number of collisions is proportional to $(N - 1) \times N$. N represents the number of molecules in the system. For all actual cases N is an exceedingly large number, so $(N-1)$ may be considered equal to N, and $(N-1) \times N$ is practically equal to N^2. When we recall that the lowest vacuum we can possibly obtain still contains billions of molecules per cubic centimeter, certainly one molecule more or less can make no appreciable difference, so we are quite justified in letting $N-1$ equal N. Accordingly, we may say that the number of collisions in such a case is proportional to N^2. But since N may be expressed as the concentration of the reacting substance, in this case A molecules, the number of collisions is proportional to the concentration of A molecules squared. For this case,

$$\text{Rate}_1 = k_1(A)^2 \tag{17}$$

The reverse reaction,

$$C + D \rightarrow 2A \tag{18}$$

is similar to that already considered in the first case, and for this reaction it was shown that

$$\text{Rate}_2 = k_2(C) \times (D) \tag{19}$$

For equilibrium,

$$2A \rightleftharpoons C + D \tag{20}$$

and

$$\text{Rate}_1 = \text{Rate}_2 \tag{21}$$

Consequently,

$$\frac{k_1}{k_2} = \frac{(C) \times (D)}{(A)^2} = K_{eq} \tag{22}$$

In this case it will be noted that the equilibrium expression involves the concentration of A to the second power.

The two hypothetical cases considered are relatively simple but more complicated reactions offer no special difficulty. Thus, for the equilibrium,

$$2A + B \rightleftharpoons 2C + D \tag{23}$$

we may think of the forward reaction as taking place in two steps, the first step resulting in the formation of some intermediate compound, say A_2, which in turns reacts with B,

$$2A \rightarrow A_2 \tag{24}$$

and

$$A_2 + B \rightarrow 2C + D \tag{25}$$

The net result is the sum of equations (24) and (25),

$$2A + B \rightarrow 2C + D$$

which is the forward reaction of (23). Therefore the rate of the forward reaction is proportional to $(A)^2 \times (B)$ or

$$\text{Rate}_1 = k_1(A)^2 \times (B) \tag{26}$$

In a similar manner the reverse reaction may be thought of as taking place in two steps, and

$$\text{Rate}_2 = k_2(C)^2 \times (D) \tag{27}$$

At equilibrium, where $\text{Rate}_1 = \text{Rate}_2$,

$$\frac{(C)^2 \times (D)}{(A)^2 \times (B)} = K_{eq} \tag{28}$$

The same result could be obtained by assuming that some other intermediate compound, such as AB, is formed by the reaction

$$A + B \rightarrow AB \tag{29}$$

which in turn reacts with A,

$$AB + A \rightarrow 2C + D \tag{30}$$

In fact, it is not even necessary to assume the formation of any intermediate compound, but rather to consider the collisions between two A molecules and one B molecule simultaneously. In this case the rate in the forward direction would be proportional to the number of B molecules times the number of collisions between two A molecules. Since the number of collisions between two A molecules is proportional to $(A)^2$, then the number of collisions between two A molecules and one B molecule will be proportional to $(N_a)^2 \times N_b$. By the same arguments used previously,

$$\text{Rate}_1 = k_1(A)^2 \times (B) \tag{31}$$

and the same result for the equilibrium expression could be obtained.

In general, for the reaction

$$nA + mB \rightleftharpoons pC + rD \tag{32}$$

where n, m, p, and r are small whole numbers, the expression for the equilibrium constant will be

$$K_{eq} = \frac{(C)^p \times (D)^r}{(A)^n \times (B)^m}$$ (33)

Expressed in mathematical language this is a generalized statement of the Law of Mass Action or the Law of Chemical Equilibrium.

In this expression it will be observed that the concentration of each reacting substance is raised to the same power as the coefficient of the respective term in the equation representing the reaction. According to convention the concentrations of the substances in the numerator of this expression are for those substances on the right side of the equation as written (products of the forward reaction), and the concentrations in the denominator are those for the substances on the left side of the equation (reactants).

Factors Influencing Equilibrium. Since at equilibrium a chemical reaction is proceeding in the forward and backward directions with equal velocities, it might be expected that those factors, such as temperature and concentration, which affect the speed of any reaction might also affect the equilibrium; that is, it might be expected that these same factors might change the balance between the two opposing reactions. To understand the problem more clearly, it might be advantageous again to consider the analogy between a chemical system in equilibrium and the horse running on a treadmill which increases its speed as the horse advances. If the horse, while running and apparently remaining stationary with respect to some fixed point, is spurred forward by a whip, he increases his speed and advances; but as he does so the speed of the treadmill also increases and again the horse comes to an apparently stationary position. For the second time, the horse and treadmill are in a state of equilibrium, but the horse has now occupied a position farther forward. If, on the other hand, a load is hitched to the horse he runs slower. Momentarily he shifts his position backward, but since the treadmill runs slower he soon assumes a new position of equilibrium. During the short interval that the horse advances or falls back the position of equilibrium is shifted.

In an analogous manner, the equilibrium position of a chemical reaction may be shifted, and it is common to speak of a *shift in equilibrium* to the right or to the left with reference to the chemical equation for the reaction taking place. Thus for the equilibrium between sulfur dioxide, oxygen and sulfur trioxide as represented by the equation

$$2SO_2 + O_2 = 2SO_3 \qquad (34)$$

all these substances are present in definite quantities and the reaction is proceeding in both directions. If now, by some influence, the equilibrium is shifted so that more sulfur trioxide is formed, we say that the equilibrium is *shifted to the right*. During the change from one equilibrium position to another the reaction proceeds momentarily faster from left to right than from right to left. The situation is analogous to the momentary shift in the position of the horse on the treadmill when he is spurred to a faster speed. With this explanatory introduction we may state the problem of this chapter more precisely. What factors shift the equilibrium of a chemical system of reacting substances?

The Effect of Changing the Concentration. The equilibrium existing in a chemical system may be shifted by increasing the speed of either the forward or backward reaction. In the hypothetical reaction

$$A + B = C + D \qquad (35)$$

the forward speed depends upon the product of the concentrations of the A and B molecules while the speed of the backward reaction depends upon the product of the concentrations of the C and D molecules. If, when the system is in equilibrium, an additional amount of A or B is added, the forward rate is increased because the concentration of the reacting molecules is increased. The forward rate will momentarily be greater than the reverse rate; the system is temporarily out of equilibrium and C and D molecules will be produced faster than they disappear. But as the concentrations of C and D increase the reverse rate also increases until eventually it again becomes equal to the forward rate. A new state of equilibrium is attained. The addition of an extra amount of either A or B is like applying a whip to the horse on the treadmill. In the same manner that the horse moves forward, the equilibrium position shifts from left to right. In the second state of equilibrium the substances on the right side of the equation are present in greater concentration than originally. By increasing the concentration of either or both C and D the equilibrium can likewise be shifted to the left.

The equilibrium may also be shifted to the right by removal of either C or D. In this case the reaction from right to left is momentarily retarded and the reaction from left to right proceeds faster than that from right to left until a new equilibrium condition is again reached.

These same conclusions may be drawn by a consideration of the equilibrium constant. For the hypothetical reaction (35)

$$\frac{(C) \times (D)}{(A) \times (B)} = K_{eq} \tag{36}$$

If, when the system is in equilibrium, the concentration of A is increased, then momentarily the value of the above expression would be smaller than K_{eq}. The system must then shift so as to make the expression equal to K_{eq}. When this is done (C) and (D) increase and (B) decreases. In other words, some B molecules react with some of the A molecules that were added to form more C and D molecules.

In general, if the concentration of one of the substances appearing on the right side of the equation is increased, the equilibrium shifts from right to left and vice versa. If the concentration of one of the substances on the right side of the equation is decreased, the equilibrium shifts from left to right.

The Rule of Le Chatelier. The effect of concentration on equilibrium, just discussed in the last section, is a special case of the general theorem known as the **Rule of Le Chatelier.**

This rule states that, for a system already in equilibrium, any change in the factors which affect this equilibrium will cause the system to shift in such a way as to neutralize the effect of this change.

The total pressure to which a system is subjected is often one of the factors affecting equilibrium. According to the Rule óf Le Chatelier, if the total external pressure is increased, the system will change in such a way as to reduce this effect, that is, the equilibrium will shift so as to decrease the pressure. For a gaseous system, the shift will take place in such a way as to decrease the total number of molecules, for this would result in a smaller pressure. This effect of pressure may be illustrated by the reaction

$$2NO_2 = N_2O_4 \tag{37}$$

Consider the substances, represented by the formulae in this equation, to be in equilibrium and to be exerting a definite total pressure on the wall of the container. If the external pressure is increased, it will be momentarily balanced by the pressure exerted by the N_2O_4 and the NO_2. But by the Rule of Le Chatelier the system will change to a condition which will reduce the effect of the increased pressure. That is, the above equilibrium will shift in the direction of a fewer number of molecules, for two NO_2 molecules are required to produce one N_2O_4. In other words, an increase in the external pressure will shift the equilibrium to the right. Conversely, a decrease in total pressure (by expansion) will shift the equilibrium from right to left.

In the system consisting of ice and water in equilibrium at 0° C as much ice melts as is formed. This is an example of a physical equilibrium but it may be treated in the same manner as a chemical equilibrium. Therefore we may write

$$ice = water \tag{38}$$

If pressure only is now applied to the system, water in equilibrium with ice, the system will change in such a way as to make the volume smaller, thereby reducing the pressure exerted on the sides of the container by its contents. Since water occupies a smaller volume than an equivalent amount of ice, some ice will melt as pressure is applied. However, as the ice melts it absorbs heat. The temperature will therefore drop and a new state of equilibrium will be reached. The melting point of ice decreases with increased pressure.

If a system of molecules in equilibrium in solution is diluted, the equilibrium will shift in such a way as to decrease the effect of dilution; that is, it will shift so as to produce more molecules or particles. Acetic acid is a weak acid which in solution consists of acetic acid molecules in equilibrium with its dissociation products, hydrogen ion and acetate ion, in accordance with the equation

$$HC_2H_3O_2 = H^+ + C_2H_3O_2^- \tag{39}$$

Dilution decreases the concentrations of all substances but this dilution effect will be counterbalanced by the production of more particles; that is, the above reaction will shift from left to right. Conversely, if the solution is concentrated by evaporation the above equilibrium will shift from right to left.

The Effect of Temperature on Equilibrium. Let us now consider the effect on equilibrium of changing the temperature. Increasing the temperature of a reacting system in equilibrium will increase the velocities of the reactions in both directions. If the forward and backward reactions were increased by exactly the same amount by an increase in temperature there would be no change in the position of equilibrium. Returning to the analogy of the horse on the treadmill, an increase in temperature is like increasing both the speed of the horse and the mill. If the speeds of both increase by exactly the same amount the horse will remain in an apparently stationary position. If, however, the speed of the horse is increased to a greater extent than that of the mill, the horse will move forward to a new equilibrium position. Likewise, if the speeds of the forward and backward reactions are not increased by the same amount, a shift in the equilibrium position will occur.

The effect of temperature on equilibria can best be judged

from the standpoint of the Rule of Le Chatelier. When any reaction proceeds in one direction, from right to left or vice versa, heat is either evolved or absorbed. Thus, when carbon monoxide reacts with oxygen to form carbon dioxide heat is evolved. This effect may be included in the equation

$$2CO + O_2 = 2CO_2 + \text{heat} \tag{40}$$

If, when all these substances are in equilibrium, the temperature is increased or heat is applied, the equilibrium will shift in such a way as to absorb the heat; that is, the equilibrium will shift from right to left, for proceeding in this direction the reaction absorbs heat. At higher temperatures, then, more CO_2 is dissociated into CO and O_2 at equilibrium than at lower temperatures.

While changing the concentration of one of the reactants and keeping the temperature constant shifts the equilibrium, it does not change the value of the equilibrium constant. The effect of temperature change, however, is to alter the value of the constant. The equilibrium expression for the reaction just considered is

$$\frac{(CO_2)^2}{(CO)^2(O_2)} = K_{eq} \tag{41}$$

K_{eq} has a definite value for each temperature and it may be deduced that the higher the temperature the lower the value of the constant. (Lower values of K_{eq} correspond to a smaller concentration of CO_2 and a larger concentration of CO and O_2.)

Catalysts Cannot Shift Equilibrium. While catalysts are used to increase the speed of a reaction, they cannot shift its equilibrium position. It can be demonstrated that a shift in chemical equilibrium by a catalyst would be equivalent to a perpetual motion machine. It would only be necessary to bring the catalyst alternately in and out of the reaction mixture. Knowing that perpetual motion is impossible, we must conclude that a catalyst cannot influence the equilibrium position. The complete argument is one which falls into the scope of chemical thermodynamics and cannot be given here.

If a catalyst can increase the velocity of a reaction but not affect its equilibrium it must follow that a catalyst which increases the speed of a forward reaction also increases the speed of the reverse reaction by an equal amount. This deduction has been verified many times by experiment. Specially prepared iron, which is a good catalyst for the formation of ammonia from hydrogen and nitrogen is also a good catalyst for the decomposition of ammonia into its elements (the reverse of the formation reaction).

Questions and Problems

1. Deduce from kinetic theory considerations that an increase in temperature will cause an increase in the velocity or rate of any given reaction.
2. If the velocity of a reaction doubles for every ten degree rise in temperature, how much faster would the reaction proceed at 100° C than at 20° C?
3. On the basis of the increase of reaction rate with increase of temperature explain why a mixture of hydrogen and oxygen explodes when ignited.
4. How much faster will the reaction, $H_2 + I_2 \rightarrow 2HI$, proceed if the partial pressures of the H_2 and I_2 are two atmospheres each than it will if their partial pressures are each one-half atmosphere (at the same temperature)?
5. What are the two classes of catalysts?
6. What is the distinction between a heterogeneous and a homogeneous reaction?
7. Is the neutralization of an acid solution by a basic solution a heterogeneous or homogeneous reaction?
8. What is meant by the term "irreversible reaction"?
9. If SO_2, O_2 and SO_3 are in equilibrium, has all reaction stopped either in the forward or reverse direction? The equation is

$$2SO_2 + O_2 = 2SO_3$$

Explain.
10. Show that for equilibrium for the hypothetical reaction

$$A + B = C + D$$

the concentrations of A, B, C and D must satisfy the condition that $\dfrac{(C) \times (D)}{(A) \times (B)}$ is equal to a constant.

11. If 5 molecules of the same kind in a given container make on the average ten collisions with each other every second, how many collisions per second would occur if 15 molecules instead of 5 were present?

12. In the equation $\dfrac{a \times b}{c \times d} = K$, where K is a constant, let the values of a, b, c and d be 3, 4, 5 and 6 respectively. What is the value of K? In each of the following cases determine the value of a, b, c or d from the value of K obtained previously and from the values of the other three letters; i.e., fill in the blanks to make the value of K the same as that previously obtained.

	a	b	c	d
(1)	3	4	10	..
(2)	3	4	20	..
(3)	..	4	5	3
(4)	..	4	5	12
(5)	3	..	5	12
(6)	3	..	5	24
(7)	6	8	5	..
(8)	12	16	5	..

13. Write the expression for the equilibrium constant for each of the following reactions:

(1) $HCN = H^+ + CN^-$
(2) $NH_4OH = NH_4^+ + OH^-$
(3) $H_2S = 2H^+ + S^{--}$
(4) $Hg_2^{++} + 2Fe^{+++} = 2Fe^{++} + 2Hg^{++}$
(5) $CO_2 + H_2 = CO + H_2O$ (gas)
(6) $2NO_2 = 2NO + O_2$
(7) $3H_2 + N_2 = 2NH_3$ (gas)

14. Consider the system represented by the equation

$$N_2 + 3H_2 = 2NH_3 + \text{heat}$$

to be in equilibrium.
(a) What will be the effect of adding more H_2 to the system? (Will the equilibrium shift to the right or left or remain stationary?)
(b) What will be the effect of adding more NH_3?

    (c) What will be the effect of increasing the total pressure?

    (d) What will be the effect of increasing the temperature?

15. What is the Rule of Le Chatelier?

16. Explain why a catalyst which accelerates the rate of a reaction in one direction must also accelerate the rate in the reverse direction.

17. At 60° C the solubility of KNO_3 is 110 g. per 100 g. of water, while at 20° C its solubility is 26 g. per 100 g. of water. Is heat liberated or absorbed when KNO_3 is dissolved?

18. When NH_4NO_3 dissolves in water heat is absorbed. Is NH_4NO_3 more or less soluble at high than at low temperatures?

19. In the game of pocket billiards there are, besides the "projectile" ball or cue ball, fifteen other balls numbered 1 to 15. The score of any player is determined by the summation of numbers of the balls he pockets (the balls must be pocketed in successive order). If any one player should pocket all the balls, show by equation (16) that his score will be 120. Confirm this result by adding all numbers from 1 to 15, inclusive.

CHAPTER 4

Equilibria Involving Weak Acids and Bases

In the previous chapter we considered a generalized treatment of the Law of Mass Action or the Law of Chemical Equilibrium, which for liquid systems can be applied only to solutions of relatively insoluble substances or to solutions of weak electrolytes. Although relatively few of the known substances belong to this latter class, the majority being either strong electrolytes or non-electrolytes, yet from the standpoint of chemical equilibrium the weak electrolytes are of the greatest importance and henceforth we shall deal to a very large extent with equilibria involving this class of compounds.

Of all the weak electrolytes weak acids are the most important, not only in the subject of qualitative analysis and in problems of a purely chemical nature but also in biological systems involving the blood, the tissue and cell materials, and the glandular secretions. In many systems it is highly important that not only the hydrogen ion concentration be controlled but that a source of hydrogen ions be at hand to replace those which may be used up. The molecules of weak acids act as such a source of hydrogen ions for, as we shall see, the Law of Mass Action demands that as hydrogen ions are removed by chemical reaction, more molecules must dissociate to replace the ions that may be consumed.

The neutralization of both a strong and a weak acid by a

solution of sodium hydroxide may be used to illustrate the action of a weak acid as a hydrogen ion reservoir. Hydrochloric acid and acetic acid, CH_3COOH, are typical examples of strong and weak acids respectively. Hydrochloric acid in a 1 molar solution is completely dissociated and the concentrations of the hydrogen ion and chloride ion are each 1 molar. Acetic acid in a 1 molar solution, on the other hand, is dissociated only to the extent of about 0.43 percent, so the hydrogen ion concentration in this solution is only .0043 molar. In spite of the difference in the hydrogen ion concentrations in the two cases cited, equal quantities of these two solutions will require the same amount of sodium hydroxide to neutralize them. When the sodium hydroxide solution is added to the solution of hydrochloric acid the reaction taking place is simply the combination of hydrogen ions and hydroxide ions of the acid and base respectively to form water, as represented by the equation

$$H^+ + OH^- = H_2O \qquad (1)$$

When sodium hydroxide is added to the solution of acetic acid we may regard the reaction as being made up of two steps or two parts. In the first place, we may regard the free hydrogen ions as combining with the hydroxide ions, the same reaction as with hydrochloric acid. As the hydrogen ions are removed, more acetic acid dissociates.

$$CH_3COOH = H^+ + CH_3COO^- \qquad (2)$$

This dissociation and combination proceeds until all the acetic acid molecules have been used up, and therefore the amount of sodium hydroxide required in the two cases will be the same. The over-all reaction for the neutralization of acetic acid by sodium hydroxide represents the summation of these two steps and is written

$$CH_3COOH + OH^- = CH_3COO^- + H_2O \qquad (3)$$

The acetic acid in solution consists principally of CH_3COOH molecules, and since it is these molecules which ultimately disappear during the course of the reaction, CH_3COOH, and not H^+ as in equation (1), must appear on the left side of the equation.

In later chapters we shall see how it is possible to calculate the hydrogen ion concentration after any given amount of sodium hydroxide has been added to the acetic acid solution. Also, in a later chapter we shall briefly discuss the rôle of weak acids in controlling the hydrogen ion concentration in the blood.

The Ionization of Weak Acids. To illustrate the application of the Law of Chemical Equilibrium to weak acids, let us consider again acetic acid and its ions in solution. The acetic acid molecules are in equilibrium with the hydrogen ions and acetate ions, which equilibrium may be expressed by the equation

$$HAc = H^+ + Ac^- \tag{4}$$

Applying the Law of Chemical Equilibrium to this case we find that $\dfrac{Conc.\ H^+ \times Conc.\ Ac^-}{Conc.\ HAc}$ equals a constant. In a more abbreviated form this is written

$$\frac{(H^+)(Ac^-)}{(HAc)} = K_I \tag{5}$$

K_I is known as the Ionization Constant. In any Law of Mass Action expression the concentrations of the substances involved in the expression are given in terms of moles per liter, never as grams per liter or as grams per 100 ml.

In a 0.1 molar solution of acetic acid the concentrations of the H^+ and Ac^- ions are the same, and by experiment we know that their concentrations are each .00135 molar. The concentration of the undissociated acid must be $0.1 - .00135$ or .09865 molar, since the total of dissociated and undissociated acid must equal 0.1 molar. (Note that the amount of undissociated acid is $0.1 - .00135$ and not $0.1 - 2 \times .00135$, as a too hasty deduction might lead one to believe. Each molecule which dissociates produces one hydrogen ion and one acetate ion. A concentration of .00135 molar of either hydrogen ions or acetate ions in this case means that .00135 moles of acetic acid molecules are dissociated in one liter of solution.) The numerical value of the foregoing expression then becomes

$$\frac{(H^+)(Ac^-)}{(HAc)} = \frac{.00135 \times .00135}{.09865} = .0000185 \text{ or } 1.85 \times 10^{-5}$$

The value of K_I at $25° C$ is then 1.85×10^{-5}. At any other temperature acetic acid is not dissociated to the same extent. At $100° C$, for example, the dissociation constant for acetic acid is 1.1×10^{-5}. In other words, the value of 1.85×10^{-5} holds for the temperature of $25° C$ only. However, at this temperature K_I has the same value for solutions other than 0.1 molar. For a .01 molar solution, for example, the same value of K_I is obtained. From this value of K_I it is now possible to calculate the concentrations of the H^+ and Ac^- ions in any solution of acetic acid which is not too concentrated.

In a .01 molar solution of acetic acid the total amount of acetic acid, both dissociated and undissociated, contained in one liter is .01 mole. If we let X be the concentration of the H^+ ion, then the concentration of the Ac^- ion is also X and the concentration of the undissociated acid is $.01 - X$. Then,

$$\frac{(H^+)(Ac^-)}{(HAc)} = \frac{X^2}{.01 - X} = 1.85 \times 10^{-5} \qquad (6)$$

In solving this equation for the value of X (the H^+ and Ac^- concentrations), let us first assume that X is very small as compared with .01; so small that the amount of undissociated acid $(.01 - X)$ is practically equal to .01. (X can be neglected in such equations only when it is added to or subtracted from some other number much larger than X. It cannot be neglected in the numerator of the foregoing expression.) The equation then simplifies to

$$\frac{X^2}{.01} = 1.85 \times 10^{-5}$$
$$X^2 = 1.85 \times 10^{-7} = 18.5 \times 10^{-8}$$
$$X = 4.3 \times 10^{-4} \text{ mole per liter}$$

The concentration of the H^+ and Ac^- ions is then calculated to be 4.3×10^{-4} molar. We may now inspect the original equation to see if we were justified in neglecting X in the denominator expression of $.01 - X$. $(.01 - .000431 = .009569.)$ This is almost equal to $.01$ and, for all practical purposes, the neglecting of X in the original expression was thus justified. If, however, X were so large that it could not be neglected (say 10 percent of the value from which it is subtracted or to which it is added) then the equation must be solved by the general solution of the quadratic equation (see the Appendix).

In a 0.1 molar solution of acetic acid the concentration of the H^+ ion is $.00135$ molar, while in a $.01$ molar solution we have just found it to be $.000431$ molar. The H^+ ion concentration is smaller in the more dilute solution. However, in the dilute solution a greater fraction of the total amount of acetic acid present is dissociated; 1.35 percent in the 0.1 molar solution and 4.3 percent in the $.01$ molar solution. We would be led to expect such a condition by a consideration of the processes taking place to maintain equilibrium. In the more dilute solutions the H^+ and Ac^- ions are farther apart and do not collide as often. Therefore a larger fraction of the molecules must remain in the dissociated state.

We can arrive at the same conclusion through an application of the Rule of Le Chatelier to this equilibrium (equation 4). Let us assume that we have a 0.1 molar solution in which, according to our calculations, 1.35 percent of the total amount of acetic acid is in the form of H^+ and Ac^- ions. These ions and the remaining undissociated acetic acid molecules are in equilibrium with each other. Now let us add some water to the solution to make it more dilute. This imposes a stress upon the equilibrium which in turn shifts in such a way as to undo its effect. The original 0.1 molar solution contained a definite number of H^+ and Ac^- ions but when water was added for dilution, temporarily the number of particles (ions plus molecules) per unit of volume became less than that originally present. To undo the effect of the stress (the dilution in this case) more acetic acid molecules dissociate to produce more ions, and since by dissociation one molecule produces two ions the net effect is to increase the total number of particles. The reaction proceeds in such a way as partially to undo the effect of the dilution. The dissociation of the acetic acid does not continue until the concentration of the ions, expressed in moles per liter, is the same as in the original 0.1 molar solution, since equilibrium is reached before dissociation has proceeded to such an extent. The removal of water from the solution would produce an opposite effect; H^+ and Ac^- ions would combine to form acetic acid molecules. There would be a shift in the equilibrium to the left (equation 4).

The Common Ion Effect. From a consideration of the Rule of Le Chatelier we can predict that the effect of adding either H^+ or Ac^- ions to a solution of acetic acid will be to shift the equilibrium in such a way as to decrease the amount of acid dissociated, i.e., to increase the amount of undissociated acid. From the Law of Chemical Equilibrium, which in fact is a more concise and exact form of the Rule of Le Chatelier, it is possible to calculate the extent to which the equilibrium is shifted and to calculate the concentrations of the H^+ and Ac^- ions present when either of these ions has been added in some form other than acetic acid. For example, let us calculate the concentration of the H^+ ion in a 0.1 molar solution of acetic acid when 0.1 mole of NaAc, sodium acetate, has been added to 1 liter of this same solution. Sodium acetate is a salt, a strong electrolyte, and is completely dissociated in this solution as well as in a solution made by adding it to pure water. The equilibrium is the same as that for the previous example except that the concentrations of the substances involved will be different. Let X equal the number of moles of HAc per liter which has dissociated. (In this case X will not have the same value as it would for a solution containing only HAc at this concentration.) The concentration of the undissociated acid is then $0.1 - X$. The dissociation of X moles of HAc produces X moles of H^+ ions and X moles of Ac^- ions, but the concentration of the Ac^- ion is not the same as that of the H^+ ion. In this case it is $0.1 + X$, since the sodium acetate supplies 0.1 mole of Ac^- ions per liter and the acetic acid supplies X moles per liter. The value of X, the H^+ ion concentration, may now be calculated.

$$\frac{(H^+)(Ac^-)}{(HAc)} = \frac{X(0.1 + X)}{(0.1 - X)} = 1.85 \times 10^{-5}$$

Again simplify the expression by considering X small as compared with 0.1. Then both $0.1 + X$ and $0.1 - X$ are practically equal to 0.1, and the equation becomes

$$\frac{(X)(0.1)}{(0.1)} = 1.85 \times 10^{-5}$$

or $$X = 1.85 \times 10^{-5} \tag{7}$$

We see that X is small as compared with 0.1 and we were justified in neglecting it in those terms in which it was added to and subtracted from 0.1.

The H^+ ion concentration in the acetic acid solution containing sodium acetate was found to be 1.85×10^{-5} M. In the pure acetic acid solution the H^+ ion concentration was 1.35×10^{-3} M, about 75 times larger. The dissociation of the HAc molecules was repressed by the addition of the common ion.

In the same way we could calculate the concentration of the Ac^- ion in a HAc solution to which H^+ ion has been added (as HCl, for example) and again we would find that under these conditions fewer HAc molecules dissociate. In other words, the addition of H^+ ion shifts the equilibrium again to the left as shown in equation (4).

The Law of Chemical Equilibrium Does Not Apply to Strong Acids. Hydrochloric and nitric are typical examples of strong acids. These electrolytes, like the majority of the salts, we regard as 100 percent ionized in solution. On the basis of the concept of complete ionization, the Law of Chemical Equilibrium cannot be applied, for in such a case the concentration of the undissociated acid would be zero and the value of the equilibrium constant, infinity. In a .01 molar solution of hydrochloric acid, for example, the concentrations of the H^+ and Cl^- ions are both .01 molar and that of the undissociated HCl molecules, zero.

$$\frac{(H^+)(Cl^-)}{(HCl)} = \frac{.01 \times .01}{0} = \text{infinity} * \tag{8}$$

The Mass Law expression applies only to systems of substances in equilibrium, and if no undissociated molecules of HCl exist, there can be no equilibrium involving this substance. However, HCl molecules were once regarded as existing in dilute solutions. As we have previously shown, solutions of HCl have a greater equivalent conductance the more dilute the solution. The fact that the more concentrated solutions do not show as high an equivalent conductance as the dilute solutions was regarded as evidence that there are relatively fewer ions present in the more concentrated solutions; hence, undissociated molecules were believed to exist. In a previous chapter it was shown that this decrease of conductance in the more concentrated solutions was due rather to a "drag-effect."

Following the older views for the moment, we shall tentatively regard hydrochloric acid as only partially dissociated. From conductance data together with this assumption we can calculate the fractional number of apparently undissociated and dissociated HCl molecules as well as the values for the apparent "dissociation constant" of hydrochloric acid at different concentrations. Table 4 gives the apparent "dissociation constants" of hydrochloric acid so calculated.

Passing from 0.2 molar to .001 molar the value of the dissociation constant so calculated varies more than tenfold. The same trend in the value of the equilibrium constant with varying concentration is obtained in the case of all other strong electrolytes. If we now compare these values with those obtained for acetic acid, which obeys the Law of Mass Action, we note a striking difference in the behavior of the two acids (Table 5).

---

* Any finite number divided by *zero* equals infinity.

TABLE 4

APPARENT DISSOCIATION CONSTANTS OF HYDROCHLORIC ACID
(Assuming Incomplete Ionization)

Concentration (Moles per Liter)	$K = \dfrac{(H^+)(Cl^-)}{(HCl)}$
0.200	1.56
0.100	1.05
0.050	0.73
0.020	0.45
0.010	0.32
0.005	0.23
0.002	0.15
0.001	0.12

TABLE 5

DISSOCIATION CONSTANTS OF ACETIC ACID
(Experimentally Determined from Conductance Data)

Concentration (Moles per Liter)	$K = \dfrac{(H^+)(Ac^-)}{(HAc)}$
0.07369	0.0000185
0.03685	0.0000186
0.01842	0.0000185
0.00921	0.0000186
0.00461	0.0000186
0.00230	0.0000186
0.00115	0.0000186
0.00057	0.0000186

In the case of acetic acid the constant has the same value
well within 1 percent for a large range of concentrations.
The lack of conformity of the strong acids and other strong
electrolytes to the Law of Chemical Equilibrium was one of
the chief arguments for abandoning the theory of incomplete
dissociation for these substances and for adopting, instead,
the theory of complete dissociation for all strong electrolytes.

The Extent of Ionization of Weak Acids. Weak acids differ considerably in their ability to ionize; the weaker acid, by definition, has a smaller tendency to dissociate. The ionization constant of an acid is of course a quantitative measure of this tendency. An acid with a very small constant has a small tendency to ionize while one with a relatively large constant ionizes to a larger extent. The following table shows a few typical weak acids together with their ionization constants at room temperature, and the percent of ionization of their 0.1 molar aqueous solutions.

TABLE 6

TYPICAL WEAK ACIDS, THEIR IONIZATION CONSTANTS
AND EXTENT OF IONIZATION

Acid	Percent Ionization of 0.1 Molar Solution	K (Ionization Constant)
Dichloracetic	52	5.5×10^{-2}
Salicylic	10	1.1×10^{-3}
Nitrous	6.5	4.5×10^{-4}
Acetic	1.36	1.85×10^{-5}
Hydrocyanic	0.0065	4.0×10^{-10}
Phenol	0.003	1.0×10^{-10}

The extreme variation among weak acids in the ability to ionize is well illustrated by this table; the extent of ionization of their 0.1 molar solutions varies from 52 percent for dichloracetic acid to .003 percent for phenol (carbolic acid).

The question which naturally arises is: When is an acid to be regarded as a weak acid and when a strong acid? Arbitrarily, we may answer this question in a simple way. An acid may be regarded as belonging to the weak class if its dilute solutions obey the Law of Mass Action. Such acids as hydrochloric, sulfuric and nitric are without question to be regarded as strong acids (100 percent ionized). When we search further for the reason that some acids are weak and some are strong, we find ourselves inquiring into the electronic structures or make-up of the molecules in question. The problem is a very complicated one which involves not only the tendencies of the different molecules to hold fast their dissociable hydrogen ions but also the tendency of surrounding water molecules to hold the dissociation products (hydrogen ions and negative ions) and thus aid the dissociation process. As we have pointed out before ions in solution do not exist independently in the condition indicated by their formulae but are surrounded by and attached, more or less firmly, to water molecules.

All Substances in the Same Solution Must Be in Equilibrium. When two or more weak acids, or in fact any weak electrolytes, are present in the same solution, they must all be in equilibrium with their respective ions. For example, if a solution contains both acetic and hydrocyanic acids, the following equilibria must be maintained:

$$HAc = H^+ + Ac^- \tag{9}$$

$$HCN = H^+ + CN^- \tag{10}$$

In this case the hydrogen ion is common to the two equilibria and since it exists in the same solution it must have only one concentration. The acetic acid ionizes to a larger extent than the hydrocyanic acid and produces more hydrogen ions, but this excess concentration of hydrogen ion represses the ionization of hydrocyanic acid and in this solution the latter is ionized to a smaller extent than it is when it exists alone in water solution. But the hydrocyanic acid also ionizes to a small extent to produce some hydrogen ions. For this reason the acetic acid is likewise ionized to a slightly smaller extent than it is in pure water. The common hydrogen ion represses the ionization of both acids in such a mixed solution. The calculation of the concentration of the hydrogen ion in a mixed solution (0.1 molar with respect to both acetic acid and hydrocyanic acid) becomes slightly more complicated than the simpler case of one acid, due to the necessity of solving simultaneous equations.

Some acids dissociate in two or more steps. Carbonic acid,

H_2CO_3, is an example of this type. The first step of the dissociation of this acid results in the formation of the bicarbonate ion, HCO_3^-, and H^+ ion in accordance with the equation

$$H_2CO_3 = H^+ + HCO_3^- \tag{11}$$

The second step consists of the dissociation of the bicarbonate ion:

$$HCO_3^- = H^+ + CO_3^{--} \tag{12}$$

In any solution containing carbonic acid, both these acids (H_2CO_3 and HCO_3^-) are present and, like a mixed solution of acids, they are in complete equilibrium with each other and their common hydrogen ion. A fuller treatment of such acids will be considered in Chapter 6.

Weak Bases. Equilibria involving weak bases may be treated in the same manner as was done above in the case of weak acids with the exception, of course, that the bases dissociate to give hydroxide ions, OH^-, in solution.

TABLE 7

IONIZATION CONSTANTS OF SOME WEAK BASES

Base	Percent Ionization in 0.1 Molar Solution	K (Ionization Constant)
Methyl ammonium hydroxide	7.0	5.0×10^{-4}
Ammonium hydroxide	1.3	1.8×10^{-5}
Hydrazine hydroxide	0.003	9.8×10^{-7}
Phenyl ammonium hydroxide	0.0007	4.6×10^{-10}

The number of common weak bases is far smaller than that of the weak acids. The most common weak base is ammonium hydroxide, NH_4OH. This base is about as weak a base as acetic acid is a weak acid; the ionization constants are practically the same for the two substances. A few examples of weak bases appear in the table above; others together with their ionization constants are listed in the Appendix.

Just as ammonium hydroxide is known only in solution and

not in the pure state, so methyl ammonium hydroxide and phenyl ammonium hydroxide are known only in solution. In the pure state these substances are known as methyl amine, CH_3NH_2, and phenyl amine, $C_6H_5NH_2$ (aniline), respectively. They are the analogues of ammonia with one hydrogen atom replaced by a methyl or phenyl group, and like ammonia, NH_3, they take up water in solution to form the hydroxide.

Indicators. Certain natural and synthetic colored substances have the property of either changing color or becoming colorless in dilute solution when the hydrogen ion concentration in the solution attains a definite and fixed value. Phenolphthalein, for example, is a colorless substance in any solution for which the hydrogen ion concentration is greater than 10^{-9} mole per liter. In solutions for which the hydrogen ion concentration is less than this value the phenolphthalein imparts a red or pink color to the solution. Methyl violet in solution is green when the hydrogen ion concentration is greater than 10^{-2} mole per liter, blue for hydrogen ion concentrations of 10^{-3} to 10^{-2} mole per liter and violet for solutions for which the hydrogen ion concentration is less than 10^{-3} mole per liter. A great number of such substances are known and enough can be selected so that the hydrogen ion concentration can be determined somewhat roughly over a wide range of concentration. The table of indicators on page 83 gives such a series, together with their colors for corresponding hydrogen ion concentrations.*

Litmus, one of the first known of the indicators, changes from blue to red when the hydrogen ion concentration becomes greater than 10^{-8} molar. The change is so gradual that it is not entirely red until the solution has a hydrogen ion concentration greater than 10^{-5} molar. Accordingly, litmus is a poor indicator for determining the hydrogen ion concentration of a solution.

* In all water solutions there is a definite relationship between the hydrogen ion and hydroxide ion concentrations. This relationship, which becomes evident from a study of the first two rows of the table, is treated fully in Chapter 7 on hydrolysis.

TABLE 8

INDICATORS

H⁺ Conc.	1	10^{-1}	10^{-2}	10^{-3}	10^{-4}	10^{-5}	10^{-6}	10^{-7}	10^{-8}	10^{-9}	10^{-10}	10^{-11}	10^{-12}	10^{-13}	10^{-14}
OH⁻ Conc.	10^{-14}	10^{-13}	10^{-12}	10^{-11}	10^{-10}	10^{-9}	10^{-8}	10^{-7}	10^{-6}	10^{-5}	10^{-4}	10^{-3}	10^{-2}	10^{-1}	1
pH	0	1	2	3	4	5	6	7	8	9	10	11	12	13	14
Methyl violet	yellow	green / blue	blue ←						—— violet						
Methyl orange		red ——			→ orange ←				—— yellow						
Methyl red		—— red			→ ←				—— yellow						
Brom cresol purple	yellow							←		—— purple					
Brom thymol blue	yellow						→ green ←					—— blue			
Phenol-phthalein	colorless			—— colorless								—— red			
Thymol blue		red —→			—— yellow ——								—— blue		
Thymol-phthalein				—— colorless									—— blue		
Tri-nitro benzene					← colorless								→ orange	red	orange

In determining the hydrogen ion concentration of any solution, a number of indicators must be used and by a process of elimination the hydrogen ion concentration can be fixed within rather narrow limits. For finer work the color of the indicator in the unknown solution should be compared with its color in some solution for which the hydrogen ion concentration is known. Such solutions can be made by mixing known quantities of acids and their salts for which the hydrogen ion concentrations have been determined by other methods. The usual method of originally determining the hydrogen ion concentration of a standard solution employs the hydrogen electrode. This method cannot be discussed in this course. It is usually treated more fully in courses in quantitative analysis and in physical chemistry.

Indicators are generally considered as weak acids or weak bases, with the color of the indicator ion different from that of the undissociated compound. The general equation for the dissociation of an indicator acting as an acid is

$$Ind = Ind^- + H^+ \tag{13}$$

With methyl orange, for example, the unionized acid (Ind) is red and the ion (Ind$^-$) is yellow. The dissociation constant for this indicator is equal to 2×10^{-4}.

$$\frac{(Ind^-)(H^+)}{(Ind)} = K_{Ind} = 2 \times 10^{-4} \tag{14}$$

When the undissociated acid form and the ion form of the indicator are present in equal amounts (Ind = Ind$^-$), it is apparent that the H$^+$ concentration equals the K_{Ind}.

pH Values. For convenience the hydrogen ion concentration is often expressed in terms of pH values. The pH value of a solution is defined as the logarithm of the reciprocal of the hydrogen ion concentration. In other words,

$$pH = \log \frac{1}{(H^+)} \tag{15}$$

The pH value of a solution for which the hydrogen ion concentration is $10^{-4} M$, for example, is 4; the pH for a solution whose hydrogen ion concentration is 10^{-9} M is 9, etc. For a fuller treatment of this quantity the student is referred to the paragraphs on exponential numbers, logarithms and pH values in the Appendix.

pK Values. Just as it is often convenient to express the hydrogen ion concentration by pH values, it may also be desirable in some cases to express equilibrium constants by pK values. The pK for any equilibrium is defined as the logarithm, to the base 10, of the reciprocal of the equilibrium constant.

$$p\text{K} = \log \frac{1}{K_{eq}} \tag{16}$$

Since $$\log \frac{1}{K_{eq}} = -\log K_{eq}$$

$$p\text{K} = -\log K_{eq}$$

Thus, for example, the pK for the equilibrium

$$\text{HAc} = \text{H}^+ + \text{Ac}^-$$

is equal to $-\log K_\text{I}$. The equilibrium constant for this reaction is equal to 1.85×10^{-5}. Therefore $\log K_\text{I} = \log 1.85 + \log 10^{-5}$ $= 0.27 - 5 = -4.73$; $p\text{K} = -(-4.73) = 4.73$.

The equilibrium constants given in the tables in the Appendix following the text are expressed in two ways. In the last column the value of the constant is given as a purely exponential number. The pK is the negative value of the exponent of this exponential number. The equilibrium constant for HCN, for example, is $10^{-9.4}$. The pK value for HCN is therefore 9.4.

Any equilibrium constant can be expressed in this manner.

The Brønsted Definitions of Acids and Bases. In the Brønsted system, acids and bases are defined in broader and more general terms than was commonly done in the past. The older established definitions restricted an acid to a substance producing hydrogen ions, and a base to a substance producing hydroxide ions in water solution. But it is well recognized that many substances other than hydroxides behave like bases in that they produce basic solutions and react with acids;

sodium carbonate for example. Furthermore, when solvents other than water are taken into consideration the number of substances which act like hydroxides in water solution increases greatly. The Brønsted definitions are so general that they include as bases all substances which combine with hydrogen ions not only in water solution but in all solvents. The definition of an acid is not greatly different from that previously used.

An acid is defined as any substance in ionic or molecular form, which produces or donates protons (H^+), *while a base is any substance which accepts or acquires protons.* We shall consider these definitions from the standpoint of the equilibrium existing between the proton donor and the proton acceptor, i.e., between the acid and the base. Since the equilibrium reactions are reversible neither an acid nor a base is considered separately; when an acid dissociates or transfers protons it produces a base and when a base accepts protons an acid is formed. This perhaps may be better expressed by the equation

$$\text{Acid} = H^+ + \text{Base} \tag{17}$$

The acid produces protons (left to right) and the base acquires protons (right to left).

Since our consideration of acids and bases is to be restricted very largely to water solutions, let us consider the equilibrium existing between the proton, water, and the hydronium ion. This relationship is expressed by the equation

$$H_3O^+ = H^+ + H_2O \tag{18}$$

Here H_3O^+, hydronium ion, is the acid (proton donor) and H_2O is the base (proton acceptor). This equilibrium is considered as being very largely in favor of H_3O^+, i.e., the concentration of free protons is very small; almost all of them are attached to water molecules. Accordingly, the hydrogen ion in solution is symbolized by H_3O^+ and not by H^+. In the older established definitions all forms of the hydrogen ion, H^+, H_3O^+ and higher hydrates are represented as a group by the symbol H^+ and the equilibrium as expressed in equation (18) is never considered explicitly because it is recognized that the protons exist very largely in the hydrated form.

According to these definitions the ammonium ion is an acid.

$$NH_4^+ = H^+ + NH_3 \tag{19}$$

In this case ammonia, NH_3, is the base. However, if this reaction takes place in water solution the protons formed attach themselves to water molecules to form hydronium ions and the complete reaction is

$$\underset{\text{Acid}_1}{NH_4^+} + \underset{\text{Base}_2}{H_2O} = \underset{\text{Acid}_2}{H_3O^+} + \underset{\text{Base}_1}{NH_3} \tag{20}$$

In effect the proton is merely transferred from the NH_4^+ ion to the water molecule and *vice versa*. The NH_4^+ and the H_3O^+ ions are acids and H_2O and NH_3 are bases. The process is that of neutralization, with the salt formation not emphasized by the equation representing it. In this reaction, the two bases NH_3 and H_2O are competing for protons, with the NH_3 having the greater tendency to acquire them.

Water itself may act as an acid as well as a base.

$$H_2O = H^+ + OH^- \tag{21}$$

In this case water is the acid molecule and the OH^- ion is the base. Again, this does not represent the complete reaction for according to reaction (18) the protons combine with water molecules. The reaction is rather represented by the equation

$$\underset{\text{Acid}_1}{H_2O} + \underset{\text{Base}_2}{H_2O} = \underset{\text{Acid}_2}{H_3O^+} + \underset{\text{Base}_1}{OH^-} \tag{22}$$

In the complete reaction water acts both as an acid and as a base. It should be borne in mind that the OH^- ion is also hydrated but this hydration is not expressed in the formula. Hydration or combination with water is only expressed in the formulae for the hydrogen ion and for amphoteric substances some of which will be considered in a later chapter.

The fact that HCl in the pure state is virtually a non-conductor while its water solution shows a high conductivity is not as easily expressed in terms of the established definitions as it is with the newer definitions. Pure HCl, a liquid with a boiling point of $-83°$ C., dissociates into protons and chloride ions. The equation for this equilibrium is

$$HCl = H^+ + Cl^- \tag{23}$$

Both the proton and the chloride ion are probably "solvated," i.e., joined to HCl molecules. In fact we might reason by analogy that the formula of the hydrogen ion is really H_2Cl^+. On the basis of the Brønsted definitions we then can write the reaction as

$$\underset{\text{Acid}_1}{HCl} + \underset{\text{Base}_2}{HCl} = \underset{\text{Acid}_2}{H_2Cl^+} + \underset{\text{Base}_1}{Cl^-} \tag{24}$$

The reaction which takes place when pure HCl is added to water may be represented by

$$\underset{\text{Acid}_1}{HCl} + \underset{\text{Base}_2}{H_2O} = \underset{\text{Acid}_2}{H_3O^+} + \underset{\text{Base}_1}{Cl^-} \tag{25}$$

In this case the hydrogen ion is present as H_3O^+ while in pure HCl it is present as H_2Cl^+. The Cl^- ions are also different in the two cases but the difference is not indicated in the formula. It is apparent that HCl in the pure state and HCl in water solution are different but there is no *a priori* reason based on these definitions alone which tells us that the conductivity is very low in pure HCl, i.e., that the equilibrium in equation (24) lies largely in the direction of undissociated HCl, while in water it lies in the direction of the dissociated form (to the right in equation 25). By the older definitions both cases are represented by equation (23); the difference between the two cases is implied and left more to the imagination or to the visualization of the experimental conditions.

Systems such as those expressed by equation (25) are known as conjugated acid-base systems. $Base_1$ is the base of $Acid_1$ and $Base_2$ is the base of $Acid_2$. A weak acid such as HAc in water solution, as indicated in the following equation, is also a part of a conjugated acid-base equilibrium system.

$$\underset{\text{Acid}_1}{HAc} + \underset{\text{Base}_2}{H_2O} = \underset{\text{Acid}_2}{H_3O^+} + \underset{\text{Base}_1}{Ac^-} \tag{26}$$

The new base indicated here is the Ac⁻ ion. It conforms in its properties with the definition of a base, that is, it shows a tendency to combine with the proton to produce the HAc molecule.

An acid which has a great tendency to donate protons is known as a strong acid while a base which has a great tendency to accept protons is a strong base. Acetate ion is a strong base and acetic acid is therefore a weak acid. Chloride ion in water solution is a very weak base; in fact it is so weak that in dilute solution it is no base at all, and therefore HCl in water solution is a very strong acid. In pure HCl, however, chloride ion is a strong base and HCl is a weak acid.

The ionization of a number of acids in water solution may be represented by the following equations. The order is given in decreasing strength of the acid.

Acid₁		Base₂		Acid₂		Base₁	
HSO_4^-	$+$	H_2O	$=$	H_3O^+	$+$	SO_4^{--}	(27)
H_3PO_4	$+$	H_2O	$=$	H_3O^+	$+$	$H_2PO_4^-$	(28)
HNO_2	$+$	H_2O	$=$	H_3O^+	$+$	NO_2^-	(29)
$HCNO$	$+$	H_2O	$=$	H_3O^+	$+$	CNO^-	(30)
H_2CO_3	$+$	H_2O	$=$	H_3O^+	$+$	HCO_3^-	(31)
H_2S	$+$	H_2O	$=$	H_3O^+	$+$	HS^-	(32)
$H_2PO_4^-$	$+$	H_2O	$=$	H_3O^+	$+$	HPO_4^{--}	(33)
HCN	$+$	H_2O	$=$	H_3O^+	$+$	CN^-	(34)
HCO_3^-	$+$	H_2O	$=$	H_3O^+	$+$	CO_3^{--}	(35)
HPO_4^{--}	$+$	H_2O	$=$	H_3O^+	$+$	PO_4^{---}	(36)
HS^-	$+$	H_2O	$=$	H_3O^+	$+$	S^{--}	(37)

For strong acids, all of which are practically completely ionized in water solution, the following examples are cited.

Acid₁		Base₂		Acid₂		Base₁	
H_2SO_4	$+$	H_2O	$=$	H_3O^+	$+$	HSO_4^-	(38)
HNO_3	$+$	H_2O	$=$	H_3O^+	$+$	NO_3^-	(39)
HCl	$+$	H_2O	$=$	H_3O^+	$+$	Cl^-	(40)

All of the anions designated as Base₁ are to be regarded as bases. These are merely representative of a much larger number of anions which behave as bases in that they all show a tendency to acquire the proton. Of this group of anions, the HSO_4^-, NO_3^-, and Cl^- ions certainly show little if any tendency to acquire the proton. According to the older definitions we have already classified the corresponding acids, H_2SO_4, HNO_3, and HCl as strong and 100 percent ionized. How then can the anions of these acids be called bases? In water solution these acids are practically completely ionized, but in the pure state as liquids these acids show very little ionization. If we consider the reaction of Cl^- ion with the hydronium ion to form HCl gas or liquid, then there is some justification for calling the Cl^- ion a base.

Returning to equation (26), we may write the equilibrium expression as

$$\frac{(H_3O^+)(Ac^-)}{(HAc)(H_2O)} = K_{eq}{}^B \qquad (41)$$

The concentration of the water in the denominator remains practically constant during the course of any reaction since the water is either produced or consumed in amounts which are negligible compared to the total amount of water present. We may consider this value as constant and include it in the value for the equilibrium constant. It is therefore omitted from the expression which may now be written.

$$\frac{(H_3O^+)(Ac^-)}{(HAc)} = K_I = 1.85 \times 10^{-5} \qquad (42)$$

The symbol for the hydronium ion, H_3O^+, is merely a symbol for expressing the same particle in solution as is denoted by the simpler symbol, H^+. We may use any symbols we choose for designating particles in solution, but it is evident that the value for the equilibrium constant is independent of our method of naming the particles participating in the equilibrium. Accordingly, $K_I{}^B$ of equation (42) has the same value as that given in the older established system, namely, 1.85×10^{-5}.

On the basis of the older definitions we have termed NH_4OH a weak base since it ionizes only slightly to produce NH_4^+ and OH^- ions. The equilibrium in solution is one which involves all three particles, the NH_4^+ and OH^- ions, and NH_4OH molecules. When NH_3 gas is passed into water the following equilibria are considered.

$$NH_3 + H_2O = NH_4OH = NH_4^+ + OH^- \qquad (43)$$

Whether NH_4OH molecules actually exist in solution we do not know, and as a matter of fact it makes no difference whether we consider the solution as one composed of NH_3 molecules, NH_4OH molecules, or both, since the equilibria are independent of our method of naming the particles.

Suppose we omit the intermediate NH_4OH molecule from our equation. We then have

$$\underset{\text{Base}_1}{NH_3} \; + \; \underset{\text{Acid}_2}{H_2O} \; = \; \underset{\text{Acid}_1}{NH_4^+} \; + \; \underset{\text{Base}_2}{OH^-} \qquad (44)$$

In applying our definitions of acids and bases, we see the NH_3 is a base since it combines with the proton to give NH_4^+ ion. This reaction can be considered as taking place in two steps, as can the other similar foregoing reactions.

$$H_2O = H^+ + OH^- \qquad (45)$$

and

$$NH_3 + H^+ = NH_4^+ \qquad (46)$$

The H_2O gives up H^+ ions which are then taken up by the NH_3 molecules. By adding equations (45) and (46), equation (44) is obtained.

The equilibrium expression for equation (44) is

$$\frac{(NH_4^+)(OH^-)}{(NH_3)} = K_{eq}^{\;B} = 1.8 \times 10^{-5} \qquad (47)$$

This expression is the same as we obtain when the ammonia in water is considered to be ammonium hydroxide, NH_4OH. The two substances, NH_3 and NH_4OH, are one and the same; different symbols are used to designate them.

In equation (44) the reaction is one in which the two bases NH_3 and OH^- ion are competing with each other for the proton. At equilibrium the reaction will predominate either to the left or to the right depending upon whether the OH^- ion or the NH_3 molecule is the stronger base, that is, whether the OH^- ion or the ammonia molecule holds the proton more firmly.

On the basis of the proton transfer concept of acids and bases, it is apparent that the term "salt" is of little significance, since the ions of most salts may be considered either as acids or bases. These ions will either lose protons or acquire protons, and these two processes are all that is essential to conform to the definitions of acids and bases. Practically all negative ions may be considered as bases since they combine with protons. Many positive ions are acids in that they will give up protons but, on the other hand, most positive ions do not show this tendency to any marked degree. If a metallic ion is to be regarded as an acid it is apparent that its formula must include protons which it can donate. Therefore for this purpose the symbol for the hydrated form of the ion is used. Such cases will be presented later.

In the following chapters of this text we shall retain the established definitions of acids and bases, except in those sections in which we deal explicitly with the Brønsted definitions.

Examples of Problems

Example 1.

Calculate the (H^+) in a 0.1 molar HCNO solution. What is the degree of ionization of cyanic acid in this same solution? $K_1 = 2 \times 10^{-4}$.

$$HCNO = H^+ + CNO^-$$

The concentration (0.1 molar) given for HCNO is that for the total HCNO in solution, both dissociated and undissociated.

Let
$$(H^+) = X$$

(CNO^-) must also be X in this case, for as many CNO^- as H^+ ions are formed by the dissociation process.

$$(HCNO) = 0.1 - X$$

Substituting these values in the equilibrium expression, we have

$$\frac{(H^+)(CNO^-)}{(HCNO)} = \frac{X^2}{0.1 - X} = 2 \times 10^{-4}$$

By inspection of this equation we see that X is relatively small as compared with 0.1, therefore for all practical purposes

$$0.1 - X \approx 0.1$$

Then

$$\frac{X^2}{0.1 - X} = \frac{X^2}{0.1} = 2 \times 10^{-4}$$

$$X^2 = 2 \times 10^{-5} = 20 \times 10^{-6}$$

$$X = 4.5 \times 10^{-3}$$

$$X = .0045 \text{ mole per liter} = (H^+) = (CNO^-)$$

From the value of X so obtained we can readily see that we were justified in neglecting X as compared with 0.1, for $0.1 - .0045 = .0955$, which is near enough to 0.1 that, for the purpose of our expected accuracy, it may be neglected. If we solve the equation

$$\frac{X^2}{0.1 - X} = 2 \times 10^{-4}$$

by the use of the quadratic solution (see Appendix), we obtain a value for X of .0044 mole per liter. This again shows the justification for the simple solution.

The degree of ionization is the fractional number of molecules dissociated, or the amount per liter of the dissociated weak electrolyte divided by the total concentration (both dissociated and undissociated). Since, in this particular example, the concentration of H^+ and CNO^- is 4.5×10^{-3} mole per liter, the amount of the dissociated HCNO has this same value, for 4.5×10^{-3} mole of HCNO gives 4.5×10^{-3} mole of H^+ and 4.5×10^{-3} mole of CNO^- upon dissociation.

$$\text{Degree of dissociation} = \frac{4.5 \times 10^{-3}}{0.1} = 4.5 \times 10^{-2} \text{ or } 4.5 \text{ percent.}$$

Example 2

In a 0.1 molar solution of a hypothetical acid, HA, the degree of dissociation is .025. Calculate the ionization constant for the acid HA.

$$HA = H^+ + A^-$$

$$.025 = \frac{\text{Concentration of dissociated HA}}{\text{Total HA}}$$

$$= \frac{(H^+)}{0.1}$$

$$(H^+) = 0.1 \times .025 = .0025 = (A^-)$$

$$\text{The ionization constant} = \frac{(H^+)(A^-)}{(HA)}$$

$$= \frac{2.5 \times 10^{-3} \times 2.5 \times 10^{-3}}{.0975}$$

$$K_I = 6.4 \times 10^{-5}$$

Example 3.

(a) What is the concentration of the H^+ in a solution containing 0.1 mole per liter HCNO and 0.1 mole NaCNO per liter?

$$HCNO = H^+ + CNO^-$$

NaCNO is completely ionized, so it contributes 0.1 mole CNO^- per liter. Let X equal the number of moles per liter of HCNO dissociated, which also equals (H^+). (CNO^-) will be $0.1 + X$ and the (HCNO) undissociated, $0.1 - X$.

$$K_I = 2 \times 10^{-4} = \frac{(H^+)(CNO^-)}{(HCNO)}$$
$$= \frac{X(0.1 + X)}{(0.1 - X)}$$

Neglecting X in comparison with 0.1, we have

$$(0.1 + X) \approx 0.1$$
$$(0.1 - X) \approx 0.1$$

Then $\qquad \dfrac{X(0.1)}{0.1} = 2 \times 10^{-4}$

$$X = 2 \times 10^{-4} \text{ mole per liter} = (H^+)$$

(b) What is the degree of ionization of the HCNO in this solution?

The degree of ionization is the fractional number of molecules ionized. This is equivalent to the concentration of the hydrogen ion divided by the total concentration of HCNO present, both in the form of ions and unionized molecules.

$$\text{Degree of ionization} = \frac{(H^+)}{0.1} = \frac{2 \times 10^{-4}}{0.1} = .002$$

The percent of ionization $= .002 \times 100 = 0.2$.

Thus, 0.2 percent of the HCNO is present in solution as H^+ and CNO^- ions.

Example 4.

If 100 ml. of 0.1 M NH_4Cl solution are added to 150 ml. of 0.1 M NH_4OH solution, what is the OH^- ion concentration in the resulting solution? $K_I(NH_4OH) = 1.8 \times 10^{-5}$.

The concentration of the NH_4^+ ion is the same as it would be if the 100 ml. of 0.1 M NH_4Cl solution were diluted to 250 ml. by adding water, so the (NH_4^+) from the $NH_4Cl = 0.1 \times \frac{100}{250} = .04$ M.

The concentration of the NH_4OH is the same as it would be if the 150 ml. of 0.1 M NH$_4$OH solution were diluted to 250 ml. by water, so the total NH$_4$OH concentration is $0.1 \times \frac{150}{250} = .06\ M$.

Substances in solution: NH$_4$OH = NH$_4^+$ + OH$^-$
Concentrations: $.06 - X$ $.04 + X$ X

$$\frac{(NH_4^+)(OH^-)}{(NH_4OH)} = \frac{(.04 + X)X}{(.06 - X)} = 1.8 \times 10^{-5}$$

Neglecting X as compared with .04 and .06,

$$\frac{(.04)X}{(.06)} = 1.8 \times 10^{-5}$$

$$X = \frac{.06}{.04} \times 1.8 \times 10^{-5} = 2.7 \times 10^{-5}\ M$$

$$\text{i.e., } (OH^-) = 2.7 \times 10^{-5}\ M$$

Example 5.

If 0.1 mole solid NaOH is added to 1 liter of 0.125 M HAc solution, what is the final H$^+$ concentration? (Assume no volume change.)

0.1 mole NaOH neutralizes 0.1 mole HAc to form 0.1 mole NaAc and leaves .025 mole HAc not neutralized in the one liter. The solution now is 0.1 M with respect to NaAc and .025 M with respect to HAc.

Substances in solution: HAc = H$^+$ + Ac$^-$
Concentrations: $.025 - X$ X $0.1 + X$

$$\frac{(H^+)(Ac^-)}{(HAc)} = \frac{X(0.1 + X)}{(.025 - X)} = 1.85 \times 10^{-5}$$

Neglecting X as compared with 0.1 and with .025,

$$\frac{X(0.1)}{(.025)} = 1.85 \times 10^{-5}$$

$$X = \frac{(.025)}{(0.1)} \times 1.85 \times 10^{-5}$$

$$X = 0.46 \times 10^{-5} = 4.6 \times 10^{-6}\ M \qquad \text{i.e., } (H^+) = 4.6 \times 10^{-6}\ M$$

Example 6.

100 ml. of 0.1 M NaOH is added to 150 ml. 0.2 M HAc. Calculate the final H$^+$ concentration.

Before reaction, 100 ml. 0.1 M NaOH contains .01 mole NaOH.
Before reaction, 150 ml. 0.2 M HAc contains .03 mole HAc.

.01 mole NaOH neutralizes .01 mole HAc, producing .01 mole NaAc in solution and leaving .02 mole HAc not neutralized.

After reaction, the .01 mole NaAc and .02 mole HAc are contained in 250 ml. solution, so the concentrations are .04 M and .08 M respectively.

Substances in solution: $HAc = H^+ + Ac^-$
Concentrations: $.08 - X$ X $.04 + X$

$$\frac{(H^+)(Ac^-)}{(HAc)} = \frac{X(.04 + X)}{(.08 - X)} = 1.85 \times 10^{-5}$$

Neglecting the X's in the terms $(.04 + X)$ and $(.08 - X)$,

$$\frac{X(.04)}{(.08)} = 1.85 \times 10^{-5}$$

$$X = \frac{(.08)}{(.04)} \times 1.85 \times 10^{-5}$$

$$X = (H^+) = 3.7 \times 10^{-5} \; M$$

Example 7.

Calculate the pH for a .01 M HCN solution.

$$K_{(HCN)} = 4 \times 10^{-10}$$

First calculate the (H^+).

Substances in solution: $HCN = H^+ + CN^-$
Concentrations: $.01 - X$ X X

$$\frac{(H^+)(CN^-)}{(HCN)} = \frac{X^2}{.01 - X} = 4 \times 10^{-10}$$

Neglecting X in the denominator,

$$\frac{X^2}{.01} = 4 \times 10^{-10}$$

$$X^2 = 4 \times 10^{-12}$$
$$X = 2 \times 10^{-6} \; M = (H^+)$$

$$pH = \log \frac{1}{(H^+)} = -\log (H^+)$$

$$\log (H^+) = \log (2.0 \times 10^{-6}) = \log 2.0 + \log 10^{-6}$$
$$\log 2.0 = 0.3$$
$$\log 10^{-6} = -6$$
$$\log (H^+) = \log (2.0 \times 10^{-6}) = 0.3 - 6 = -5.7$$
$$pH = -\log (H^+) = -(-5.7) = 5.7$$

(See also mathematical operations in the Appendix.)

EXAMPLES OF PROBLEMS

Example 8.

The pH of a solution is 6.38.   What is the concentration of the hydrogen ion in this solution?

$$pH = - \log (H^+) = 6.38 = - (- 6.38)$$
$$\log (H^+) = - 6.38 = - 6.00 + (- 0.38)$$
$$\log (H^+) = - 7.00 + 0.62$$
$$\text{antilog of } - 7 = 10^{-7}$$
$$\text{antilog } 0.62 = 4.17$$
$$(H^+) = 4.17 \times 10^{-7} \, M$$

Example 9.

What is the concentration of a HCN solution which is 0.2 percent ionized?

$$HCN = H^+ + CN^-$$

Let α = the degree of ionization = $\dfrac{(H^+)}{C}$, where C is the total HCN concentration.   Therefore

$$(H^+) = C \times \alpha$$
$$(CN^-) = (H^+) = C \times \alpha$$
$$(HCN) = C(1 - \alpha)$$

$$\frac{(H^+)(CN^-)}{(HCN)} = K_I = 4 \times 10^{-10}$$

$$\frac{C\alpha \times C\alpha}{C(1 - \alpha)} = \frac{C^2\alpha^2}{C(1 - \alpha)} = \frac{C\alpha^2}{1 - \alpha} = 4 \times 10^{-10}$$

$$\frac{C \times (.002)^2}{1 - .002} = \frac{C \times 4 \times 10^{-6}}{0.998} = 4 \times 10^{-10}$$

$$C = \frac{4 \times 10^{-10} \times 0.998}{4 \times 10^{-6}} = 10^{-4} \, M \text{ HCN}$$

Example 10.

A 0.2 M HCN solution is found to have a (H^+) of $1 \times 10^{-6} \, M$. Calculate the (CN^-) necessary to maintain this (H^+).

$$HCN = H^+ + CN^-$$

$$\frac{(H^+)(CN^-)}{(HCN)} = K_I = 4 \times 10^{-10}$$

At equilibrium, the (HCN) has a value of $0.2 - .000001$ or $0.2 \, M$, while the (H^+) is maintained at $1 \times 10^{-6} \, M$.   Then

$$\frac{(H^+)(CN^-)}{(HCN)} = \frac{1 \times 10^{-6}(CN^-)}{0.2} = 4 \times 10^{-10}$$

$$(CN^-) = \frac{0.2 \times 4 \times 10^{-10}}{1 \times 10^{-6}} = 8 \times 10^{-5} \; M$$

Questions and Problems *

1. Will 0.1 mole of a weak acid in solution require more, less or the same amount of sodium hydroxide solution to neutralize it as 0.1 mole of a strong acid? Explain.

2. Is the percentage of molecules of HAc which are dissociated in a .001 M solution smaller, greater or the same as in a .01 M solution?

3. Considering HAc and its ions to be in a state of equilibrium,

$$HAc = H^+ + Ac^-$$

how can this equilibrium be shifted to the left and how to the right?

4. How does the application of the Law of Mass Action help support the theory of complete dissociation of strong electrolytes?

5. Which two indicators would you use to show that the hydrogen ion concentration in a given solution is less than 10^{-4} molar but greater than 10^{-7} molar?

6. Rewrite equations (1), (2), (3), (6), (9), (10), (11), and (12) of this chapter in terms of the Brønsted definitions.

7. What pH values correspond to the following H^+ ion concentrations:

   (a) 10^{-5} (b) 10^{-9} (c) 10^{-1} (d) $10^{-7.38}$ (e) $10^{-2.1}$

8. What is the concentration of the H^+ ion in moles per liter in each of the following solutions?

   (a) 0.1 M CH_3COOH (HAc)   (f) 0.02 M HCNO
   (b) 0.01 M CH_3COOH (HAc)   (g) 0.001 M HN_3
   (c) 1 M CH_3COOH (HAc)   (h) 0.08 M $ClCH_2COOH$
   (d) 0.05 M HCN   (i) 0.004 M HCN
   (e) 0.01 M HNO_2 (j) 0.0001 M C_6H_5COOH

   Use quadratic equation for (e) and (j) (see Appendix).

9. Calculate the concentration of the OH^- ion in solutions of the following:

* Values for dissociation constants are given in the Appendix.

(a) 1 M NH$_4$OH   (f) 0.01 M CH$_3$NH$_3$OH
(b) 0.1 M NH$_4$OH   (g) 0.2 M (CH$_3$)$_2$NH$_2$OH
(c) 0.01 M NH$_4$OH   (h) 0.1 M C$_2$H$_5$NH$_3$OH
(d) 0.001 M NH$_4$OH   (i) 0.002 M C$_6$H$_5$NH$_3$OH
(e) 0.04 M NH$_4$OH

10. Solutions of the following weak acids and bases are ionized as indicated. Calculate the ionization constant in each case.

Solution	Percent Ionized
(a) 0.1 M CH$_3$COOH (HAc)	1.35
(b) 0.01 M CH$_3$COOH	4.20
(c) 0.1 M NH$_4$OH	1.33
(d) 0.01 M NH$_4$OH	4.15
(e) 0.1 M HNO$_2$	6.5
(f) 0.1 M HCN	0.0065
(g) 0.005 M HCN	0.029

11. Two grams of HAc are dissolved in 1 liter of water. Calculate the concentration of the H$^+$ ion and the Ac$^-$ ion.

12. To the above solution (problem 11) 2 g. of NaAc are added. Now what is the concentration of the H$^+$ and Ac$^-$ ions?

13. Calculate the degree of ionization of the solutes in the following aqueous solutions:

(a) 0.1 M HNO$_2$ (d) 0.02 M NH$_4$OH
(b) 0.01 M HCN   (e) 0.08 M CH$_3$NH$_3$OH
(c) 0.05 M HAc

14. If the H$^+$ concentration of a solution which contains 0.1 mole of HAc and a certain amount of NaAc per liter is .000025 M, what must be the concentration of the Ac$^-$ ion?

15. It is desired to make the concentration of the H$^+$ ion 3.5×10^{-8} M in a .05 M solution of HCN. This can be accomplished by the addition of KCN. What must be the concentration of the CN$^-$ ion in such a solution?

16. A 0.1 M solution of NH$_4$OH, also containing some NH$_4$Cl, is found to have an OH$^-$ ion concentration of 0.25×10^{-5} M. What is the concentration of the NH$_4^+$ ion in this solution?

17. How many moles of NH$_4$Cl must be added to 1 liter of a 0.1 M solution of NH$_4$OH to make the OH$^-$ ion concentration 1×10^{-5} M per liter?

18. If .01 mole HCl is added to 1 liter of the resulting solution in problem (17), what will be the OH$^-$ ion concentration?

19. If .01 mole NaOH is added to 1 liter of the resulting solution in problem (17), what will be the final OH$^-$ ion concentration?

20. A hypothetical acid, HA, dissociates as follows:

$$HA = H^+ + A^-$$

(a) If in a 0.1 M solution the degree of ionization is 1 percent, calculate the ionization constant for the acid.

(b) Calculate the concentration of the H$^+$ ion in a .01 M solution.

(c) Calculate the degree of ionization in (b).

(d) Calculate the concentration of H$^+$ ion in a solution which contains 0.1 M of the salt NaA and 0.1 M of the weak acid HA, the total volume of the mixture being 1 liter.

21. Calculate the molar concentration of a solution of NH$_4$OH which is known to be 4 percent ionized.

22. What is the molar concentration of a solution of HCN which by experiment is found to be ionized to the extent of .01 percent?

23. Five ml. of 3 M HAc is added to 50 ml. of 1 M NaAc solution. Calculate the concentration of the H$^+$ ion in this solution. (The total volume is 55 ml.)

24. Five grams of NH$_4$Cl is added to 100 ml. of 0.1 M NH$_4$OH solution. Calculate the concentration of the OH$^-$ ion.

25. Fifty ml. of 0.1 M HCl is mixed with 75 ml. of 0.1 M NH$_4$OH solution. Calculate the concentration of OH$^-$ ion in the mixture.

26. Repeat problem (25) using NaOH in place of NH$_4$OH.

27. To 100 ml. of a .02 M solution of C$_6$H$_5$COOH is added 250 ml. of .02 M solution of sodium benzoate (C$_6$H$_5$COONa). What is the concentration of the H$^+$ ion in the resulting solution?

28. 4.75 g. of NH$_4$Cl is added to a solution already containing 2.5 g. of NH$_3$ and the total volume is made 500 ml. by the addition of water. What is the concentration of the OH$^-$ ion in this solution?

29. Calculate the pH of the following solutions:

(a) 0.1 M HCl

(b) A solution containing 1 g. HCl per liter

(c) 0.1 M HAc

(d) A solution containing 0.1 M HAc and 0.1 M NaAc per liter

30. Using HAc and NaAc in different amounts in each case, give the concentrations of each of these substances for three dif-

ferent solutions, each solution having a H^+ ion concentration of 10^{-4}.

31. One hundred ml. of a 0.1 M HCl solution is added to 100 ml. of a 0.2 M NH$_4$OH solution.

    (a) What fraction of the NH$_4$OH does the HCl neutralize?

    (b) What is the concentration of the NH$_4^+$ ion? (Neglect that amount of NH$_4^+$ ion contributed by the NH$_4$OH not neutralized.)

    (c) What is the concentration of the NH$_4$OH not neutralized?

    (d) Calculate the OH$^-$ ion concentration in the resulting solution.

32. In the following problem solid NaOH is to be added gradually to a solution of HAc. As the NaOH is added part of the HAc is neutralized. Even after the final addition of NaOH, the HAc will not be completely neutralized. The H^+ ion concentration and the pH of the solution are to be calculated after each addition of NaOH.

    One-hundredth of a mole of solid NaOH is added to 1 liter of a 0.1 M HAc solution. (Neglect any volume change.)

    (a) What fraction of the HAc is neutralized?

    (b) What is the concentration of the Ac$^-$ ion? (Neglect that contributed by the HAc not neutralized.)

    (c) What is the concentration of the HAc?

    (d) Calculate the H^+ ion concentration.

    (e) What is the pH of the solution?

    To the resulting solution another .01 mole of NaOH is added. Again answer (a), (b), (c), (d), and (e). NaOH is added portionwise (.01 mole at a time) until, in all, .07 mole has been added. After the addition of each .01 mole portion calculate the H^+ ion concentration and the pH of the solution.

    Make a plot of pH as the ordinates (vertical axis) against the number of moles NaOH added as abscissae (horizontal axis). Note particularly that the pH does not vary greatly between .04 and .06 mole additions of NaOH. This phenomenon will be discussed in a later chapter under "Buffer Solutions."

33. From the data given in Table 20 calculate the approximate values of the indicator constants (K_{Ind}) for the following indicators, assuming them to be weak acids:

    (a) methyl orange

    (b) brom cresol purple

    (c) brom thymol blue

    (d) phenolphthalein

    (e) thymolphthalein

CHAPTER 5

Heterogeneous Equilibrium — The Solubility Product — Colloids

Any equilibrium which involves some kind of boundary surface is a heterogeneous one. The evaporation of water in a closed vessel is a simple example of this type of equilibrium. Here the water vapor in the enclosing container is in contact with the liquid water through the water surface. Although all heterogeneous equilibria involve boundary surfaces, yet the concentrations of the various substances involved are independent of the area of this surface. For example, the concentration of the water vapor, or the pressure exerted by the water vapor, in any container in which liquid water is also present is independent of the amount of surface exposed by the liquid. The rate at which water evaporates from the surface is greater, the greater the extent of the surface, but the condensation of the water vapor, i.e., the return of the water molecules from the gaseous state to the liquid state, is also greater, the greater the amount of exposed liquid surface. As a result of increasing the surface both the rate of evaporation and the rate of condensation are increased in such a way that the concentration of water remaining in the vapor state is constant.

For a given temperature the rate of evaporation depends only upon the amount of surface exposed; in other words, the rate of evaporation is proportional to the amount of surface exposed. This statement may be expressed in symbols in the following manner:

$$\text{Rate of evaporation} = k_1 S \qquad (1)$$

where k_1 is some proportionality constant and S the amount of surface.

The rate of condensation is proportional to the rate at which vapor molecules strike a unit area of surface and to the amount of surface. The rate at which molecules strike unit area of surface will depend upon the pressure exerted by the vapor. (If, for any given case, the pressure exerted by the vapor is doubled, twice as many molecules strike a unit surface per second.)

$$\text{Rate on unit surface} \propto \text{pressure}$$

Therefore

$$\text{Rate of condensation} \propto P \times S$$

where P is the pressure.

Or

$$\text{Rate of condensation} = k_2 P \times S \qquad (2)$$

where k_2 is some proportionality constant. At equilibrium the rate of evaporation equals the rate of condensation and

$$k_1 S = k_2 S \times P$$

Cancelling the surface term S from both sides of the equation,

$$P = \frac{k_1}{k_2} = K_{eq} \qquad (3)$$

This means that for a given temperature the vapor pressure of water vapor (or of any liquid) is a constant and is independent of the surface exposed, since the surface factor S does not appear in the final equilibrium equation.

Another type of heterogeneous equilibrium with which we are to deal to a very great extent is the equilibrium between a solid and its ions in solution, i.e., the solubility of some electrolyte in water. To illustrate this type of equilibrium let us consider a specific example, the equilibrium existing between solid barium sulfate and its saturated solution, and let us apply the Law of Mass Action to this case.

According to the theory of complete ionization, the small amount of barium sulfate which exists in water is present only as barium ions and sulfate ions. Although barium sulfate is very slightly soluble in water, it is nevertheless a salt and therefore is completely ionized. It would be considered as practically completely ionized even on the basis of the theory of incomplete ionization, since its concentration is so small in the saturated solution. When equilibrium conditions are attained, that is, when the solution is saturated with the barium sulfate, the rate at which barium sulfate passes into solution from the solid crystals is equal to the rate at which barium ions and sulfate ions collide and deposit on the surface of the crystal. The rate at which barium ions and sulfate ions leave the solid barium sulfate will depend upon the amount of surface of barium sulfate in contact with the water. If in one case the surface of barium sulfate exposed to the water is three times as great as that in another case, the rate at which it enters the solution will be three times as large.

$$\text{Rate of solution} = k_1 S \qquad (4)$$

where S is the amount of surface of barium sulfate exposed to the solution.

The rate of deposition of the barium sulfate will depend upon the rate of which barium ions and sulfate ions collide in juxtaposition on the surface. For a barium ion to deposit, it is also necessary that a sulfate ion deposit next to it, for in the barium sulfate crystals these ions lie next to each other. It would be impossible for only barium ions to deposit, since a positive charge would then develop on the crystal and crystals of barium sulfate could not be formed. The rate of combination of the barium and sulfate ions will then be proportional to the rate at which they collide with each other on the surface of the solid barium sulfate. The rate of formation of the crystal will then be proportional to the concentration of the barium ions, the concentration of the sulfate ions, and the surface. If the surface is doubled, twice as many collisions between barium ions and sulfate ions occur on the surface in a given period of time. We may then write

$$\text{Rate of deposition} = k_2(\text{Ba}^{++})(\text{SO}_4^{--})S \tag{5}$$

Under equilibrium conditions the rate of solution equals the rate of deposition, and

$$k_1S = k_2(\text{Ba}^{++})(\text{SO}_4^{--})S$$

The same amount of surface is involved in both processes of solution and deposition; the S cancels from both sides of the expression and we have

$$(\text{Ba}^{++})(\text{SO}_4^{--}) = \frac{k_1}{k_2} = K_{\text{S.P.}} \tag{6}$$

$K_{\text{S.P.}}$ is an equilibrium constant which is designated more specifically as the solubility product constant, while the product $(\text{Ba}^{++})(\text{SO}_4^{--})$ under equilibrium conditions is known as the *solubility product*.

Analyzing this expression we see that as the concentration of the barium ion is increased, if equilibrium is to be maintained, the concentration of the sulfate ion must decrease in the inverse ratio. For example, in a saturated solution of barium sulfate in pure water the concentrations of both the barium ions and the sulfate ions are each about 4×10^{-5} mole per liter. The value of $K_{\text{S.P.}}$ for barium sulfate is then $4 \times 10^{-5} \times 4 \times 10^{-5} = 1.6 \times 10^{-9}$. If now the concentration of the sulfate ions in this same solution is increased tenfold, that is, to 4×10^{-4} mole per liter by the addition of a small amount of sodium sulfate, then to maintain equilibrium the concentration of the barium ions must be decreased tenfold to 4×10^{-6} mole per liter, and now $(\text{Ba}^{++})(\text{SO}_4^{--}) = 4 \times 10^{-6} \times 4 \times 10^{-4} = 1.6 \times 10^{-9}$.

The product of the two concentrations must always equal 1.6×10^{-9}, the solubility product constant for the temperature in question. A decrease in the concentration of barium ions by the addition of sulfate ions, as just described, can only take place by the precipitation of barium sulfate. In other words, the barium ions can be removed from the solution only by the formation of solid barium sulfate. This general conclusion can be qualitatively deduced from a consideration of the Rule of Le Chatelier. The equilibrium is represented by the equation,

$$BaSO_4(solid) = Ba^{++} + SO_4^{--} \tag{7}$$

By increasing the concentration of the sulfate ions the equilibrium is shifted to the left, i.e., solid barium sulfate is formed, and this shift proceeds until a new equilibrium condition is established which, in the case cited above, results in a concentration of 4×10^{-4} mole per liter for sulfate ions and 4×10^{-6} mole per liter for barium ions.

We may apply the Law of Mass Action directly to this equilibrium without considering the rate processes involved and arrive at the same conclusion. Applying the Law of Mass Action to the equilibrium for equation (7) we may write

$$\frac{(Ba^{++})(SO_4^{--})}{(BaSO_4, solid)} = k_1 \tag{8}$$

or

$$(Ba^{++})(SO_4^{--}) = k_1(BaSO_4, solid)$$

But the concentration of solid barium sulfate does not change. Its concentration depends only upon the density of solid barium sulfate, which remains practically constant under all ordinary conditions. Therefore the product $k_1 \times (BaSO_4, solid)$ is a constant, which we designate as $K_{s.p.}$ or

$$(Ba^{++})(SO_4^{--}) = K_{s.p.} \tag{9}$$

This is the same expression as that previously obtained (equation 6).

Applying these same considerations to silver chromate which dissolves slightly in water to give two silver ions for each chromate ion,

$$Ag_2CrO_4(solid) = 2Ag^+ + CrO_4^{--} \tag{10}$$

we obtain

$$(Ag^+)^2(CrO_4^{--}) = K_{s.p.} \tag{11}$$

In this case, however, for the deposition of silver chromate from its solution it is necessary that two silver ions and one chromate ion collide on the surface of the solid silver chromate, and therefore the concentration of the silver ion is squared.

Conditions Necessary for Precipitation. Every pure substance has a definite solubility in water at a given temperature. When the concentration of the substance in water solution exceeds this solubility value, either precipitation of the substance from solution or a supersaturated solution will be the result. The solubility product is a quantitative statement of the limit of solubility of any difficultly soluble substance which forms ions. When the product of the concentrations of the ions in the solution exceeds the value of the solubility product constant either precipitation will ensue or a supersaturated solution will be formed. Supersaturated solutions form with difficulty and precipitation is the usual result of excess concentration of the ions.

To illustrate this condition let us consider a specific example. If a solution contains chloride ion at a concentration of 10^{-5} mole per liter in the form of dissolved sodium chloride or calcium chloride, will a precipitate be formed when enough silver nitrate is added to make the silver ion concentration equal to 10^{-3} mole per liter? The condition necessary for precipitation is

$$(Ag^+)(Cl^-) = K_{s.p.} \tag{12}$$

The solubility product constant for silver chloride at room temperature is 2.8×10^{-10}. In the solution under consideration $(Ag^+)(Cl^-) = 10^{-3} \times 10^{-5} = 10^{-8}$, which is greater than 2.8×10^{-10}. We see that the product of the silver ion concentration and the chloride ion concentration exceeds the solubility product constant; hence, either precipitation will follow or a supersaturated solution will be formed.

If, in the above case, the concentration of the silver ion were made 10^{-5} mole per liter rather than 10^{-3} mole per liter, no precipitation would take place under any circumstances, for now the product $(Ag^+)(Cl^-)$ would be less than the solubility product constant,

$$(Ag^+)(Cl^-) = 10^{-5} \times 10^{-5} = 10^{-10} < 2.8 \times 10^{-10}$$

Supersaturation of Difficultly Soluble Substances. As we have already indicated, precipitation will not always occur when the concentrations of the ions exceed the solubility product constant, due to the slow rate of precipitation. However, once the small crystals are formed, the precipitation

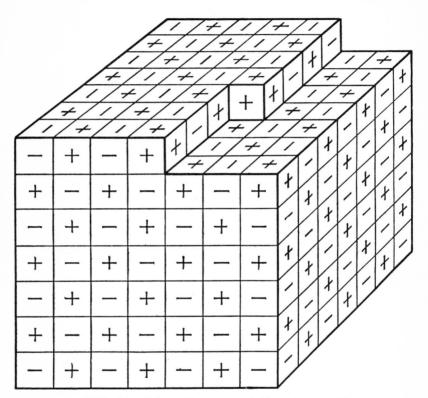

FIG. 5.1 Schematic representation of a crystal.

proceeds rapidly. The process of forming the first nucleus about which crystallization takes place is entirely different from the later crystallization. Any crystal which is within the limit of visibility even with the best microscope contains thousands of ions. Such a crystal is pictured in a general way in Figure 5.1.

In this case the ions only need find their regular positions and thus build up the crystal. When the crystal is started, however, the situation becomes entirely different. Figure 5.2 illustrates in a general way an incipient crystal. Here the forces holding the ions are certainly different since each ion occupies a corner and edge position. An additional condition is that four or more ions be sufficiently close to each other simultaneously to allow the nucleus to form. This situation is probably rather rare. We see from these illustrations that the process of incipient crystallization is undoubtedly a more complicated phenomenon than is usually imagined. Barium oxalate, BaC_2O_4, and calcium chromate, $CaCrO_4$, are two well-known examples of difficultly soluble salts which easily form supersaturated solutions.

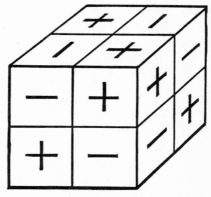

FIG. 5.2 Formation of first crystal nucleus.

Solubility of Very Small Crystals. Experiments have shown definitely that small crystals of any substance are more soluble than larger ones. Barium sulfate crystals, 10^{-4} cm. in diameter, are almost twice as soluble as crystals twenty times this diameter. The difference between the solubility of crystals 10^{-3} cm. in diameter and the solubility of larger crystals becomes inappreciable and it is only for very small crystals that this factor must be considered. Calculations have shown that ions in the interior of a crystal are bound with greater forces than are those on the faces or edges. Evidently a greater fraction of the ions occupy external positions for small than for larger crystals, and therefore the average tendency to enter the solution will be greater for the smaller crystal. From these considerations it can be deduced that crystals will grow in such a way as to produce as many interior ions (as few surface ions) as possible. Such a condition is attained only by the growth of larger crystals at the expense of smaller ones.

Since small crystals are more soluble than large crystals, the smallest crystals will in time dissolve and the larger ones will grow still larger. No real equilibrium is attained until the crystals are relatively large. Minute crystals will pass through filters and it is often possible to "digest" such precipitates to remove this condition. Heat increases the rate of solution, crystallization, and the rate at which the large crystals will grow from the smaller ones. Very often the precipitate will become sufficiently coarse, i.e., digested, either by heating or allowing the suspended precipitate to stand overnight.

The fact that small crystals have a greater solubility means that a different and larger solubility product constant must apply to these than to the larger crystals. The solubility product constants are calculated for solutions in contact with relatively large crystals. When calculating the concentrations of the different ions necessary for precipitation it must be borne in mind that a slight excess concentration over that demanded by the solubility product constant is required, since the first crystals formed are necessarily small. However, after crystallization has set in and relatively larger crystals are formed, the concentrations of the ions left in solution will be in accord with the solubility product constant.

Limit of Visibility of Precipitates Is Often the Determining Factor in Qualitative Analysis. Even though a precipitate may form from very dilute solutions of the reactants, yet that precipitate may exist in such small quantities that it is not visible. Such a precipitate would be of no consequence in qualitative analysis. For example, calculations show that a precipitate will be formed when a solution which contains as little as 10^{-20} mole per liter of copper ion, Cu^{++}, is saturated with hydrogen sulfide. Obviously, such a precipitate could not be seen. With silver chloride a precipitate is only visible when the solution before precipitation contains either silver ion or chloride ion at a concentration greater than 2×10^{-5} mole per liter. For the detection of a precipitate it is necessary that the ions producing the precipitate be present at concentrations sufficient to render the solid phase visible.

The lower limit of "visible" concentration is about 10^{-4} mole per liter for most substances.

Increase in Solubility by the Formation of Weak Acids. The addition of any acid to a saturated solution will increase the solubility of the salt if the hydrogen ion combines with the anion of the salt to form a weak acid. Thus, the equilibrium between silver acetate and its ions,

$$AgAc(solid) = Ag^+ + Ac^- \qquad (13)$$

is shifted to the right by the addition of hydrogen ion in the form of a strong acid, such as nitric acid since the hydrogen ions combine with the acetate ions to form acetic acid.

All carbonates are soluble in acid solution due to the formation of the weak acid, carbonic acid, $H_2CO_3(CO_2 + H_2O)$. Barium carbonate is readily dissolved by hydrochloric and by nitric acid solutions. The solubility of barium sulfate, on the other hand, is not increased appreciably by the addition of hydrochloric acid because sulfate ions show little tendency to combine with hydrogen ions.

The solubility of any sulfide is increased by the addition of hydrogen ion, since the weak acid, hydrogen sulfide, and its weak ion, HS^-, are formed. In some cases, however, the sulfide may be so insoluble that an increase in its solubility as much as a millionfold will not be appreciable. In other words, for the very insoluble sulfides the addition of acid to the solution does not allow an appreciable amount of the sulfide to dissolve even though the solubility is increased enormously. Equilibria involving the sulfides will be considered in detail in a later chapter.

Colloids. If any relatively insoluble substance is prepared in a finely divided state and added to a liquid, such as water, a suspension of the solid in the liquid will be formed, which will ultimately settle to the bottom of the container provided that the suspended material is not too finely divided. Very finely divided suspended material will remain in continued suspension if no subsequent coagulation of the particles takes place. Such a system is a heterogeneous one and the substance in the finely divided state is known as the ***dispersed phase*** and the liquid, the ***dispersing medium.***

When the particles in the dispersed phase are so small that they can no longer be seen or detected with the microscope, we may well ask whether this system is a suspension or a solution. If the particles were of molecular size, the system would be a solution, and if the particles were visible, a suspension or mixture would be formed. There is no sharp distinction between solutions and suspensions, and systems for which the suspended particles lie in this intermediate condition are known as ***colloidal suspensions*** or ***colloidal solutions.*** The finely divided dispersed phase in such a system is known as a ***colloid.***

As we have said previously, molecules or ions at the surface of a crystal or particle behave somewhat differently from those in the interior. The properties of any substance which has a large surface compared to its volume are more like those of the surface molecules. A very finely divided substance has a very much larger surface than one consisting of large particles. Since colloidal particles are very finely divided the increased surface is responsible for some of the properties which distinguish this class of substances from substances as we ordinarily know them. For simplicity, let us consider the total surface area of the cubic particles contained in one cm.^{3} of a given substance. If only one particle is present, each edge has a length of 1 cm. and the surface area of the cube is 6 cm.^{2} By decreasing the size of the particle, the number of particles in one cm.^{3} and the surface area are greatly increased, as is demonstrated by Table 9 on page 113.

While the limit of distinct visibility with the microscope is about 10^{-5} cm., yet particles somewhat smaller than this can be detected but not seen in outline. Such very small particles when viewed through a microscope with illumination from the side will reflect light and sparkle. Such a microscopic arrangement is known as the ultra-microscope.

The Brownian Movement. When very small particles are viewed through the microscope or ultra-microscope, they appear to be darting about in constant zig-zag motion. This

TABLE 9

SURFACE OF ONE CM.^{3} OF MATERIAL FOR
DIFFERENT PARTICLE SIZES

Size of Cubic Particle, cm.	Surface, cm.^{2}
1	6
0.1	60
0.01	600
0.001	6000
0.0001	60000
0.00001 *	600000
0.000001	6000000

* Limit of visibility.

motion of small particles is known as the Brownian Movement and is characteristic of all colloidal suspensions. When we seek an explanation of this motion we are led back to the kinetic theory of matter, which postulates that all molecules are in motion. Any particle in suspension is bombarded on all sides by the moving molecules of the dispersing medium. When the particles are sufficiently large the impact of the molecules on the side of the particle is not great enough to cause any appreciable movement. Furthermore, the bombardment on one side of the particle is counterbalanced by the bombardment on the opposite side, so the net result is that there is no appreciable momentum imparted to the particle in any particular direction. When the particle is very small the probability that it will be struck simultaneously with equal force on two opposite sides becomes small, and since the particle itself is small its velocity acquired by impact will be large and a visible motion results.

Classes of Colloids. Colloidal systems are not confined to the suspension of solids in liquids, although such suspensions are of most importance in qualitative analysis and in most problems in chemistry. One liquid dispersed in another is known as an emulsion; mayonnaise dressing is an example of an emulsion, essentially an oil in water. The different general types of colloidal systems are given below in tabular form.

TABLE 10

TYPES OF COLLOIDAL SYSTEMS

Dispersing Phase	Dispersed Phase	Type
gas	gas	none (homogeneous)
gas	liquid	fog
gas	solid	smoke
liquid	gas	foam
liquid	liquid	emulsion (mayonnaise dressing)
liquid	solid	suspension (muddy water)
solid	gas	solidified foam (pumice)
solid	liquid	
solid	solid	ruby glass

Adsorption. Any molecule, atom, or ion may be conceived as being surrounded by a field of force, which field is not neutralized or "satisfied" when the particle is existing alone in space. This attractive force varies considerably with different particles. Thus the helium atom has a very small field, as evidenced by its very low boiling point, while the molecules of a substance having a high melting point or high boiling point possess relatively large attractive forces. When a molecule or ion is situated in the interior of a crystal these forces are neutralized or satisfied to the greatest possible extent. At the surface of a crystal, however, the attractive forces are not completely neutralized and the residual force of the surface molecules attracts other particles and holds them fast to the surface. This adherence of foreign particles to any surface is known as *adsorption.* The smaller the particle the greater will be the amount of surface and the larger the total effect of surface forces. Not all finely divided particles are perfect crystals and the less perfect the crystalline form the greater will be the adsorptive forces, for under such conditions the the attractive forces of the molecules in the crystal are less satisfied by each other. Gelatinous precipitates like aluminum hydroxide and ferric hydroxide are very probably imperfectly crystallized and these substances have very great adsorptive capacities.

The small size of colloidal particles, because of the increased surface area, makes them particularly good adsorbents. Not only are neutral molecules adsorbed to their surfaces but ions as well. The adsorption of ions on the surface of colloidal particles is preferential, i.e., not all ions are adsorbed alike. In some cases negative ions are adsorbed more readily than positive ions. In such cases the colloidal particles become negatively charged. Some colloids, on the other hand, become positively charged through the adsorption of positive ions. If all the colloidal particles have the same charge, they will repel each other and prevent coagulation. The adsorption of ions of like charge, therefore, stabilizes the colloidal solution. When placed in an electric field — between two charged plates — negatively charged particles will move toward the positive plate and positively charged particles toward the negative plate. Under some conditions these particles become neutralized at the electrode and "plate out" just as ions may be plated from solution. By such a process rubber may be "plated out" of its suspension.

Finely divided barium sulfate has a great tendency to adsorb other ions from solution. In fact this tendency is so great that it becomes very difficult to obtain pure barium sulfate by precipitation.

Coagulation of Colloids. Not all colloidal suspensions are stable. Many of them tend to coagulate through the adherence of the particles for each other. When silver chloride is precipitated from solution it first forms a very finely divided suspension but in a short time these fine particles coagulate and settle to the bottom of the container. This process is hastened by heating, and in many instances this simple expedient is sufficient to cause coagulation.

When a negatively charged colloid such as arsenic trisulfide, As_2S_3, is in suspension, it may be coagulated by adding certain positive ions to the solution in the form of salts, acids or bases, which have a tendency to be adsorbed. The adsorbed positive ions neutralize the negative ions already adsorbed and the more nearly neutral particles then coagulate. In general, the hydrogen ion is highly adsorbed and the addition of an acid to this suspension precipitates it.

In general, those ions which are multiply charged are more effective in causing coagulation than singly charged ions. Aluminum ion is more effective than magnesium ion, Mg^{++}, and this ion in turn is more effective than sodium ion, Na^+.

In qualitative analysis finely divided precipitates are often very troublesome and annoying. Coagulation may often be effected by either heating or by the addition of an acid. It is evident that salts can very seldom be added to the solution, since in most cases they will interfere with the analysis.

The applications of dyestuffs to cloth fiber is usually a process of adsorption, the dyestuff being adsorbed on the fiber. Dyes will not "take" to certain fibers and in such a case the material to be dyed may be coated with a coagulant such as aluminum hydroxide or stannic acid, which in turn will adsorb the dye and bind it to the cloth fiber. Coagulants used for such purposes are known as **mordants** and the combination between the mordant and the dye is called a **lake.**

In qualitative analysis use is made of the adsorptive properties of aluminum hydroxide in its detection. This substance possesses the property of adsorbing a dyestuff known as aluminon. When the latter is added to a suspension of aluminum hydroxide, $Al(OH)_3$, it is adsorbed preferentially by the hydroxide and the suspension, which is a lake, assumes a characteristic red color.

Catalysts. Preferential adsorption is the property that gives contact catalysts their special effectiveness. The substances which react with each other are adsorbed on the surface of the catalyst and the products formed are adsorbed to a lesser extent and thus leave the surface of activity.

The preparation of a catalyst usually greatly influences its activity. If the catalyst is prepared in such a way that the substance formed is not well crystallized, it usually becomes more active. Thus, when iron is used as a catalyst it is most active when prepared from iron oxalate. This compound is broken down at low temperatures to ferric oxide, carbon monoxide and carbon dioxide, and the ferric oxide in turn is reduced with hydrogen at a low temperature. At the low temperature perfect iron crystals form with difficulty; the imperfect crystals are the better adsorbers, hence the greater their catalytic activity. The addition of foreign substances such as sodium hydroxide or aluminum oxide often enhances this activity of the catalyst. These substances, known as *promoters,* very probably prevent the formation of perfect or large crystals by keeping the iron atoms apart.

Examples of Problems Involving the Solubility Product Principle

Example 1.

The solubility of $BaSO_4$ in water is .00092 g. per 100 ml. What is the value of the $K_{S.P.}$ for $BaSO_4$?

First, calculate the solubility of $BaSO_4$ in moles per liter. .00092 g. per 100 ml. is equivalent to .0092 g. per liter.

The molecular weight of $BaSO_4$ is 233.4.

$$\frac{9.2 \times 10^{-3}}{233.4} \text{ mole per liter} = 3.9 \times 10^{-5} \text{ mole per liter}$$

This means that there is 3.9×10^{-5} mole each of the barium ion and sulfate ion in solution.

The solubility product constant is therefore

$$(Ba^{++})(SO_4^{--}) = 3.9 \times 10^{-5} \times 3.9 \times 10^{-5} = 1.5 \times 10^{-9}$$

Example 2.

Silver chromate, Ag_2CrO_4, is soluble to the extent of .0259 g. per liter. Calculate the solubility product constant.

The molecular weight of silver chromate is 331.8. The solubility in moles per liter is

$$\frac{.0259 \text{ g. per liter}}{331.8 \text{ g. per mole}} = 7.8 \times 10^{-5} \text{ mole per liter}$$

Since silver chromate is completely ionized there is 7.8×10^{-5} mole of chromate ion and $2 \times 7.8 \times 10^{-5}$ mole of silver ion in solution.

The $K_{S.P.}$ is then

$$(Ag^+)^2(CrO_4^{--}) = (2 \times 7.8 \times 10^{-5})^2 \times 7.8 \times 10^{-5} = 1.9 \times 10^{-12}$$

Example 3.

Calculate the solubility of $SrSO_4$ in g. per 100 ml. from its solubility product constant. $K_{S.P.} = 7.6 \times 10^{-7}$.

Let X be the number of moles of $SrSO_4$ in 1 liter of solution.

Since $SrSO_4$ is completely dissociated, there will be X moles of Sr^{++} ion and X moles of SO_4^{--} ion in solution.

$$SrSO_4(solid) = Sr^{++} + SO_4^{--}$$
$$X \quad \rightarrow \quad X \qquad X$$
$$(Sr^{++})(SO_4^{--}) = X^2$$
$$X^2 = 7.6 \times 10^{-7} = 76 \times 10^{-8}$$
$$X = 8.7 \times 10^{-4} \text{ mole per liter}$$

This is not only the concentration of the strontium ion and of the sulfate ion, but it also represents the concentration of the total amount of strontium sulfate in solution. The molecular weight of strontium sulfate is 184. There are therefore

$$8.7 \times 10^{-4} \times 184 = 0.16 \text{ g. } SrSO_4 \text{ per liter or .016 g. per 100 ml.}$$

Example 4.

Calculate the solubility of $Mg(OH)_2$ in g. per liter from the solubility product constant. $(K_{S.P.} = 8.9 \times 10^{-12})$.

X = number of moles of $Mg(OH)_2$ dissolved — (total)
X = number of moles of Mg^{++} ion in solution at equilibrium
$2X$ = number of moles of OH^- ion in solution at equilibrium

$$(Mg^{++})(OH^-)^2 = X(2X)^2 = 4X^3 = 8.9 \times 10^{-12}$$
$$X^3 = 2.2 \times 10^{-12}$$
$$X = 1.3 \times 10^{-4} \text{ mole per liter}$$

The molecular weight of $Mg(OH)_2$ is 58.3. Therefore the solubility is

$$1.3 \times 10^{-4} \times 58.3 = 76 \times 10^{-4} = .0076 \text{ g. per liter}$$

Example 5.

What is the concentration of the Ag^+ ion in moles per liter left in solution if AgCl is precipitated by adding enough HCl to a solution of $AgNO_3$ to make the final Cl^- ion concentration 0.1 molar?

$$K_{S.P.}(AgCl) = 2.8 \times 10^{-10}$$
$$(Ag^+)(Cl^-) = 2.8 \times 10^{-10}$$
$$(Ag^+) \times 0.1 = 2.8 \times 10^{-10}$$
$$(Ag^+) = \frac{2.8 \times 10^{-10}}{0.1} = 2.8 \times 10^{-9} \text{ mole per liter}$$

Example 6.

(a) A solution contains .01 mole Cl^- ion and .001 mole CrO_4^{--} ion per liter. Ag^+ ion is gradually added to this solution in the form of $AgNO_3$. Which will be precipitated first, AgCl or Ag_2CrO_4?

$$K_{S.P.} (AgCl) = 2.8 \times 10^{-10}$$
$$K_{S.P.} (Ag_2CrO_4) = 1.9 \times 10^{-12}$$

(1) Calculate (Ag^+) necessary to precipitate AgCl.

$$(Ag^+)(Cl^-) = (Ag^+) \times .01 = 2.8 \times 10^{-10}$$

$$(Ag^+) = \frac{2.8 \times 10^{-10}}{.01} = 2.8 \times 10^{-8} \text{ mole per liter}$$

(2) Calculate (Ag^+) necessary to precipitate Ag_2CrO_4.

$$(Ag^+)^2(CrO_4^{--}) = (Ag^+)^2 \times .001 = 1.9 \times 10^{-12}$$
$$(Ag^+)^2 = \frac{1.9 \times 10^{-12}}{10^{-3}} = 1.9 \times 10^{-9} = 19 \times 10^{-10}$$

$$(Ag^+) = 4.35 \times 10^{-5} \text{ mole per liter}$$

A greater concentration of Ag^+ ion is necessary to cause precipitation of Ag_2CrO_4 than AgCl, so AgCl will precipitate first.

(b) What will be the concentration of the Cl^- ion in this solution when the Ag_2CrO_4 begins to precipitate by the continued addition of $AgNO_3$? Bear in mind that as the AgCl is precipitated by the addition of Ag^+ ion the Cl^- ion concentration is reduced.

The Ag^+ ion concentration necessary to precipitate the Ag_2CrO_4 is 4.35×10^{-5} mole per liter. For this concentration of Ag^+ ion the Cl^- ion concentration will be

$$(Cl^-) = \frac{2.8 \times 10^{-10}}{(Ag^+)} = \frac{2.8 \times 10^{-10}}{4.35 \times 10^{-5}} = 0.644 \times 10^{-5}$$

$$= 6.44 \times 10^{-6} \text{ mole per liter}$$

(c) What fraction of the amount of Cl^- ion originally present remains in solution when Ag_2CrO_4 begins to precipitate?

$$(Cl^-) \text{ (original)} = .01 \text{ mole per liter}$$

(Cl^-) when precipitation of Ag_2CrO_4 begins $= 6.44 \times 10^{-6}$ mole per liter

$$\frac{6.44 \times 10^{-6}}{.01} = 6.44 \times 10^{-4} = .000644$$

$$= .0644 \text{ percent of original } Cl^- \text{ ion present.}$$

*Calculations Involving Both the Ionization Constant
and Solubility Product Constant*

Example 7.

How many moles of NH_4Cl must be added to 100 ml. of 0.1 M NH_4OH solution to prevent precipitation of $Mn(OH)_2$ when this solution is added to 100 ml. of a .02 M solution of $MnCl_2$?

$$K_{SP.} (Mn(OH)_2) = 2 \times 10^{-13}$$
$$K_I (NH_4OH) = 1.8 \times 10^{-5}$$

In working this problem consider the concentrations of all substances in the final solution after the two original solutions are mixed. The concentration of the Mn^{++} ion will be .01 M and the OH^- ion just necessary to begin the precipitation of the $Mn(OH)_2$ can be calculated from its solubility product constant.

$$(Mn^{++}) \times (OH^-)^2 = .01 \times (OH^-)^2 = 2 \times 10^{-13}$$
$$(OH^-)^2 = 20 \times 10^{-12}$$
$$(OH^-) = 4.5 \times 10^{-6} \text{ mole per liter}$$

If the (OH^-) exceeds this calculated value, $Mn(OH)_2$ will be precipitated. To prevent precipitation, the (OH^-) must be less than this value. The (OH^-) can be diminished by the addition of NH_4^+ ion, in the form of NH_4Cl. The concentration of the NH_4^+ ion is equilibrium with this low concentration of OH^- ion can be calculated from the K_I for NH_4OH.

$$\frac{(NH_4^+)(OH^-)}{(NH_4OH)} = 1.8 \times 10^{-5}$$

The concentration of the NH_4OH is practically .05 mole per liter.

$$\frac{(NH_4^+) \times 4.5 \times 10^{-6}}{.05} = 1.8 \times 10^{-5}$$

$$(NH_4^+) = \frac{1.8 \times 10^{-5} \times .05}{4.5 \times 10^{-6}}$$

$$= 0.2 \text{ mole per liter}$$

$$= .040 \text{ mole per 200 ml.}$$

Since this is the total amount of NH_4^+ ion which must be added in the form of NH_4Cl, it is this amount which must be added to the original 100 ml. of NH_4OH. The amount of NH_4^+ ion formed by the dissociation of NH_4OH is negligibly small and therefore has been neglected in the calculations.

Questions and Problems

(In all of the following problems in this Chapter the hydrolysis of the ions is neglected)

1. What is a heterogeneous equilibrium?
2. If solid barium sulfate is in equilibrium with its ions, Ba^{++} and SO_4^{--}, in solution, will this equilibrium be effected by the addition of more solid barium sulfate?
3. If in a saturated solution of silver chloride, the concentrations of the Ag^+ ion and Cl^- ion are each 1.67×10^{-5} M, what will be the final concentration of the Ag^+ ion if sufficient sodium chloride is added to the solution to increase the Cl^- ion concentration one hundredfold?
4. What are the conditions necessary for the precipitation of a relatively insoluble salt?
5. If the product of the concentrations of the ions exceeds the solubility product will precipitation always occur? Explain.
6. Is the solubility product for very small crystals the same as that for large crystals?
7. Explain why small crystals would be expected to be more soluble than large crystals.
8. What is the order of magnitude of the concentration of the ions necessary to produce a precipitate visible to the naked eye?
9. If a cube 1 cm. on the side is divided into one million cubes each of the same size, how much is the total surface increased?

10. Why do the surfaces of imperfect crystals adsorb substances to a greater extent than do those of perfect crystals?
11. How may colloids be coagulated?
12. Explain the use of "aluminon" reagent in qualitative analysis.
13. Why are catalysts more active when prepared at low temperatures?
14. The solubility of each of the following salts is given below in terms of grams per 100 ml. of solution. Calculate the solubility product constant for each substance.

Substance	*Solubility in grams per 100 ml.*
(a) AgCl	2.40×10^{-4}
(b) AgBr	1.35×10^{-5}
(c) AgI	2.15×10^{-7}
(d) $BaSO_4$	8.95×10^{-4}
(e) Ag_2CrO_4	2.56×10^{-3}
(f) $CaCO_3$	8.3×10^{-4}
(g) SrF_2	7.3×10^{-3}

15. The solubility product constants are given below for a few difficultly soluble substances. Calculate the solubility of each in terms of grams of solute per 100 ml. of solution.

Substance	*Solubility Product Constant*
(a) $Mg(OH)_2$	8.9×10^{-12}
(b) $BaCO_3$	1.6×10^{-9}
(c) Ag_2CrO_4	1.9×10^{-12}
(d) $Fe(OH)_3$	6×10^{-38}
(e) MgC_2O_4	8.6×10^{-5}
(f) $SrSO_4$	7.6×10^{-7}
(g) CuI	1×10^{-12}
(h) AgCN	1.6×10^{-14}

16. The solubility product constant for $BaCrO_4$ is 8.5×10^{-11}. If the concentration of the barium ion in a solution is .04 M, calculate the minimum concentration of the chromate ion, in terms of moles per liter, that will be required to begin the precipitation of barium chromate, assuming that a supersaturated solution is not formed. How many grams of sodium chromate must be added to 200 ml. of water to produce this amount of chromate ion?

17. How many grams of silver chromate will dissolve in 100 ml. of 0.1 M potassium chromate solution?

18. (a) Calculate the number of grams of PbS that would precipitate from 1 liter of saturated solution of PbI_2, if the solution is saturated with H_2S, assuming that the concentration of the sulfide ion is kept at 1×10^{-15} mole per liter.
    (b) How many moles of Pb^{++} are left in solution?

19. Calculate the number of moles of AgCl that will dissolve (a) in 1 liter of 0.1 M KCl solution; (b) in 1 liter of 0.1 M $CaCl_2$ solution.

20. If $AgNO_3$ is added slowly to each of the following solutions, calculate the concentration of the Ag^+ ion in the resulting solution just after the first trace of precipitate appears.
    (a) 0.1 M KBr solution.　　　　(b) 0.1 M K_2CrO_4 solution.
    (c) A solution containing 1 mole HCl and .001 mole KI per liter.

21. The solubility of PbI_2 is .058 g. per 100 ml. at room temperature.
    (a) What is the concentration of Pb^{++}? Of I^-?
    (b) Write the solubility product expression for PbI_2.
    (c) Calculate the solubility product constant for PbI_2.

22. The solubility product constant for calcium oxalate at room temperature is 1.3×10^{-9}.
    (a) What is the concentration of Ca^{++} and of $C_2O_4^{--}$ in a saturated solution of calcium oxalate?
    (b) Calculate the number of grams of calcium oxalate dissolved in a liter of saturated solution.

23. The solubility product constant for lead iodate at room temperature is 2.6×10^{-13}. How many grams of lead iodate are required to make 200 ml. of a saturated solution?

24. Calculate the concentration of the OH^- in a saturated solution of silver hydroxide.

25. How many grams of NaOH are required to start the precipitation of $Mg(OH)_2$ in 100 ml. of a solution which contains 0.1 g. of $MgCl_2$?

26. If to a liter of solution containing 0.1 mole of Ag^+ enough Cl^- is added to make the final concentration of the Cl^- ion remaining in solution 1×10^{-4} mole per liter, what fraction of Ag^+ is left in solution? (Assume no volume change.)

27. $AgNO_3$ is added to a solution containing .001 mole Cl^- and .001 mole Br^- per liter. What are the concentrations of Cl^- and of Br^- remaining when the AgCl just begins to precipitate?

28. How many grams of Ag^+ are present in (a) 5 ml. of a saturated solution of AgBr?

(b) 5 ml. of a saturated solution of AgCl?

29. How many moles of AgCl would dissolve in 1 liter of the following solutions:

(a) 0.1 M NaCl

(b) 0.1 M KNO$_3$

(c) Pure water

(d) 0.1 M AgNO$_3$

(e) 1×10^{-5} M HCl

30. Solid AgCl is added to a 0.1 M KBr solution. What is the ratio of the (Cl^-) to the (Br^-) in the solution when equilibrium is attained?

31. The solubility of the AgI is 2.15×10^{-7} g. per 100 ml. in water, and that of AgCl is 2.4×10^{-4} g. per 100 ml. Assuming that there is no volume change when pulverized solid AgNO$_3$ is added little by little to 1 liter of a solution containing 0.1 mole of KCl and 0.1 mole of KI:

(a) At what concentration of Ag^+ will AgI first precipitate?

(b) At what concentration of Ag^+ will AgCl begin to precipitate?

(c) Which precipitates first, AgI or AgCl?

(d) What will be the concentration of I^- when AgCl starts to precipitate?

(e) What percentage of the I^- initially present will remain in solution when AgCl begins to precipitate?

(f) What will be the ratio of the concentration of Cl^- to that of I^- in the solution when AgCl begins to precipitate? (Use result of (d) to obtain answer.)

(g) When half of the Cl^- initially present has been precipitated as AgCl, what will be the concentration of (1) Ag^+ and (2) I^- in the supernatant liquid?

(h) What is the ratio of the concentration of Cl^- to that of I^- in the supernatant liquid of part (g)?

32. The solubility of PbI$_2$ is 1.28×10^{-3} mole per liter and that of AgI 9.2×10^{-9} mole per liter at room temperature. Assuming that there is no volume change when solid NaI is added slowly to 1 liter of a solution which is .01 M in Pb^{++} and .01 M in Ag^+:

(a) At what concentration of I^- will AgI first precipitate?

(b) At what concentration of I^- will PbI$_2$ first precipitate?

(c) Which will precipitate first, AgI or PbI$_2$?

(d) What will be the concentration of Ag^+ in the solution when PbI$_2$ first starts to precipitate?

(e) What is, therefore, the ratio of the concentration of Pb^{++} to that of Ag^+ at this point?

(f) When the concentration of Pb^{++} has been reduced to half of its original value, what will be the concentration of I^-?

(g) Then what will the concentration of Ag^+ be at this concentration of Pb^{++}?

(h) What is then the ratio of the concentration of Pb^{++} to that of Ag^+ at the point described in parts (f) and (g)? Compare with the answer to part (e).

(i) When AgI and PbI_2 precipitate together, show from the solubility product constants that the concentration of the Ag^+ is always proportional to the square root of the concentration of the Pb^{++} under these conditions.

(j) Why are the ratios found in parts (c) and (h) not the same, whereas similar ratios in Problem 31 were found equal?

33. How many moles of $AgAc$ will dissolve in a liter of a 0.1 M HNO_3 solution? (The $K_{S.P.}$ for $AgAc$ is 4×10^{-3}.) (Note that in the resulting solution the concentration of HAc (unionized) is approximately 0.1 M.)

34. A solution contains .01 M Mg^{++} and .05 M NH_4Cl. How much NH_4OH must be added to 1 liter of this solution to begin the precipitation of $Mg(OH)_2$?

35. How many grams of NH_4Cl must be added to 50 ml. of 0.2 M NH_4OH to prevent the precipitation of $Mn(OH)_2$ when this solution is added to 50 ml. of .02 M $MnCl_2$ solution?

36. If 50 g. of $MgCl_2$ and 50 ml. of 6 M NH_4OH are added to enough water to make 1 liter of solution, how much NH_4Cl in grams must be added to this same solution to prevent precipitation of $Mg(OH)_2$? (Assume no volume change.)

37. A solution is .01 M in hydrogen ion and 0.1 M with respect to acetic acid. Calculate the concentration of the silver ion, in moles per liter, that will be required to just start precipitation of silver acetate.

CHAPTER 6

Polybasic Acids
— Precipitation with
Hydrogen Sulfide

Polybasic acids are those acids the molecules of which have more than one replaceable hydrogen atom and therefore dissociate to produce hydrogen ions in more than one step. Dibasic acids and tribasic acids, which are special classes of polybasic acids, have two and three replaceable hydrogen atoms respectively. Phosphoric acid, an example of a tribasic acid, dissociates to produce hydrogen ion in three steps, which are represented by the equations:

$$H_3PO_4 = H_2PO_4^- + H^+ \tag{1}$$

$$H_2PO_4^- = HPO_4^{--} + H^+ \tag{2}$$

$$HPO_4^{--} = PO_4^{---} + H^+ \tag{3}$$

The process represented by equation (1) takes place to a greater extent than either (2) or (3), and (2) to a greater extent than (3). The ions, $H_2PO_4^-$ and HPO_4^{--}, resulting from the dissociation of phosphoric acid, are likewise acids and the relative strengths of H_3PO_4 and these ions as acids can be readily determined by a consideration of the three dissociation constants for phosphoric acid. The dissociation constant for the process represented by equation (1) is 7.5×10^{-3}; for the process represented by equation (2), 6.2×10^{-8}; and for (3), 1×10^{-12}. A 0.1 molar solution of phosphoric acid dissociates according to equation (1) to the extent of about 25 percent, while the concentration of PO_4^{---} in this same solution produced by step (3) is only about 10^{-18} molar. This small concentration of PO_4^{---} ion is the reason that most insoluble phosphates cannot be precipitated from phosphoric acid solution.

Sulfuric acid, the commonest example of a dibasic acid, is 100 percent dissociated into H^+ and HSO_4^- ions. The bisulfate ion, which dissociates according to the equation

$$HSO_4^- = H^+ + SO_4^{--} \tag{4}$$

behaves like a weak acid. Its dissociation constant is 1.26×10^{-2} and in a 0.1 molar H_2SO_4 solution the concentration of the SO_4^{--} is approximately .01 molar; i.e., about 10 percent of the HSO_4^- dissociates in sulfuric acid of this concentration. The bisulfate ion in a 0.1 molar solution of $NaHSO_4$, on the other hand, dissociates to the extent of about 30 percent. The dissociation of the HSO_4^- in sulfuric acid solution is less than that in a solution of $NaHSO_4$ of the same concentration because the excess H^+ has a common ion effect in the H_2SO_4 solution and represses the ionization of the HSO_4^-. There are no polybasic acids which are 100 percent dissociated in every step of the ionization.

Two common examples of dibasic acids which are weak in both stages of ionization are hydrogen sulfide, H_2S, and carbonic acid, H_2CO_3.

The first stage in the dissociation of hydrogen sulfide produces hydrogen and bisulfide ions.

$$H_2S = H^+ + HS^- \tag{5}$$

The HS^- formed in this reaction in turn dissociates to form hydrogen ion and sulfide ion.

$$HS^- = H^+ + S^{--} \tag{6}$$

The equilibrium expression for the first stage (equation 5) is

$$\frac{(H^+)(HS^-)}{(H_2S)} = K_1 = 1 \times 10^{-7} \tag{7}$$

and for the second stage,

$$\frac{(H^+)(S^{--})}{(HS^-)} = K_2 = 1.3 \times 10^{-13} \tag{8}$$

It will be observed that the constant for the second stage of ionization is almost 10^6 times smaller than that for the first stage; the HS^- ion is a very much weaker acid than is H_2S. The bisulfide ion is such a weak acid that of the amount formed by the dissociation of hydrogen sulfide only a very small fraction dissociates. For this reason, the concentrations of the H^+ and HS^- ions are practically equal to each other in a solution of pure hydrogen sulfide. The concentration of hydrogen sulfide in a solution saturated with the gas at 1 atmosphere pressure is very nearly 0.1 molar at room temperature, $25°$ C. With this information it is not difficult to calculate the concentration of both the hydrogen ion and the bisulfide ion in a solution saturated with hydrogen sulfide. Since only a very small fraction of the hydrogen sulfide dissociates we may consider the concentration of the undissociated portion of the hydrogen sulfide to be 0.1 molar (the amount which dissociates is negligible compared with 0.1). If we let X be the concentration of the hydrogen ion at equilibrium, X will also be the concentration of the bisulfide ion. We then have:

$$\frac{(H^+)(HS^-)}{(H_2S)} = \frac{X^2}{0.1} = 1 \times 10^{-7}$$

$$X^2 = 1 \times 10^{-8}$$

$$X = 1 \times 10^{-4} \text{ molar} = (H^+) = (HS^-)$$

If hydrogen ion is added to a saturated solution of hydrogen sulfide, the concentration of the undissociated hydrogen sulfide molecules will not be changed appreciably but the concentration of the bisulfide ion will be decreased and its concentration will be inversely proportional to the concentration of the hydrogen ion. The greater the concentration of the hydrogen ion, the smaller will be the concentration of the bisulfide ion.

A calculation of the concentration of the sulfide ion involves the second stage of ionization. For a saturated solution of hydrogen sulfide, we have just calculated the concentration of the hydrogen ion and of the bisulfide ion to be 1×10^{-4} molar. Since the dissociation constant for the second stage is so small, only a very small amount of the bisulfide ion dissociates; that is, the second dissociation (equation 6) does not lower the concentration of the bisulfide ion appreciably. Its concentration may then be considered to be 1×10^{-4} molar even after the second stage of dissociation has been taken into account. Likewise, the amount of hydrogen ion produced by the second stage of ionization does not add appreciably to the hydrogen ion concentration produced by the dissociation of the H_2S. Hence we may take the final equilibrium value of the hydrogen ion concentration to be the same as that calculated for the first stage of ionization, namely 1×10^{-4} mole per liter. In other words, even after the second stage of ionization has been considered, the hydrogen ion and bisulfide ion concentrations are practically the same. We may then calculate the sulfide ion concentration:

$$\frac{(H^+)(S^{--})}{(HS^-)} = K_2 = 1.3 \times 10^{-13}$$

$$\frac{1 \times 10^{-4}(S^{--})}{1 \times 10^{-4}} = 1.3 \times 10^{-13}$$

$$(S^{--}) = 1.3 \times 10^{-13} \text{ mole per liter} \qquad (9)$$

Since the concentration of the hydrogen ion of the numerator in this expression cancels the bisulfide ion concentration of the denominator, the concentration of the sulfide ion is 1.3×10^{-13} molar. It will be noted that this value will be the approximate concentration of the sulfide ion even though the solution may not be saturated with hydrogen sulfide, for even under these conditions the concentration of the hydrogen ion and the concentration of the bisulfide ion will be practically equal to each other and will cancel in the equilibrium expression, leaving the sulfide ion concentration still 1.3×10^{-13} molar. In fact, for any weak polybasic acid the concentration of the doubly charged anion is practically equal to the second ionization constant.

The product of the equilibrium expressions for stages one and two of ionization (equations 7 and 8) is

$$\frac{(H^+)(HS^-)}{(H_2S)} \times \frac{(H^+)(S^{--})}{(HS^-)} = \frac{(H^+)^2(S^{--})}{(H_2S)} = K_1 \times K_2 = K_{12} \quad (10)$$

$$K_{12} = 1 \times 10^{-7} \times 1.3 \times 10^{-13} = 1.3 \times 10^{-20}$$

or

$$\frac{(H^+)^2(S^{--})}{(H_2S)} = 1.3 \times 10^{-20} \quad (11)$$

This last expression cannot be used by itself to calculate both the concentration of the hydrogen ion and the sulfide ion in a solution which contains only hydrogen sulfide because both the concentration of the hydrogen ion and the concentration of the sulfide ion are unknown quantities and two equations are necessary to solve for two unknowns. The other equation necessary would involve K_1 alone. If the hydrogen ion concentration is determined from K_1 alone, then the sulfide ion concentration may be determined from equations (8) or (11).

Since a saturated solution of hydrogen sulfide in water is 0.1 molar with respect to the gas, we may write

$$\frac{(H^+)^2(S^{--})}{0.1} = 1.3 \times 10^{-20}$$

or

$$(H^+)^2(S^{--}) = 1.3 \times 10^{-21} = K_{12}(sat.) \quad (12)$$

Equation (12) may be used when the hydrogen ion concentration of the saturated solution of H_2S is known or calculated from equation (7).

When the hydrogen ion is added to the solution in the form of a strong acid then the sulfide ion concentration may be determined from equation (12), since the hydrogen ion concentration is now known from the amount of strong acid added; the amount produced by the dissociation of hydrogen sulfide is negligible. For example, suppose we wish to calculate the sulfide ion concentration in a saturated solution of hydrogen sulfide to which hydrochloric acid has been added to make the hydrogen ion concentration 0.1 molar. Applying equation (12), we have

$$(H^+)^2(S^{--}) = (0.1)^2(S^{--}) = 1.3 \times 10^{-21}$$

$$(S^{--}) = \frac{1.3 \times 10^{-21}}{.01} = 1.3 \times 10^{-19} \text{ molar}$$

In the same way we may calculate the sulfide ion concentration for solutions of any hydrogen ion concentration. The concentration of the sulfide ion is thus inversely proportional to the square of the hydrogen ion concentration. If the hydrogen ion concentration is increased tenfold over that in any given case, the sulfide ion concentration will accordingly be decreased one hundredfold. The following table gives the sulfide ion concentration for different solutions containing hydrogen sulfide. For the sake of completeness the table includes solutions of the sulfides for which calculations of the sulfide ion concentrations are considered in the next chapter on hydrolysis.

TABLE 11

CONCENTRATION OF THE SULFIDE ION IN
DIFFERENT SOLUTIONS

Solution	(S^{--}) (Molar Concentrations)
0.1 molar H_2S	1.3×10^{-13}
0.1 molar H_2S and 0.001 molar H^+ ion	1.3×10^{-15}
0.1 molar H_2S and 0.01 molar H^+ ion	1.3×10^{-17}
0.1 molar H_2S and 0.1 molar H^+ ion	1.3×10^{-19}
0.1 molar H_2S and 1.0 molar H^+ ion	1.3×10^{-21}
0.1 molar $(NH_4)_2S$	2×10^{-5}
0.1 molar Na_2S	5×10^{-2}

Precipitation of the Sulfides. The concentration of the sulfide ion, in a solution saturated with hydrogen sulfide and which contains hydrogen ion in 1 molar concentration, has the exceedingly low value of about 1.3×10^{-21} mole per liter. Since there are 6×10^{23} molecules in one mole, 1.3×10^{-21} mole per liter corresponds to about 800 sulfide ions per liter — roughly, one ion per ml. (milliliter). Yet when this solution is added to one containing .001 mole of copper ion, Cu^{++}, per liter, a black precipitate is formed immediately. It might seem inconceivable that such a small concentration of sulfide ions could cause this rapid precipitation of cupric sulfide, CuS, if the reaction mechanism were the simple combination between sulfide and cupric ions as represented by the equation,

$$Cu^{++} + S^{--} = CuS(\text{solid}) \qquad (13)$$

The concentration of the bisulfide ion in such a solution is very much larger than the concentration of the sulfide ion, and conceivably the bisulfide ion, HS^-, could combine with the cupric ions, and hydrogen sulfide would be liberated in such a way that the final result would be

$$2HS^- + Cu^{++} = CuS(\text{solid}) + H_2S \qquad (14)$$

In fact, it is not out of the question that an unstable intermediate compound, $Cu(HS)_2$, could be formed which immediately breaks down to form CuS and H_2S. Such processes are known in the formation of oxides by precipitation. For example, when a solution of silver nitrate is added to one of sodium hydroxide, there results a dark brown precipitate of silver oxide, Ag_2O. If the solutions used are dilute, a yellow-brown precipitate is first observed, very probably AgOH, and this changes to the brown precipitate of silver oxide with the loss of water,

$$2AgOH = Ag_2O + H_2O \qquad (15)$$

Likewise, cupric hydroxide, $Cu(OH)_2$, a blue precipitate formed by the addition of a sodium hydroxide solution to one containing cupric ion, such as a copper sulfate solution, slowly changes to black cupric oxide, CuO, when the precipitate is heated to 100° C.

$$Cu(OH)_2 = CuO + H_2O \qquad (16)$$

Sulfur and oxygen are in the same group in the periodic system, and hydrogen sulfide is therefore the analogue of water. Since hydrogen sulfide dissociates in two steps to give sulfide ions, so water undoubtedly does the same to give the oxide ion, O^{--} ion, but since we have no means of measuring the oxide ion concentration, we have neglected it entirely. The oxide ion must be present at extremely low concentration, much lower than that of the sulfide ion in water solution. In view of these considerations it would not be surprising if we found that in the case of the precipitation of a sulfide the unstable hydrosulfide first formed and the breakdown of this to the sulfide and hydrogen sulfide then occurred.

The mechanism of the formation of a sulfide precipitate, or any precipitate for that matter, is immaterial in our calculations or reasoning involving the solubility product principle. We always assume that equilibrium is maintained, and when such is the case, the concentrations of the substances left in solution are those calculated by this principle, provided of course that the data upon which the calculations are based (solubility product constants) are correct. The precipitation of a given sulfide will take place for a given sulfide ion concentration even though this sulfide precipitate is not formed directly from its ions. The equilibrium involving a relatively insoluble salt in solution behaves as though the reaction takes place directly between its ions, regardless of what intermediate compounds may be formed. *Equilibrium has to do only with the final result and not with the means by which the result is obtained.*

The Separation of Sulfides into Groups. If the concentration of the sulfide ion in a solution containing some metal ion, Me^{++}, is so small that the product, $(Me^{++})(S^{--})$, does not exceed the solubility product constant for the metallic sulfide, then no precipitate will be formed. On the other hand, if the sulfide ion concentration is such that this product exceeds the solubility product constant, then a precipitate will appear providing (1) that a supersaturated solution is not formed and (2) that the amount of the metallic ion in the solution is sufficiently great to give a visible effect. The largest concentration of hydrogen ion which can be used conveniently in analysis is about 1 molar. This concentration of hydrogen ion in a saturated solution of hydrogen sulfide, as we have seen (see

Table 11), provides a sulfide ion concentration of about 10^{-21} molar. It has been shown experimentally that sulfide precipitates are not visible if they are precipitated from solutions more dilute than 10^{-4} molar. This concentration is therefore taken as the limit of visibility of the precipitate. Therefore any sulfide of a bivalent metallic ion for which the solubility product constant is smaller than the product ($10^{-4} \times 10^{-21}$ $= 10^{-25}$) should be precipitated in barely detectable amounts in a solution which is 1 molar in hydrogen ion. By referring to the table of solubility product constants for some of the sulfides given in the Appendix, it will be observed that the sulfides of cadmium, copper, lead and mercury are included in this group. Other sulfides with greater solubility product constants require a greater sulfide ion concentration, hence a smaller hydrogen ion concentration, to bring about precipitation.

The sulfides are then divided into two groups, (1) those which precipitate in acid solution and (2) those which precipitate in solutions of low hydrogen ion concentration. In practice one group is often precipitated in acid solution and filtered, the other group is precipitated by hydrogen sulfide after neutralizing the solution and making it alkaline. This last procedure then increases the sulfide ion concentration sufficiently to precipitate all sulfides that were not precipitated in the acid solution.

In practically all cases the precipitation of a metallic sulfide requires a much smaller H^+ ion concentration (larger S^{--} ion concentration) than is necessary to dissolve the already precipitated sulfide. This may be explained on the basis that crystal nuclei of the sulfides are not present in the solution and that higher concentrations of S^{--} ion are necessary to form them. Once these have been formed the precipitation takes place rapidly. In the case of some sulfides, notably NiS, CoS, and ZnS, the freshly precipitated sulfide is not in the form of perfect crystals — somewhat amorphous. This freshly precipitated form of the sulfide is less stable than the crystalline form. However, there is good evidence to indicate that the freshly precipitated form rapidly rearranges to the more stable crystalline form and therefore becomes less soluble in acid solution. The solubility product therefore varies with time. For some purposes we need to know the solubility product of the most stable form. However, for purposes of qualitative analysis we should like to know the solubility product of the freshly precipitated form, for it is with that form that we are dealing. The solubility product constants given in Tables in the Appendix, wherever data are available, are those of the freshly precipitated product. The solubility products of the sulfides are less reliable than those of other relatively insoluble precipitates.

The Precipitation of Ferrous and Zinc Sulfides. If acetic acid is added to a solution which is 0.1 molar with respect to both ferrous, Fe^{++}, and zinc, Zn^{++}, ions, until its concentration is approximately 0.1 molar, and then hydrogen sulfide is passed into this solution, a white precipitate of zinc sulfide will be formed. Under these conditions ferrous sulfide, FeS, which is black, is not precipitated. The hydrogen ion concentration of a 0.1 M acetic acid solution is approximately 10^{-3} M. From equation (12) we calculate the sulfide ion concentration to be about 10^{-15} M. Since precipitation occurs we may now conclude that the solubility product constant for zinc sulfide, ZnS, is less than $10^{-1} \times 10^{-15}$ or 10^{-16}. Since the ferrous sulfide does not precipitate under these conditions we might conclude that the solubility product constant for ferrous sulfide is greater than 10^{-16}. However, we should not be entirely justified in this conclusion for (1) a supersaturated solution may form and (2) the solubility product is different for the first formed small crystals. The value given in the tables is usually determined for large crystals. As a matter of fact, the solubility product constant given in the tables (see the Appendix) for ferrous sulfide (4×10^{-17}) is slightly smaller than 10^{-16}. The data from which we made our calculation may be in error by this small amount (a factor of about two or so) or the effects of supersaturation and small crystals may play a significant rôle here.

If sodium acetate is added to the solution considered above, a black precipitate of the ferrous sulfide is obtained. The effect of the addition of sodium acetate is to lower the concentration of the hydrogen ion through the formation of the weak acetic acid.

$$H^+ + Ac^- = HAc$$

Lowering the hydrogen ion concentration raises the sulfide ion concentration to a point sufficient to cause the precipitation of ferrous sulfide. The same result could have been achieved by the addition of either sodium hydroxide or ammonium hydroxide. The hydroxide ion is even more effective than the acetate ion in reducing the hydrogen ion concentration.

When any metallic sulfide is precipitated with hydrogen sulfide the hydrogen ion concentration in the solution is increased during the course of the reaction.

$$H_2S + Me^{++} = MeS_{(s)}{}^* + 2H^+ \tag{17}$$

This increase in hydrogen ion concentration may become great enough to render the precipitation incomplete. However, if hydroxide ion, acetate ion, ammonium hydroxide, or any ion or molecule which combines with hydrogen ion, is present in the solution the reaction proceeds readily with the formation of the sulfide, MeS.

While a 10^{-4} molar solution of the metallic ion is the approximate limit of visibility of a precipitate, yet this is not the lower limit of concentration which will discolor some other precipitate which might be formed. For example, if zinc sulfide, which when pure is white, is precipitated from a solution which contains only a slight trace of ferrous ion, the resulting precipitate will be gray. In fact, zinc sulfide seldom appears pure white when other ions are also in the solution. The small amount of ferrous sulfide which gives rise to the gray color may be prevented from precipitating by dissolving the gray precipitate in acetic acid and diluting to about 0.1 molar and again adding hydrogen sulfide. The presence of the hydrogen ions from the acetic acid lowers the sulfide ion concentration

---

* (s) is used to denote a solid phase.

to a value which will prevent the formation of ferrous sulfide and the zinc sulfide will now appear white.

The precipitation of zinc sulfide and ferrous sulfide have been discussed here in order to show the important rôle that the hydrogen ion concentration plays in the precipitation of sulfides. The solubility product constants of copper and mercuric sulfides are so small that the hydrogen ion concentration cannot be increased sufficiently to prevent precipitation. Any sulfide which precipitates from acid solutions will of course precipitate from alkaline solutions for which the hydrogen ion concentration has a smaller, and the sulfide ion concentration a larger value.

Carbonic Acid and the Precipitation of the Carbonates. The ionization of carbonic acid in two steps is entirely analogous to the ionization of hydrogen sulfide. These two steps are represented by the equations:

$$H_2CO_3 = H^+ + HCO_3^- \tag{18}$$

and

$$HCO_3^- = H^+ + CO_3^{--} \tag{19}$$

The bicarbonate ion, like the bisulfide ion, is a very much weaker acid than the acid from which it is derived. The dissociation constants for carbonic acid, however, are somewhat larger than the similar constants for hydrogen sulfide.

$$\frac{(H^+)(HCO_3^-)}{(H_2CO_3)} = 4.2 \times 10^{-7} \tag{20}$$

and

$$\frac{(H^+)(CO_3^{--})}{(HCO_3^-)} = 4.8 \times 10^{-11} \tag{21}$$

By multiplying equation (20) by equation (21), we obtain

$$\frac{(H^+)(HCO_3^-)}{(H_2CO_3)} \times \frac{(H^+)(CO_3^{--})}{(HCO_3^-)} = \frac{(H^+)^2(CO_3^{--})}{(H_2CO_3)}$$

$$= 4.2 \times 10^{-7} \times 4.8 \times 10^{-11}$$

Therefore,

$$\frac{(H^+)^2(CO_3^{--})}{(H_2CO_3)} = 2 \times 10^{-17} \tag{22}$$

A saturated solution of carbon dioxide in water at 1 atmosphere pressure and at 25° C contains about .034 mole per liter. Since in this solution such a small fraction of the acid dissociates, the undissociated portion is present at very nearly the same concentration, i.e., .034 molar. Since the second stage of ionization occurs to an extremely small extent, it may be neglected in calculating the concentration of the hydrogen ion or the concentration of the bicarbonate ion. If X is the concentration of each of these ions then, according to equation (20),

$$\frac{(H^+)(HCO_3^-)}{(H_2CO_3)} = \frac{X^2}{.034} = 4.2 \times 10^{-7}$$

$$X^2 = 14.3 \times 10^{-9} = 1.43 \times 10^{-8}$$

$$X = 1.2 \times 10^{-4} \text{ mole per liter} = (H^+) = (HCO_3^-)$$

In calculating the carbonate ion concentration in such a solution from equation (21), we observe that since the hydrogen ion and bicarbonate ion concentrations are very nearly the same, they cancel in this expression and the carbonate ion concentration is equal in value to the second ionization constant, namely, 4.8×10^{-11} mole per liter.

The insoluble carbonates differ markedly from the sulfides in the magnitude of their solubility product constants; the solubility product constants for the most soluble of the so-called insoluble sulfides are considerably smaller in magnitude than those for the least soluble of the carbonates. Whereas most of the sulfides can be precipitated by the addition of hydrogen sulfide to solutions of their salts, this is not the case for any of the carbonates. They cannot be precipitated by the direct addition of carbon dioxide gas to solutions containing the appropriate metal ions. The product of the concentrations of the carbonate ion and the metal ion in such solutions is not larger than the solubility product constants of the respective carbonates. From an inspection of the values of the solubility product constant of lead carbonate it might appear that it could be precipitated from a solution containing lead ions by the direct addition of carbon dioxide gas, but the salts of this metal hydrolyze (subject to be considered in the next chapter) sufficiently to give an appreciable hydrogen ion concentration, which in turn lowers the carbonate ion concentration. Just as in the case of hydrogen sulfide where an increase in the hydrogen ion concentration is accompanied by a decrease in the sulfide ion concentration, so in this case increasing the hydrogen ion concentration decreases the carbonate ion concentration.

The insoluble carbonates can then be precipitated only when the carbonate ion concentration is increased. This may be easily brought about by lowering the hydrogen ion concentration through the addition of a base. As a matter of fact, carbonic acid is not used for the precipitation of the carbonates but rather solutions of soluble carbonates such as sodium carbonate or ammonium carbonate, in which the concentration of the carbonate ion is relatively high. In qualitative analytical procedures these soluble carbonates are used to precipitate $CaCO_3$, $SrCO_3$, and $BaCO_3$.

Examples of Problems Involving Polybasic Acids and Sulfide Precipitation

Example 1.

Calculate the CO_3^{--} concentration in a solution which is 0.1 molar in HCl and saturated with CO_2 at 1 atmosphere. In this solution the solubility is practically the same as that in water, namely .034 molar.

Since HCl is a strong acid the H^+ concentration is 0.1 M. The increase in the concentration of this ion, because of the dissociation of H_2CO_3, is negligibly small and may be left out of consideration.

$$\frac{(H^+)^2(CO_3^{--})}{(H_2CO_3)} = 2 \times 10^{-17}$$

$$\frac{(0.1)^2(CO_3^{--})}{.034} = 2 \times 10^{-17}$$

$$(CO_3^{--}) = \frac{.034 \times 2 \times 10^{-17}}{10^{-2}} = 6.8 \times 10^{-17} \ M$$

Example 2.

Calculate the (H^+) necessary to give a (S^{--}) of 1×10^{-18} molar in a saturated solution of hydrogen sulfide. H_2S is soluble to the extent of 0.1 M.

$$\frac{(H^+)^2(S^{--})}{(H_2S)} = 1.3 \times 10^{-20}$$

$$\frac{(H^+)^2 \times 1 \times 10^{-18}}{0.1} = 1.3 \times 10^{-20}$$

$$(H^+)^2 = 1.3 \times 10^{-3} = 13 \times 10^{-4}$$

$$(H^+) = 3.6 \times 10^{-2} \ M$$

Example 3.

Calculate the minimum (H^+) necessary to prevent precipitation of ZnS when a .01 M $ZnCl_2$ solution is saturated with H_2S. The $K_{S.P.}$ for ZnS $= 1 \times 10^{-20}$.

The (S^{--}) below which no precipitation of ZnS takes place can be calculated from the solubility product constant.

$$(Zn^{++})(S^{--}) = .01 \times (S^{--}) = 1 \times 10^{-20}.$$

$$(S^{--}) = 1 \times 10^{-18}$$

The (H^+) which will be in equilibrium with this (S^{--}) may be obtained from the expression

$$\frac{(H^+)^2(S^{--})}{(H_2S)} = \frac{(H^+)^2 \times 1 \times 10^{-18}}{0.1} = 1.3 \times 10^{-20}$$

$$(H^+)^2 = 1.3 \times 10^{-3} = 13 \times 10^{-4}$$

$$(H^+) = 3.6 \times 10^{-2} = .036 \ M$$

Note: This answer should be regarded as only an approximation, inasmuch as the solubility product for freshly precipitated ZnS, like that of many sulfides, is not accurately known.

Example 4.

A solution contains .02 mole of Cd^{++} ion, .02 mole of Zn^{++} ion, and 1 mole of HCl per liter, and is saturated with H_2S at room temperature.

    (a) What is the concentration of the S^{--} ion in this solution?

    (b) Will CdS precipitate?

    (c) Will ZnS precipitate?

Since the solubility of H_2S in the solution is 0.1 M then we may write

EXAMPLES OF PROBLEMS

$$\frac{(H^+)^2(S^{--})}{(H_2S)} = \frac{(H^+)^2(S^{--})}{0.1} = 1.3 \times 10^{-20}$$

or
$$(H^+)^2(S^{--}) = 1.3 \times 10^{-21}$$

If the (H^+) is 1 M, then

$$(1)^2(S^{--}) = 1.3 \times 10^{-21} \quad \text{and} \quad (S^{--}) = 1.3 \times 10^{-21}$$

If precipitation of both sulfides takes place, then at equilibrium the reactions are

$$CdS_{(s)} = Cd^{++} + S^{--}$$
$$ZnS_{(s)} = Zn^{++} + S^{--}$$

The solubility product expressions are respectively

$$(Cd^{++})(S^{--}) = 6 \times 10^{-27}$$
$$(Zn^{++})(S^{--}) = 1 \times 10^{-20}$$

In the case of CdS, the ion product, $(.02)(1.3 \times 10^{-21}) = 2.6 \times 10^{-23}$, is greater than the solubility product constant, so CdS precipitates. On the other hand, the ion product for ZnS, 2.6×10^{-23}, is less than the solubility product constant, so ZnS does not precipitate.

Example 5.

Calculate the concentration of the PO_4^{---} ion in a 0.1 M solution of H_3PO_4.

The H_3PO_4 ionizes in three stages, as follows:

$$H_3PO_4 = H^+ + H_2PO_4^- \tag{1}$$
$$H_2PO_4^- = H^+ + HPO_4^{--} \tag{2}$$
$$HPO_4^{--} = H^+ + PO_4^{---} \tag{3}$$

The equilibrium expressions for the three stages of ionization are respectively

$$\frac{(H^+)(H_2PO_4^-)}{(H_3PO_4)} = K_{I_1} = 7.5 \times 10^{-3}$$

$$\frac{(H^+)(HPO_4^{--})}{(H_2PO_4^-)} = K_{I_2} = 6.2 \times 10^{-8}$$

$$\frac{(H^+)(PO_4^{---})}{(HPO_4^{--})} = K_{I_3} = 1 \times 10^{-12}$$

First calculate (H^+) and $(H_2PO_4^-)$ from the first stage of ionization.

$$H_3PO_4 \;=\; H^+ \;+\; H_2PO_4^-$$

Concentrations: $0.1 - X$ X X

Therefore $\dfrac{(H^+)(H_2PO_4^-)}{(H_3PO_4)} = \dfrac{X^2}{0.1 - X} = 7.5 \times 10^{-3}$

Since the ionization constant is relatively large, X cannot be neglected in the denominator. Therefore

$$X^2 = 7.5 \times 10^{-3} \,(0.1 - X) = 7.5 \times 10^{-4} - 7.5 \times 10^{-3}\, X$$

or $X^2 + 7.5 \times 10^{-3}\, X - 7.5 \times 10^{-4} = 0$

Solution of the quadratic equation (see Appendix) gives $X = 2.4 \times 10^{-2}\, M = (H^+) = (H_2PO_4^-)$

Now calculate the (HPO_4^{--}) from the second stage of ionization.

$$H_2PO_4^- \;=\; H^+ \;+\; HPO_4^{--}$$

Concentrations: $(2.4 \times 10^{-2} - X)$ $(2.4 \times 10^{-2} + X)$ X

Therefore

$$\frac{(H^+)(HPO_4^{--})}{(H_2PO_4^-)} = \frac{(2.4 \times 10^{-2} + X)(X)}{(2.4 \times 10^{-2} - X)} = 6.2 \times 10^{-8}$$

Since the ionization constant is small, the value of X is negligible as compared with 2.4×10^{-2}; consequently, X may be neglected when it is subtracted from or added to this number. Then

$$X = (HPO_4^{--}) = 6.2 \times 10^{-8}\, M$$

Finally calculate (PO_4^{---}) from the third stage of ionization.

$$HPO_4^{--} \;=\; H^+ \;+\; PO_4^{---}$$

Concentrations: $(6.2 \times 10^{-8} - X)$ $(2.4 \times 10^{-2} + X)$ X

Therefore

$$\frac{(H^+)(PO_4^{---})}{(HPO_4^{--})} = \frac{(2.4 \times 10^{-2} + X)(X)}{(6.2 \times 10^{-8} - X)} = 1 \times 10^{-12}$$

Again neglecting X in comparison with 2.4×10^{-2} and with 6.2×10^{-8} on the basis of the extremely small value of the ionization constant (1×10^{-12}), the expression becomes

$$\frac{(2.4 \times 10^{-2})(X)}{(6.2 \times 10^{-8})} = 1 \times 10^{-12}$$

$$X = \frac{(1 \times 10^{-12})(6.2 \times 10^{-8})}{(2.4 \times 10^{-2})} = 2.6 \times 10^{-18}$$

Therefore $X = (PO_4^{---}) \approx 2.6 \times 10^{-18} \ M$. The concentration of the PO_4^{---} ion in a 0.1 M solution of H_3PO_4 is approximately $10^{-18} \ M$.

Example 6.

To 50 ml. of 0.11 M $CdSO_4$ solution is added 5 ml. of 3 M HCl solution. The mixture is then saturated with H_2S at room temperature and CdS is found to precipitate. What is the concentration of the Cd^{++} ion left in solution? (Do not neglect the (H^+) produced by the reaction.)

Before precipitation the (Cd^{++}) has a value of $\frac{50}{55} \times 0.11$ or 0.1 M. The (H^+) is $\frac{5}{55} \times 3$ or 0.28 M. The reaction which takes place as the CdS precipitates is

$$Cd^{++} \ + \ H_2S \ = \ CdS_{(s)} \ + \ 2H^+$$

Since the reaction proceeds practically to completion, the increase in the (H^+) during the course of the reaction is 0.2 M. Thus, the total (H^+) in the solution when equilibrium is reached is 0.28 M + 0.2 M or 0.48 M. In a solution of this (H^+), saturated with H_2S, the (S^{--}) is

$$(H^+)^2(S^{--}) = 1.3 \times 10^{-21}$$
$$(0.48)^2(S^{--}) = 1.3 \times 10^{-21}$$
$$(S^{--}) = 5.6 \times 10^{-21}$$

Since the Cd^{++} ion is in equilibrium with the S^{--} ion,

$$(Cd^{++})(S^{--}) = K_{S.P.} = 6 \times 10^{-27}$$
$$(Cd^{++})(5.6 \times 10^{-21}) = 6 \times 10^{-27}$$
$$(Cd^{++}) = 1.1 \times 10^{-6} \ M$$

Therefore, the (Cd^{++}) left in solution is 1.1×10^{-6} mole per liter.

Questions and Problems

1. Sulfuric acid is usually regarded as a strong acid. In what respect could it be placed in the category of weak acids?
2. Explain without calculation why zinc sulfide cannot be precipitated from a solution which is 1 molar with respect to H^+ while copper sulfide can.
3. Is it necessary that we know the mechanism or steps by which a

given reaction takes place in order to apply the Law of Mass Action to an equilibrium involving this reaction?

4. How could you precipitate ZnS from a solution containing Zn^{++} and Fe^{++} without precipitating FeS?

5. Why cannot insoluble carbonates be precipitated from solution by CO_2 or H_2CO_3 in a way that is analogous to the precipitation of the sulfides by H_2S?

6. Explain why it is not possible to precipitate slightly soluble phosphates from solution with phosphoric acid.

7. Explain why $BaCO_3$ dissolves in dilute HCl solution while $BaSO_4$ does not.

8. What is the concentration of the $C_2O_4^{--}$ ion in a 0.1 M $H_2C_2O_4$ solution? Will such a solution precipitate MgC_2O_4 if $MgCl_2$ is added to make the solution 0.1 M with respect to Mg^{++} ion? (Note: in the $H_2C_2O_4$ solution the concentration of the H^+ ion is practically the same as that for the $HC_2O_4^-$ ion.)

9. What is the concentration of the S^{--} ion in a solution saturated with H_2S at one-half atmosphere pressure and room temperature? What is the concentration of the H^+ ion in this solution? (The solubility of a gas is proportional to the saturation pressure — Henry's Law.)

10. What is the H^+ concentration in a water solution of H_2CO_3 saturated with CO_2 at a pressure of 500 lb. per square inch (34 atmospheres)? (A solution saturated with CO_2 at 1 atmosphere pressure at the same temperature contains .034 mole CO_2 per liter. Assume Henry's Law applies.)

11. Calculate the concentration of the H^+ ion in the following solutions. Neglect all but the first step of ionization.

   (a) 0.1 M H_2CO_3 (e) 0.2 M $ClCH_2COOH$
   (b) 0.01 M H_2CO_3 (f) 0.1 M H_3PO_4
   (c) 0.01 M H_2S (g) 0.1 M $H_2C_2O_4$
   (d) 0.04 M H_3BO_3

12. Solutions of HCl are saturated with H_2S. From the total H^+ ion concentrations given below, calculate the corresponding S^{--} ion concentrations.

$$H^+ \text{ concentration}$$

   (a) 1×10^{-4} M (d) 1×10^{-1} M
   (b) 1×10^{-3} M (e) 1 M
   (c) 1×10^{-2} M

13. Plot the results of problem (12) using (H^+) as ordinates and (S^{--}) as abscissae. It may be convenient to save this plot for future reference.

14. Five ml. of 6 M HCl is added to 95 ml. of a solution containing 1 g. $ZnSO_4$ and 1 g. $CdSO_4$, and the solution is saturated with H_2S at room temperature.

(a) What is the concentration of the H^+ ion before H_2S is introduced?

(b) What is the concentration of the S^{--} ion after the solution becomes saturated with H_2S?

(c) Will CdS precipitate?

(d) Will ZnS precipitate?

(e) Explain your conclusions in detail.

15. Hydrogen sulfide is gradually added to a neutral solution which is 0.1 M in Cd^{++} ion and 0.1 M in Zn^{++} ion. Calculate the concentration of the Cd^{++} ion when ZnS begins to precipitate.

16. To 100 ml. of a hot .03 M solution of $PbCl_2$ is added 5 ml. of 6 M HCl solution. When the resulting solution is saturated with H_2S, PbS precipitates. How many moles of Pb^{++} ion are left in solution after it has cooled to room temperature? (Do not neglect the H^+ ion produced by the reaction.)

17. Hydrogen sulfide is added to separate solutions containing 50 mg. each of the following positive ions in 1 liter of solution. What is the S^{--} ion concentration when precipitation begins?

(a) Cu^{++} (b) Pb^{++} (c) Zn^{++} (d) Hg^{++} (e) Cd^{++}

18. A quantitative determination of zinc as ZnS is to be made. What must be the maximum concentration of the H^+ ion in the solution if no more than 0.3 mg. of Zn^{++} ion is to be left in a 100 ml. sample of the solution when saturated with H_2S?

19. Calculate the S^{--} ion concentration in a 0.1 M acetic acid solution which is saturated with H_2S.

20. Calculate the approximate concentrations of the following ions in a .05 M solution of phosphoric acid.

(a) H^+ (b) $H_2PO_4^-$ (c) HPO_4^{--} (d) PO_4^{---}

21. Ten ml. of 3 M HCl is added to 200 ml. of a solution containing .05 mole of $CuSO_4$ and .05 mole of $CdSO_4$, and the solution is saturated with H_2S at room temperature. Both CuS and CdS precipitate. How many moles of Cu^{++} ion and of Cd^{++} ion are left in solution? (Do not neglect the H$^+$ ion produced by the reactions.)

22. What must be the minimum concentration of a HCl solution to dissolve .01 mole of freshly precipitated ZnS in a liter of the solution?

23. What must be the minimum concentration of a HCl solution to dissolve .01 mole of CuS in a liter of the solution? Would it be possible to dissolve the CuS under these conditions?

24. One-tenth mole of Na$_2$SO$_4$ and 0.1 mole NaHSO$_4$ are added to enough water to make 100 ml. of solution. What is the H$^+$ ion concentration in this solution? HSO$_4^-$ ion is a weak acid with a dissociation constant equal to .0126.

This solution is then made .02 M with respect to each of the ions, Zn^{++}, Co^{++}, and Ni^{++}. It is then saturated with H$_2$S. Show by calculation that all three sulfides should precipitate. In practice only ZnS precipitates under these conditions. This is due to the fact that the rate of precipitation of ZnS is rapid whereas the rate of precipitation of CoS and of NiS is too slow under these conditions.

CHAPTER 7

The Ionization of Water — Hydrolysis

The Equilibrium between Water and Its Ions. Water is often regarded as a non-conductor of electricity. When the instruments used in measuring conductance are not exceedingly sensitive and when the voltage used is not exceedingly high, pure water shows no appreciable conductance. Very sensitive instruments, however, show that pure water actually does conduct electricity to a very small extent. This conductance is due to the dissociation of a very small fraction of the water molecules into hydrogen and hydroxide ions, and in pure water the concentrations of these ions must be identical. Therefore, water may be regarded both as an acid and as a base.

Since water is the medium in which all electrolytes are dissociated and since water solutions are by far the most commonly occurring solutions in chemistry, the equilibrium between water and its ions is one of the greatest importance in all phases of chemistry that deal with solutions, not only in qualitative analysis but particularly in the chemistry of all plant and animal systems.

The reaction representing the equilibrium between water and its ions is

$$H_2O = H^+ + OH^- \tag{1}$$

If we followed the previously discussed rule regarding equilibrium constants, we would write the equilibrium expression for the reaction

$$\frac{(H^+)(OH^-)}{(H_2O)} = K$$

But the concentration of the hydrogen and hydroxide ions is so small in comparison with the large concentration of undissociated molecules that, for all practical purposes, the concentration of the undissociated molecules (denominator of above expression) may be regarded as a constant. One liter of water contains 55.5, i.e., $\frac{1000}{18}$, moles of water, and if this concentration should vary as much as 0.1 of a mole in any given reaction, the change in the concentration of the water molecules, (H_2O), would be negligible. Suppose, for example, that 0.1 mole of water was used up by some reaction which also involved this equilibrium. The amount of water left in the original 1 liter of solution, after the reaction was completed, would now be 55.4 moles instead of 55.5 moles. The difference between these two values is less than 0.2 percent and for all practical purposes we may regard the concentration of the undissociated water molecules as not having changed, i.e., (H_2O) is constant.

We may, therefore, write

$$(H^+)(OH^-) = K(H_2O)$$
$$(H^+)(OH^-) = K \times constant$$
$$(H^+)(OH^-) = K_w \tag{2}$$

where $K_w = K \times constant = K(H_2O)$. K_w is known as the dissociation constant of water. It has a value of 1×10^{-14} at room temperature. This means that for pure water

$$(H^+)(OH^-) = 1 \times 10^{-14}$$

and

$$(H^+) = (OH^-) = 1 \times 10^{-7} \text{ mole per liter}$$

The equilibrium existing between water and its ions (not the value of the equilibrium constant) can be shifted or changed

(1) by the addition of hydroxide ions in the form of a base or by the addition of hydrogen ions in the form of an acid, or

(2) by the removal of hydrogen ions or hydroxide ions through the addition of some other substance.

Let us consider the equilibrium between water and its ions

(equation 1) and reiterate what is meant by the shifting of an equilibrium. By increasing the concentration of any of the substances on the right side of the equation, hydrogen ion or hydroxide ion, the equilibrium is shifted to the left. The equilibrium cannot be shifted to the right by increasing the concentration of the substance on the left for there is no way in which we can increase the concentration of water. The water molecules are already as close together as it is possible for them to be. By decreasing the concentration of either the hydrogen ion or the hydroxide ion, however, the equilibrium is shifted to the right.

Suppose some sodium hydroxide is added to pure water. This increases the concentration of the hydroxide ion with the final result that the hydrogen and hydroxide ions are still in equilibrium with each other, but the conditions of equilibrium are not the same as those existing in pure water. Strictly speaking, we should not say that the equilibrium is changed, for in the end condition there is still an equilibrium involving the same substances and the value of the equilibrium constant remains the same, but the *conditions* of equilibrium are changed. During the change in the conditions of equilibrium it is necessary that the concentration of the hydrogen ion decrease because the concentration of the hydroxide ion increases. The only way that the concentration of the hydrogen ion can decrease is by the combination of the hydrogen ions with some of the hydroxide ions to form water. In other words, the equilibrium under these conditions is said to shift from right to left to establish the new conditions; i.e., referring to equation (1), the reaction that re-establishes equilibrium is that proceeding from right to left. The original concentrations of the hydrogen and hydroxide ions were each 10^{-7} molar before the extra hydroxide ions were introduced. If the final concentration of the hydroxide ions, after equilibrium was re-established, was 10^{-5} molar, i.e., 100 times larger, then the final concentration of the hydrogen ion must be 10^{-9} molar or 100 times smaller than originally. Thus, under these new conditions,

$$(H^+)(OH^-) = 10^{-9} \times 10^{-5} = 10^{-14}$$

The concentration of the hydrogen ion is always inversely proportional to the concentration of the hydroxide ion. If one is increased tenfold, the other *must* be decreased tenfold; if one is increased fiftyfold, the other *must* be decreased fiftyfold of the original concentration. In no case does the concentration of either the hydroxide ion or the hydrogen ion become zero, because the Law of Mass Action would then require the concentration of the other ion to be infinite. The concentration of the hydrogen ion in a 1 molar solution of sodium hydroxide is about 10^{-14} molar. Likewise, the concentration of the hydroxide ion in a .01 molar solution of hydrochloric acid is 10^{-12} molar.

In the process of removing one of the ions of water by the addition of some other substance, new conditions of equilibrium are established by the dissociation of water to produce more ions and the equilibrium is shifted to the right (equation 1). It is with this process of partial removal of one of the ions of water that we are concerned in the problem of *hydrolysis*.

Hydrolysis. To understand better the process of hydrolysis let us consider this same equilibrium from a kinetic standpoint; i.e., from the standpoint of the motions of the molecules. In the equilibrium

$$H_2O = H^+ + OH^-$$

we may regard the reaction proceeding from left to right, as taking place through collisions of water molecules with each other. In the reverse reaction it is necessary that hydrogen ions and hydroxide ions collide with each other to react and form water molecules. At equilibrium both processes are proceeding at the same rate; as much water forms as dissociates. Now if it were possible to capture and remove a large part of the hydrogen ions as fast as they are formed, how would this equilibrium be affected? Water molecules would continue to dissociate at the same rate as they did previously, and since under these conditions the hydroxide ions could find fewer hydrogen ions, the reverse reaction would be temporarily blocked and the hydroxide ions would accumulate and increase in concentration.

There are substances which capture hydrogen ions and thereby cause an increase in the hydroxide ion concentration. The negative ion of any weak acid is a captor of hydrogen ions since a weak acid is formed. This process of capture does not go on indefinitely, for evidently the weak acid will itself dissociate to some extent to give hydrogen ions and a negative ion, eventually feeding hydrogen ions back into the medium at the same rate at which they are removed. The net result is that some hydrogen ions are removed and the number of hydroxide ions is increased.

This is the process taking place in hydrolysis. Let us consider a specific case, that of adding sodium acetate to water. The acetate ions, Ac^-, from sodium acetate capture some of the hydrogen ions from water to form weak acetic acid molecules.

$$H_2O \rightleftharpoons \boxed{\begin{array}{c} H^+ \\ + \\ Ac^- \end{array}} + OH^-$$

$$\updownarrow$$
$$HAc$$

The acetic acid molecules dissociate to give back hydrogen ions, but a great number have been effectively removed from the medium and as a consequence the concentration of the hydroxide ion is increased. Another way of expressing this is: when acetate ions are added to the solution both acetate and hydroxide ions are competing for the hydrogen ions and therefore the concentration of the hydrogen ion is lowered. Reasoning on the basis of the equilibrium expression for water, the hydroxide ion concentration must be increased if the hydrogen ion concentration is decreased.

Similarly, the hydroxide ion may be captured, thereby increasing the concentration of the hydrogen ion. Ammonium ion, NH_4^+, is a captor of hydroxide ions. Any salt of ammonium hydroxide, such as ammonium chloride, ammonium sulfate, or ammonium nitrate, when added to water, will hydrolyze to produce a small amount of NH_4OH and give an acid solution. It follows then that salts of weak acids and strong bases give alkaline solutions (OH^- ions in excess) and salts of strong acids and weak bases give acid solutions (H^+ ions in excess).

Salts of strong acids and strong bases do not hydrolyze. The ions of these salts do not have the ability to capture either hydrogen ions or hydroxide ions. To illustrate this point let us consider a solution of sodium chloride which is a salt of a strong acid (HCl) and a strong base ($NaOH$). In this solution neither the sodium ion nor the chloride ion has any tendency to capture either the hydrogen ion or the hydroxide ion, for both HCl and $NaOH$ in solution are 100-percent ionized.

The salts of weak acids and weak bases hydrolyze to a relatively large extent, capturing both the hydrogen ion and the hydroxide ion, and their solutions will be either basic or acidic depending upon which is the weaker, the acid or the base formed in the hydrolysis process. For example, a solution of ammonium cyanide, NH_4CN, will give an alkaline reaction because hydrocyanic acid, HCN, is weaker as an acid than is ammonium hydroxide as a base; that is, HCN tends to hold the hydrogen ions more tightly than NH_4OH holds the hydroxide ions.

We may write the reaction occurring during the hydrolysis of sodium acetate as follows:

$$Ac^- + H_2O = HAc + OH^- \qquad (3)$$

The reaction proceeding from left to right is that which represents the capture of hydrogen ions by acetate ions. It is to be noted that this equation represents the over-all reaction. By this we mean that it tells us only what disappears and what is formed regardless of the intermediate steps. The reaction for hydrolysis is *not*, as one might expect,

$$H^+ + Ac^- = HAc$$

even though the water might first dissociate to give hydrogen ion. It is only one step of the hydrolysis reaction. In the over-all process water molecules and acetate ions ultimately disappear while hydroxide ions and acetic acid molecules are formed.

The equilibrium expression for reaction (3) is

$$\frac{(HAc)(OH^-)}{(Ac^-)} = K_H \tag{4}$$

As in the case of the equilibrium expression for water, the concentration of the water molecules, (H_2O), does not vary appreciably and is therefore omitted from the denominator of this expression. We may obtain the value of K_H from the values for the ionization constants of water and of acetic acid, the only two weak substances involved in the equilibrium. In every aqueous solution the H^+ and OH^- ions are in equilibrium with each other and

$$(H^+)(OH^-) = K_W \quad \text{or} \quad (OH^-) = \frac{K_W}{(H^+)}$$

Substituting $\frac{K_W}{(H^+)}$ for (OH^-) in equation (4), we obtain

$$\frac{(HAc)K_W}{(Ac^-)(H^+)} = K_H$$

But $\frac{(HAc)}{(Ac^-)(H^+)}$ is equal to $\frac{1}{K_A}$. Therefore

$$\frac{K_W}{K_A} = K_H = \frac{1 \times 10^{-14}}{1.85 \times 10^{-5}} = 5.4 \times 10^{-10} \tag{5}$$

We may verify this relationship in the following way

$$\frac{K_W}{K_A} = \frac{(H^+)(OH^-)}{\frac{(H^+)(Ac^-)}{(HAc)}} = \frac{(HAc)(H^+)(OH^-)}{(H^+)(Ac^-)} = \frac{(HAc)(OH^-)}{(Ac^-)} = K_H$$

Similarly, the equilibrium expression for the hydrolysis of an ammonium salt,

$$NH_4^+ + H_2O = NH_4OH + H^+ \tag{6}$$

becomes

$$\frac{(H^+)(NH_4OH)}{(NH_4^+)} = K_H \tag{7}$$

Substituting $\dfrac{K_W}{(OH^-)}$ for (H^+) in equation (7) we obtain

$$K_H = \frac{K_W}{K_I \text{ (for the base)}} \tag{8}$$

A salt of a weak acid and a weak base hydrolyzes to a large extent. This is to be expected since both H^+ and OH^- ions are captured by the negative and positive ions of the salt. Ammonium cyanide is a salt derived from ammonium hydroxide and hydrocyanic acid. In water ammonium cyanide hydrolyzes in accordance with the equation,

$$NH_4^+ + CN^- + H_2O = NH_4OH + HCN \tag{9}$$

The equilibrium expression for this reaction is

$$\frac{(NH_4OH)(HCN)}{(NH_4^+)(CN^-)} = K_H$$

By multiplying both the numerator and the denominator by $(H^+)(OH^-)$, it can easily be shown that

$$K_H = \frac{K_W}{K_I \text{ (acid)} \times K_I \text{ (base)}} \tag{10}$$

The salts of polybasic acids hydrolyze in two or more steps. For example, sodium sulfide, Na_2S, a salt of a dibasic acid, hydrolyzes as follows:

$$S^{--} + H_2O = HS^- + OH^- \tag{11}$$

and

$$HS^- + H_2O = H_2S + OH^- \tag{12}$$

The hydrolysis constant for reaction (11) is

$$\frac{(HS^-)(OH^-)}{(S^{--})} = \frac{K_W}{K_2} = \frac{1 \times 10^{-14}}{1.3 \times 10^{-13}} = .077$$

and that for reaction (12) is

$$\frac{(H_2S)(OH^-)}{(HS^-)} = \frac{K_w}{K_1} = \frac{1 \times 10^{-14}}{1 \times 10^{-7}} = 1 \times 10^{-7}$$

It will be observed that the hydrolysis constant for reaction (11) is very much larger than that for reaction (12). This fact is very significant, for it means that the hydrolysis produced by the second step is negligible as compared with that for the first step, and in calculating the hydroxide ion concentration or the sulfide ion concentration in solutions of soluble sulfides only the first step of hydrolysis need be considered.

Note that in equation (11) for the hydrolysis of the sulfide ion (*first* step) an equilibrium exists between the sulfide ion and the bisulfide ion. The same ions are also involved in the equilibrium for the *second* step of ionization of hydrogen sulfide ($HS^- = H^+ + S^{--}$). Therefore in calculating the hydrolysis constant for the *first* step of hydrolysis, K_w and the ionization constant for the *second* step of ionization are involved. Conversely, the *second* step of hydrolysis (equation 12) is concerned with the *first* step of ionization of hydrogen sulfide, ($H_2S = H^+ + HS^-$).

The concentration of the hydrogen ion produced in solutions of salts of weak acids and strong bases, besides varying with the concentration of the salt, varies considerably from salt to salt, depending upon the relative weakness of the acid which is formed in the hydrolysis process. The larger the hydrolysis constant for such a salt, the greater will be the degree or extent of hydrolysis, and therefore the greater the hydroxide ion concentration. *The degree of hydrolysis is the fractional amount of the ions which hydrolyze,* i.e., the fractional part of the ions of the weak acid or base that have reacted with water. Equation (5) tells us that the hydrolysis constant will be larger the smaller the dissociation constant for the acid, i.e., the weaker the acid. The hydroxide ion concentration in a 0.1 molar solution of sodium acetate is about 10^{-5} molar; in a solution, 0.1 molar in sodium cyanide, about 10^{-3} molar; in a 0.1 molar solution of sodium carbonate, approximately 5×10^{-3} molar, while that in a 0.1 molar solution of sodium sulfide is almost .06 molar. In the last case about 60 percent of the sulfide ion hydrolyzes to produce the hydroxide ion. These examples are summarized in Table 12. Note that as the constant for the acid decreases the constant for hydrolysis and the hydroxide ion concentration increases.

TABLE 12

HYDROLYSIS OF SALTS OF WEAK ACIDS

Solution	Weak acid formed	K_I	K_H	(OH^-) in. 0.1 M soln (approx.)
Sodium nitrite	Nitrous	4.6×10^{-4}	2.2×10^{-11}	1.5×10^{-6}
Sodium acetate	Acetic	1.85×10^{-5}	5.4×10^{-10}	7×10^{-6}
Sodium carbonate	Bicarbonate ion	4.8×10^{-11}	2.1×10^{-4}	5×10^{-3}
Sodium sulfide	Bisulfide ion	1.3×10^{-13}	$.077$	6×10^{-2}

Examples of Hydrolysis. When a solution of ferric chloride is added to one containing sodium carbonate, a dark red precipitate of ferric hydroxide is formed and carbon dioxide is liberated from the solution. The hydroxide ion concentration in the sodium carbonate solution, formed by hydrolysis, is sufficient to precipitate the ferric hydroxide. Even though the carbonate ion concentration in the solution may be more than 100 times as great as the hydroxide ion concentration, the ferric hydroxide will still precipitate in preference to ferric carbonate. If ferric carbonate were very insoluble as compared with ferric hydroxide, this would not be the case. Then the carbonate would precipitate in preference to the hydroxide. (If a soluble silver salt is added to a solution containing sodium carbonate, the carbonate and not the hydroxide (or oxide) will precipitate.)

The reaction taking place when ferric hydroxide is precipitated by a solution of sodium carbonate is

$$Fe^{+++} + 3CO_3^{--} + 3H_2O = 3HCO_3^- + Fe(OH)_{3(s)} \quad (13)$$

This is followed by the reaction,

$$Fe^{+++} + 3HCO_3^- + 3H_2O = 3H_2CO_3 + Fe(OH)_{3(s)} \quad (14)$$

The carbonic acid formed in the last reaction breaks down into water and carbon dioxide. It is to be noted that it is only by virtue of the hydrolysis of the carbonate and bicarbonate ions that the precipitation of ferric hydroxide takes place. These reactions may be written:

$$CO_3^{--} + H_2O = HCO_3^- + OH^- \qquad (15)$$
$$HCO_3^- + H_2O = H_2CO_3 + OH^- \qquad (16)$$

The ferric ion may then be considered to combine with the hydroxide ion produced by equations (15) and (16) to form ferric hydroxide:

$$Fe^{+++} + 3OH^- = Fe(OH)_{3(s)} \qquad (17)$$

However, the over-all reaction includes only those substances which ultimately disappear and those which are formed and is expressed by the summation of equations (13) and (14).

$$2Fe^{+++} + 3CO_3^{--} + 6H_2O = 3H_2CO_3 + 2Fe(OH)_{3(s)} \quad (18)$$

The soluble aluminum and chromium salts behave in an entirely analogous manner; aluminum hydroxide, $Al(OH)_3$, and chromium hydroxide, $Cr(OH)_3$, are formed in these cases. The same argument that has been given for the precipitation of ferric hydroxide by the carbonate solution may be applied, part for part, to the precipitation of the hydroxides of these two metals.

Ferric hydroxide is so insoluble that it may be precipitated from a solution containing a ferric salt by the addition of the relatively insoluble barium carbonate. The small amount of carbonate ion which enters the solution ($K_{s.p.}BaCO_3 = 1.6 \times 10^{-9}$) is sufficient to produce enough hydroxide ion to precipitate ferric hydroxide, but (CO_3^{--}) is not great enough to precipitate the carbonates of the zinc group. Therefore, since the hydroxides of the aluminum group are precipitated by this solution, $BaCO_3$ is sometimes used as a means for the separation of the zinc and the aluminum groups.

Ferrous hydroxide, $Fe(OH)_2$, is not precipitated by solutions of soluble carbonates. The basic ferrous carbonate,

$Fe_2(OH)_2CO_3$, is sufficiently insoluble so that it precipitates in preference to the normal carbonate when a solution of sodium carbonate is added to one containing ferrous ion. If, however, ammonium carbonate is used in place of the sodium carbonate solution, ferrous carbonate rather than the basic ferrous carbonate will be precipitated. The presence of the ammonium ion in the ammonium carbonate solution lowers the hydroxide ion concentration (ammonium hydroxide is formed) to such an extent that the precipitation of ferrous carbonate is favored. As would be expected, the hydroxide ion concentration in a solution of ammonium carbonate, due to the hydrolysis of the ammonium ion, is smaller than the hydroxide ion concentration in a solution of sodium carbonate of the same concentration. The hydrolysis of the ammonium ion furnishes hydrogen ions which in turn use up available hydroxide ions in the solution.

When salts are said to be unstable in solution, these substances usually are decomposed in solution through hydrolysis with the formation of a precipitate or with the evolution of a gas. Aluminum sulfide, for example, when dissolved in water will form the insoluble aluminum hydroxide and hydrogen sulfide gas will be evolved. The aluminum ion, Al^{+++}, first formed reacts with the hydroxide ion of water, and the sulfide ion with the hydrogen ion of water. The net result of this double hydrolysis is

$$2Al^{+++} + 3S^{--} + 6H_2O = 2Al(OH)_{3(s)} + 3H_2S_{(g)} \qquad (19)$$

There are many examples of salts of this kind that cannot be dissolved in water and recovered again by crystallization. In fact, many salts hydrolyze to such an extent that they are decomposed by the water vapor in air.

When a relatively insoluble carbonate such as barium carbonate, $BaCO_3$, is dissolved in water an appreciable amount of the carbonate ion hydrolyzes to form the bicarbonate ion. The concentration of the barium ion accordingly is not the same as the concentration of the carbonate ion under these conditions. The concentration of the barium ion is practically equal to the sum of the concentrations of the carbonate and bicarbonate ions. Through this process of hydrolysis the solution becomes very slightly alkaline. This equilibrium is represented in the following equation:

$$BaCO_3(solid) = Ba^{++} + CO_3^{--}$$
$$+$$
$$H_2O = HCO_3^- + OH^-$$

or, $\quad BaCO_3(solid) + H_2O = Ba^{++} + HCO_3^- + OH^- \qquad (20)$

The hydrolysis of the bicarbonate ion to form carbonic acid and hydroxide ion is negligible.

The relatively insoluble sulfides behave in exactly the same way; the sulfide ion hydrolyzes to give bisulfide and hydroxide ions. In calculating the solubility of either a relatively insoluble sulfide or carbonate from the solubility product constant, account must be taken of this hydrolysis process which involves the sulfide or the carbonate ion, as the case may be.

The concentrations of the different ions in equilibrium in a solution of a soluble bicarbonate such as sodium bicarbonate, $NaHCO_3$, cannot be accounted for by a simple process of hydrolysis. The equilibrium in this case is somewhat more complicated. The bicarbonate ion hydrolyzes to produce carbonic acid and the hydroxide ion,

$$HCO_3^- + H_2O = H_2CO_3 + OH^- \qquad (21)$$

but the bicarbonate ion produces hydrogen ion through dissociation.

$$HCO_3^- = H^+ + CO_3^{--} \qquad (22)$$

The hydrogen ion and the hydroxide ion produced according to equations (22) and (21) respectively, will combine to form water. If processes (21) and (22) were to occur to the same extent, then a solution of sodium bicarbonate would be neutral. By experiment we find that a sodium bicarbonate solution is very slightly alkaline, a fact which indicates that process (21) occurs to a slightly greater extent than process (22). By summing up the reactions considered above, we obtain the over-all reaction,

$$2HCO_3^- = H_2CO_3 + CO_3^{--} \tag{23}$$

The H_2CO_3 and the CO_3^{--} ion concentrations in a solution of sodium bicarbonate are very nearly the same.

Hydrolysis must also be taken into account to explain the properties of some of the common substances that are encountered in everyday life. Lye (sodium hydroxide) and ammonium hydroxide are two well known cleansing agents. The cleansing property of these substances is attributed in part to the hydroxide ion which reacts with fats and oils to produce soaps. Since the hydroxide ions can be produced by the hydrolysis of salts of weak acids, these substances also have the same property as that of the two hydroxides just mentioned. The common salts used for this purpose are washing soda, Na_2CO_3, borax, $Na_2B_4O_7$, water glass, Na_2SiO_3, and tri-sodium phosphate, Na_3PO_4. The weaker the acid which is produced by hydrolysis, the greater will be the concentration of the hydroxide ions. Of the four substances just considered, tri-sodium phosphate produces the greatest hydroxide ion concentration, since the ion, HPO_4^{--}, is the weakest acid involved.

$$PO_4^{---} + H_2O = HPO_4^{--} + OH^- \tag{24}$$

Sodium silicate is one of the constituents of laundry soap and through its hydrolysis action increases the concentration of the hydroxide ion of the soap solution. Washing powders contain some hydrolyzable salt.

The common constituent of all baking powders is sodium bicarbonate. The other chief constituent is a substance which in solution furnishes the hydrogen ion which reacts with the bicarbonate ion to produce carbon dioxide gas. In some brands of baking powders the hydrogen ion is produced by a weak acid such as tartaric acid or an acid salt, while in others aluminum sulfate is used, which through the process of hydrolysis produces the hydrogen ion and aluminum hydroxide.

The Neutralization of Weak Acids and Weak Bases.
When 0.1 mole of hydrochloric acid is neutralized in solution
by 0.1 mole of sodium hydroxide, the solution produced could
be exactly reproduced by the addition of 0.1 mole of sodium
chloride to the same amount of water. When the acid and the
base have just neutralized each other, the solution is neither
acidic nor alkaline, for sodium chloride does not hydrolyze.
If, on the other hand, 0.1 mole of acetic acid is neutralized in
solution by exactly 0.1 mole of sodium hydroxide, the sodium
acetate solution does not contain the same number of hydrogen
ions as hydroxide ions. When a weak acid is neutralized by
a strong base the end point of the neutralization does not occur
when the concentrations of the hydrogen and hydroxide ions
are the same, but rather when the solution is slightly alkaline.
The concentration of the hydrogen ion or of the hydroxide ion
at the neutralization point will depend upon the concentrations
of the substances involved and upon the ionization constant of
the acid formed in the hydrolysis process.

The process of neutralization of weak acids by strong bases
may be illustrated by a specific example. Suppose 50 ml. of
a 0.1 molar solution of hydrocyanic acid, HCN, is to be neutralized by 50 ml. of a 0.1 molar solution of sodium hydroxide.
What will be the hydrogen and hydroxide ion concentrations
at the point of neutralization? The final solution, through
the addition of the two equal volumes, will be .05 molar with
respect to sodium cyanide. The problem is then to calculate
the hydrogen ion and the hydroxide ion concentrations in this
solution. The equation representing the hydrolysis equilibrium is

$$CN^- + H_2O = HCN + OH^- \tag{25}$$

Let X be the concentration of the hydroxide ion. Then X
must also be the concentration of the HCN, and $.05 - X$ is
the concentration of the cyanide ion at equilibrium. Since
we might expect the amount of cyanide ion hydrolyzed to be
small as compared with the total amount of cyanide ion present,
we may simplify this and let the concentration of the cyanide

ion be practically equal to .05 molar rather than $.05 - X$. Then,

$$\frac{(\text{HCN})(\text{OH}^-)}{(\text{CN}^-)} = \frac{X^2}{.05} = \frac{K_W}{K_A} = \frac{10^{-14}}{4 \times 10^{-10}} = 2.5 \times 10^{-5}$$

$$X^2 = 1.25 \times 10^{-6}$$

$$X = 1.1 \times 10^{-3} \text{ mole per liter} = (\text{OH}^-)$$

The concentration of the hydrogen ion is $\dfrac{10^{-14}}{1.1 \times 10^{-3}} = 9 \times 10^{-12}$

mole per liter. The hydrogen ion concentration in this solution is 11,000 times smaller than that for pure water (10^{-7} molar), and the hydroxide ion concentration is 11,000 times larger.

In selecting an indicator for this reaction under the conditions stipulated above, we should choose one that changes color as near as possible to the calculated hydrogen ion concentration. By referring to the table on page 83, we find that thymol phthalein would be the most suitable indicator. If methyl orange were used, the final solution obtained would still contain a large excess of the acid at the end point and would not be neutralized.

Buffer Solutions. Buffer solutions are solutions containing weak acids or weak bases together with the salts of weak acids or bases and have the property of maintaining a hydrogen ion concentration which is affected only slightly by the addition of appreciable amounts of either acid or base.

A solution containing 0.1 mole of acetic acid and 0.1 mole of sodium acetate per liter is such a buffer solution. Its hydrogen ion concentration is about 1.85×10^{-5} molar. A solution containing 1.85×10^{-5} mole of hydrochloric acid per liter would also have the same hydrogen ion concentration as the buffer solution described above, but its action toward acids and bases would be entirely different from that of the buffer solution. If 1.85×10^{-5} mole of sodium hydroxide is added to 1 liter of the above hydrochloric acid solution, the resulting solution would be neutral to the hydrogen ion, i.e., the hydrogen ion concentration would be 10^{-7} molar. Upon the addition of 1.85×10^{-5} mole of sodium hydroxide to 1 liter of the buffer solution, the hydrogen ion concentration would not be appreciably affected.

To understand better the action of the buffer solution, let us consider the equilibrium between the acid and its ions:

$$HAc = H^+ + Ac^-$$

$$\frac{(H^+)(Ac^-)}{(HAc)} = 1.85 \times 10^{-5}$$

$$(H^+) = \frac{(HAc)}{(Ac^-)} \times 1.85 \times 10^{-5} \qquad (26)$$

When the concentrations of the acetic acid molecules and of the acetate ions are made equal as they were in the example above, the concentration of the hydrogen ion has the same value as the dissociation constant. If as much as .05 mole of sodium hydroxide is added to 1 liter of the buffer solution (0.1 mole acetic acid and 0.1 mole of sodium acetate per liter), the hydrogen ion concentration will be affected relatively little. Under these conditions, .05 mole of the acetic acid has been neutralized by the added sodium hydroxide, and the solution now consists of .05 mole acetic acid and 0.15 mole of sodium acetate. Now the hydrogen ion concentration is

$$(H^+) = \frac{(HAc)}{(Ac^-)} \times 1.85 \times 10^{-5} = \frac{.05}{0.15} \times 1.85 \times 10^{-5} = 0.6 \times 10^{-5}$$

The hydrogen ion concentration has been lowered only threefold by the addition of the sodium hydroxide. In a like manner, the addition of .05 mole of hydrochloric acid to the original buffer solution will increase the hydrogen ion concentration only threefold. In this case, the hydrogen ions produced by the hydrochloric acid combine with the acetate ions and are removed in the form of acetic acid molecules. After the hydrochloric acid has been added, the final solution will contain 0.15 mole of acetic acid and .05 mole of acetate ion and

$$(H^+) = \frac{0.15}{.05} \times 1.85 \times 10^{-5} = 5.5 \times 10^{-5} \text{ mole per liter}$$

The following table illustrates the buffer action of an acetic acid–sodium acetate solution in its ability to absorb either a strong acid, such as hydrochloric acid, or a strong base, such as sodium hydroxide, with but little change in the concentration of the hydrogen ion. By adding as much as

TABLE 13

BUFFER ACTION OF A SOLUTION CONTAINING 0.1 MOLE OF ACETIC ACID AND 0.1 MOLE OF SODIUM ACETATE PER LITER

ml. of 0.1 molar NaOH added to 1 liter of buffer solution	(H$^+$) of final solution	ml. of 0.1 molar HCl added to 1 liter of buffer solution	(H$^+$) of final solution
0	0.0000185	0	0.0000185
5	0.0000183	5	0.0000187
10	0.0000181	10	0.0000189
25	0.0000175	25	0.0000195
50	0.0000167	50	0.0000204
75	0.0000159	75	0.0000215
100	0.0000151	100	0.0000226

100 ml. of either 0.1 molar hydrochloric acid solution or 0.1 molar sodium hydroxide solution to 1 liter of the buffer solution, the hydrogen ion concentration remains within the limits 1.51×10^{-5} and 2.26×10^{-5} mole per liter. By this treatment the hydrogen ion concentration of the original solution does not vary more than 25 percent. In contrast to this, if 100 ml. of 0.1 molar hydrochloric acid were added to pure water, the hydrogen ion concentration would increase 100,000-fold.

The above solution was such as to maintain the hydrogen ion concentration in the neighborhood of 10^{-5} molar. If it is desired to maintain the hydrogen ion concentration at a different value, a different acid and salt should be chosen. If it is desired to maintain the hydrogen ion concentration at about 10^{-9} molar (OH$^-$ ion concentration of 10^{-5} molar), then hydrocyanic acid and potassium cyanide might be used, for this acid has an ionization constant equal to 4×10^{-10}. However, for most work this acid would be unsuitable because of its toxic nature.

Ions and salts of polybasic acids also form buffer solutions. For example, a solution of sodium bicarbonate is a buffer solution. The bicarbonate ion, HCO_3^-, is an ion of a salt of a weak acid; $NaHCO_3$ is the salt and H_2CO_3 the acid from which it is derived. Furthermore, the bicarbonate ion is itself a weak acid, dissociating to form hydrogen ions and carbonate ions. When hydrochloric acid is added to a solution of sodium bicarbonate, carbonic acid is formed and the hydrogen ion concentration of the solution is changed very little. If sodium hydroxide is added to this same solution, the carbonate ion is formed,

$$HCO_3^- + OH^- = H_2O + CO_3^{--} \qquad (27)$$

and again the hydrogen ion concentration is little affected.

Blood is a good example of a buffer solution. The principal ion and acid responsible for the buffer action of blood are the HCO_3^- ion and H_2CO_3. When excess hydrogen ion enters the blood stream it is absorbed principally by the reaction

$$H^+ + HCO_3^- = H_2CO_3 \qquad (28)$$

and when excess hydroxide ion is formed it disappears through the reaction

$$OH^- + H_2CO_3 = H_2O + HCO_3^- \qquad (29)$$

By this mechanism the hydrogen ion concentration in the blood stream remains remarkably constant — very slightly alkaline. Besides the HCO_3^- and H_2CO_3, there are other buffering substances, such as HPO_4^{--}, $H_2PO_4^-$, and hemoglobin, which also help control the H^+ ion concentration.

When carbon dioxide is produced in the tissues by metabolic processes, carbonic acid is formed, which in turn dissociates to produce hydrogen and bicarbonate ions. The hydrogen ion produced by this reaction is absorbed by the buffer action of the blood. When oxygen is breathed into the lungs it reacts with the hemoglobin and as a result of this reaction the hemoglobin becomes a stronger acid and a large excess of hydrogen ions results. These hydrogen ions, which locally cannot be completely absorbed by the buffer action of the blood, now combine with the bicarbonate ions to form excess carbonic acid (CO_2 and H_2O). The carbon dioxide is then exhaled from the lungs.

The Hydrolysis of Metal Ions. A large number of metal ions hydrolyze to give acid solutions. We therefore conclude that the corresponding bases of these ions are weak. Many of these metal ions form polyacid bases, i.e., more than one ionizable OH radical is associated with the metal ion. Before considering the problem of the hydrolysis of these ions let us first examine the properties of these polyacid bases. Most of the polyacid bases are very insoluble, e.g., $Al(OH)_3$, $Pb(OH)_2$ and $Fe(OH)_3$. Without doubt these hydroxides ionize in two or more stages just as polybasic acids ionize in more than one stage. The equilibrium reactions between $Fe(OH)_3$, for example, and its ions, when it is dissolved in water, can be expressed by the following equations.

$$Fe(OH)_{3(s)} = Fe(OH)_{3\,(soln.)} \tag{30}$$

$$Fe(OH)_{3\,(soln.)} = Fe(OH)_2{}^+ + OH^- \tag{31}$$

$$Fe(OH)_2{}^+ = Fe(OH)^{++} + OH^- \tag{32}$$

$$Fe(OH)^{++} = Fe^{+++} + OH^- \tag{33}$$

Just as there are no polybasic acids which in moderate concentration ionize to the extent of 100 per cent in any but the first stage of ionization so we may assume that polyacid bases behave similarly. But it must be borne in mind that most of the polyacid bases are very insoluble and therefore the concentrations of the ions in equilibrium with them must be very small. Because of the small concentration — which is equivalent to a very high dilution in solutions of soluble bases — all stages can be considered as being practically completely dissociated.

Zinc hydroxide, for example, is very insoluble. Therefore

the amount of undissociated and dissolved $Zn(OH)_2$ in equilibrium with the solid must be very small.

$$Zn(OH)_{2(s)} = Zn(OH)_{2(soln.)} \tag{34}$$

The undissociated $Zn(OH)_2$ will ionize first as

$$Zn(OH)_{2(soln.)} = Zn(OH)^+ + OH^- \tag{35}$$

and then will be further ionized in the following manner:

$$Zn(OH)^+ = Zn^{++} + OH^- \tag{36}$$

Just as a $1 \times 10^{-5} M$ solution of HAc is ionized to the extent of 70 percent, while a $1 M$ solution is ionized to the extent of only 0.4 percent so, because of the low concentration, we might expect these insoluble bases to be highly ionized in spite of the fact that the ionization constants may be small. We lack data on the ionization constants for the various steps involved in the dissociation of most polyacid bases and therefore we group all stages of dissociation into a single reaction. For example, reactions (34), (35), and (36) may be grouped into the one reaction

$$Zn(OH)_{2(s)} = Zn^{++} + 2OH^- \tag{37}$$

In view of the extreme insolubility of many polyacid bases this procedure will often be satisfactory. But when we consider the hydrolysis of the metal ions the problem is quite different since the concentration of these ions is usually not small.

If 0.1 mole of $ZnCl_2$ is dissolved in one liter of water the solution is found to be decidedly acidic. The reason for this is that the Zn^{++} ion undergoes hydrolysis, the first stage of which may be represented by the equation

$$Zn^{++} + H_2O = Zn(OH)^+ + H^+ \tag{38}$$

The concentration of the Zn^{++} ion is high (approximately $0.1 M$) but since the amount of hydrolysis is relatively small the concentrations of the $Zn(OH)^+$ and of the H^+ ions are small. The second stage of hydrolysis is much smaller than that of the first stage and may be neglected, since the concentration of the $Zn(OH)^+$ ion is itself very small. However, the reaction for the second stage of hydrolysis is

$$Zn(OH)^+ + H_2O = Zn(OH)_{2(soln.)} + H^+ \qquad (39)$$

To calculate the hydrolysis constant for equation (38) it is necessary that we know the value of the ionization constant for equation (36). It cannot be calculated by using the ionization constant for equation (37). The ionization constant for (36) is known to have a value of 4×10^{-5}. The hydrolysis constant for the reaction represented by equation (38) is therefore equal to

$$\frac{(Zn(OH)^+)(H^+)}{(Zn^{++})} = \frac{K_W}{K_{2(base)}} = \frac{1 \times 10^{-14}}{4 \times 10^{-5}} = 2.5 \times 10^{-10} = K_H$$

If we let X equal the number of moles of Zn^{++} ion undergoing hydrolysis, then at equilibrium $(Zn(OH)^+)$ will be X, (H^+) will also equal X, and (Zn^{++}) will have a value of $(0.1 - X)$. Neglecting X as compared with 0.1 we have

$$\frac{X^2}{0.1} = 2.5 \times 10^{-10} \quad \text{or} \quad X^2 = 25 \times 10^{-12}$$

$$X = 5 \times 10^{-6} \text{ mole per liter} = (H^+)$$

Therefore the degree of hydrolysis is $\dfrac{5 \times 10^{-6}}{0.1}$ or 5×10^{-5}.

On a percentage basis the extent of hydrolysis is therefore .005 percent. The solution is found to be decidedly acidic, according to the calculation we have just carried out.

The constants for the different stages of ionization are not known for most hydroxides. Therefore we cannot calculate the hydrolysis constants for most positive metal ions which we know are hydrolyzed in solution.

If the hydroxide of a metal ion is insoluble we may conclude that the metal ion will hydrolyze to give an acidic solution. We base this conclusion on the assumption that the insolubility of the hydroxide is in part due to a firm binding between the metal ion and the OH^- ions. We may also assume that if all of the OH^- ions are held firmly, for example by the Al^{+++} ion in forming $Al(OH)_3$, then there should also be a firmer binding between the Al^{+++} ion and the first OH^- ion to form $Al(OH)^{++}$. If such is the case, Al^{+++} ion in water should hydrolyze. This reasoning can be applied to any ion which forms an insoluble hydroxide; the facts are in accord with this postulate. Practically all metal ions other than those of the alkali or alkaline earth groups hydrolyze to give acidic solutions.

It has been our custom to write the symbol for a multivalent positive ion in its simplest form. For example, if $SnCl_4$ is dissolved in water we often write the formula for the resulting stannic ion as Sn^{++++}. Certainly this cannot be correct. Very probably most of the ions in such a solution are present as $SnCl^{+++}$ and $SnCl_2^{++}$ ions and very few of them are in the form of Sn^{++++} ion. If HCl is present in the solution in excess, then the predominating ion is probably $SnCl_6^{--}$. However, we have no definite information relative to the composition of many ions of this type and therefore we use the simplest symbols or formulae possible. The same situation undoubtedly exists with Fe^{+++}, Al^{+++} and other trivalent and higher valent ion salts.

*Hydrolysis and the Brønsted Definitions.** If the Brønsted definitions of acids and bases are to be adopted consistently, then the term hydrolysis becomes superfluous. What the older established definitions called hydrolysis becomes merely an acid-base reaction. But the terms hydrolysis and salt have become so firmly entrenched in chemical thought and in chemical literature that hydrolysis cannot be brushed aside without consideration. The introduction of this term into the Brønsted definitions, however, is apt to lead to some confusion if hydrolysis is not already understood in the light of the older definitions.

According to the older established definitions ions which hydrolyze in water solution can be divided into two classes; those which produce acidic and those which produce basic

* Before reading this section the student is advised to review the section on the Brønsted Definitions of Acids and Bases on pages 85–92.

solutions. Let us consider these two types of hydrolysis separately and as an example of the first kind let us consider the hydrolysis of the ammonium ion. According to the older definitions the equation for the hydrolysis reaction is

$$NH_4^+ + H_2O = NH_4OH + H^+ \tag{40}$$

The mental picture for the process is that of competition between the H^+ ion and the NH_4^+ ion for the OH^- ion. As the result of this competition, some H^+ ions are left in excess of OH^- ions and the solution is acidic.

According to the Brønsted definitions this same hydrolysis reaction is expressed as follows.

$$\underset{\text{Acid}_1}{NH_4^+} + \underset{\text{Base}_2}{H_2O} = \underset{\text{Base}_1}{NH_3} + \underset{\text{Acid}_2}{H_3O^+} \tag{41}$$

Examining equations (40) and (41) formally we see that the difference between them is that in equation (40) the water molecule is associated with the NH_3 molecule to form NH_4OH (a formula which emphasizes the basic nature of ammonia in water solution), and in equation (41) the water is associated with the H^+ ion, which is written as H_3O^+. According to the Brønsted definitions equation (41) represents merely an acid-base reaction and the NH_4^+ ion is regarded as a weak acid. The NH_3 and the H_2O molecules are competing for the proton. Equation (40) does not represent the actual process taking place any more than does equation (41); these details of the reaction are not known. Whether one uses equation (41) or equation (40), i.e., Brønsted or the older established definitions, is merely a question of convenience and ease of acquiring an understanding of the acid-base reaction in solution.

According to the older definitions hydrolysis is the reverse of neutralization, i.e., equation (40) reading from right to left represents a process of neutralization while from left to right, it represents hydrolysis. With the Brønsted definitions the reactions represented by both directions of equation (41) are acid-base reactions. Only if we borrow the concepts of hydrolysis and of neutralization from the older definitions may we define the process from left to right in equation (41) as hydrolysis and the process from right to left as neutralization. In general, on the basis of the newer definitions, hydrolysis is defined as a proton transfer reaction between a cation-acid or an anion-base and water, to produce the hydronium ion or the hydroxide ion respectively. But again it must be emphasized that if the Brønsted definitions had been common usage for many years the term hydrolysis in inorganic chemistry would not be necessary.

Let us consider the equilibrium expression for reaction (41) and show the relationship between the constant for this expression and the constants for other reactions from which the value of the former may be calculated. As has been previously pointed out, reaction (41) may be regarded as one of dissociation of a weak acid, and its constant may then be designated as $K_{I\,(acid)}^B$.*

$$K_{I\,(acid)}^B = \frac{(NH_3)(H_3O^+)}{(NH_4^+)} \tag{42}$$

The concentration of the water molecules is omitted from the expression since its value remains constant for all practical purposes. Consider next the two reactions

$$H_2O + H_2O = H_3O^+ + OH^- \tag{43}$$

and

$$NH_3 + H_2O = NH_4^+ + OH^- \tag{44}$$

The equilibrium expressions for (43), (44) are $(H_3O^+)(OH^-)$ and $\frac{(NH_4^+)(OH^-)}{(NH_3)}$ respectively. The first of these is equal to the equilibrium constant for water and is denoted by K_w^B, the second we shall denote merely by K_{eq}^B.

$$K_w^B = (H_3O^+)(OH^-) \tag{45}$$

$$K_{eq}^B = \frac{(NH_4^+)(OH^-)}{(NH_3)} \tag{46}$$

* Constants referring to the Brønsted definitions are distinguished from those of the older definitions by the superscript B.

From equation (45) $(H_3O^+) = \dfrac{K_W^B}{(OH^-)}$

Substituting $\dfrac{K_W^B}{(OH^-)}$ for (H_3O^+) in equation (42), we obtain

$$K_{I(acid)}^B = \frac{(NH_3)K_W^B}{(NH_4^+)(OH^-)} = \frac{K_W^B}{\dfrac{(NH_4^+)(OH^-)}{(NH_3)}} \tag{47}$$

But the denominator in the last expression in equation (47) is equal to K_{eq}^B (equation 46). Therefore

$$K_{I(acid)}^B = \frac{K_W^B}{K_{eq}^B} \tag{48}$$

Let us now return to the older definitions with which we previously showed that

$$K_H = \frac{K_W}{K_{I(base)}} \tag{49}$$

What was previously called the hydrolysis constant is now the acid constant ($K_{I(acid)}^B$ is equivalent to K_H), and what was previously known as the dissociation constant for the base is designated merely as an equilibrium constant, (K_{eq}^B is equivalent to $K_{I(base)}$). Obviously K_W^B is the same as K_W. Again we see only different names for the same phenomena; the relationships are the same.

Let us next consider the hydrolysis of an anion to produce an alkaline solution, and as an example we shall again use the acetate ion.

$$\underset{\text{Acid}_1}{H_2O} \; + \; \underset{\text{Base}_2}{Ac^-} \; = \; \underset{\text{Acid}_2}{HAc} \; + \; \underset{\text{Base}_1}{OH^-} \tag{50}$$

The hydrolysis reaction is expressed by the same equation (50) whether the Brønsted or the older definitions are used; the terminology only is different. The equilibrium expression for the reaction is $\dfrac{(HAc)(OH^-)}{(Ac^-)}$.

By the older terminology this expression is equal to the hydrolysis constant. By the Brønsted definitions it would more properly be called an acid-base equilibrium constant. Thus,

$$\frac{(\text{HAc})(\text{OH}^-)}{(\text{Ac}^-)} = K_{eq}{}^{B} \tag{51}$$

It can be shown that

$$K_{eq}{}^{B} = \frac{K_{w}{}^{B}}{K_{I(acid)}^{B}} \tag{52}$$

where $K_{I(acid)}^{B}$ is the constant for the reaction

$$\text{HAc} + \text{H}_2\text{O} = \text{H}_3\text{O}^+ + \text{Ac}^- \tag{53}$$

Using the older definitions, we previously showed that

$$K_{H} = \frac{K_{w}}{K_{I(acid)}} \tag{54}$$

In this case the older K_H is equivalent to the newer $K_{eq}{}^{B}$.

The Ac^- ion is known as a strong base; it has a great tendency to take up protons. The strongly basic character of the Ac^- ion may be visualized in terms of the older concepts if we consider it in its hydrated form. Suppose that instead of representing the acetate ion by the symbol Ac^- we used AcHOH^- ($\text{Ac}^- + \text{H}_2\text{O}$); i.e., included in its formula one molecule of water. Then it is easy to see that if the OH^- ion dissociated from this complex the HAc molecule would be formed and the stronger the base, the greater the concentration of OH^- ions produced. The tendency to acquire protons is equivalent to a tendency to produce OH^- ions.

$$\text{AcHOH}^- = \text{HAc} + \text{OH}^- \tag{55}$$

This reaction is effectively the same as that represented by equation (50). This procedure, however, is not conventional. The hydrolysis of positive metal ions, according to the Brønsted definitions, will be considered in the next chapter.

Examples of Hydrolysis Problems

Example 1.

(a) Calculate the concentration of the OH^- ion in a 0.1 M NaAc solution.

(b) What is the value of the concentration of the H^+ ion in this same solution?

(c) What is the degree of hydrolysis?

Sodium acetate is the salt of a strong base and a weak acid and therefore its solution will show an alkaline reaction. The equation representing the hydrolysis reaction is

$$Ac^- + H_2O = HAc + OH^-$$

Concentrations: $(0.1 - X)$ X X

Therefore

$$\frac{(HAc)(OH^-)}{(Ac^-)} = \frac{X^2}{0.1 - X} = \frac{K_w}{K_I} = \frac{1 \times 10^{-14}}{1.85 \times 10^{-5}} = 0.54 \times 10^{-9}$$

Neglecting X as compared with 0.1 in the denominator of the second expression, we have

$$\frac{X^2}{0.1} = 0.54 \times 10^{-9}$$

$$X^2 = 0.54 \times 10^{-10}$$
$$X = 0.75 \times 10^{-5} \text{ mole per liter} = (OH^-) = (HAc)$$

To calculate (H^+) we use the dissociation constant for water.

$$(H^+) = \frac{K_w}{(OH^-)} = \frac{1 \times 10^{-14}}{0.75 \times 10^{-5}} = 1.3 \times 10^{-9} \text{ mole per liter}$$

It is also possible to calculate the (H^+) in the following way. The HAc in solution is in equilibrium with its two ions, H^+ and Ac^-. The concentration of the undissociated HAc in this solution is the same as that of the OH^- ion and was found to be 0.75×10^{-5} M. The value for (Ac^-) is practically 0.1. We may therefore use the ionization constant for HAc to determine the (H^+).

$$\frac{(H^+)(Ac^-)}{(HAc)} = \frac{(H^+) \times 0.1}{0.75 \times 10^{-5}} = 1.85 \times 10^{-5}$$

$$(H^+) = \frac{1.85 \times 10^{-5} \times 0.75 \times 10^{-5}}{0.1}$$

$$(H^+) = 1.3 \times 10^{-9} \text{ mole per liter}$$

The following short-cut method may be used to obtain (H^+) in a solution which hydrolyzes to produce a basic solution:

$$\frac{(HAc)(OH-)}{(Ac^-)} = \frac{X^2}{0.1 - X} = \frac{K_w}{K_I}$$

EXAMPLES OF HYDROLYSIS PROBLEMS

For generalization let $(Ac^-) = C$; C being the final concentration of the hydrolyzing ion — in this case $.01 - X$, or for practical purposes 0.1, (X is neglected as compared with 0.1). Therefore

$$\frac{(HAc)(OH^-)}{C} = \frac{K_W}{K_I}$$

Since

$$(HAc) = (OH^-)$$

$$(OH^-)^2 = \frac{K_W \times C}{K_I}$$

$$(H^+)^2 = \frac{(K_W)^2}{(OH^-)^2}$$

Therefore

$$(H^+)^2 = \frac{K_W{}^2 \times K_I}{K_W \times C} = \frac{K_W \times K_I}{C}$$

$$(H^+) = \sqrt{\frac{K_W \times K_I}{C}}$$

Calculating the (H^+) from this last equation we obtain

$$(H^+) = \sqrt{\frac{10^{-14} \times 1.85 \times 10^{-5}}{.1}}$$

$$(H^+) = \sqrt{1.85 \times 10^{-18}}$$

$$(H^+) = 1.3 \times 10^{-9} \text{ mole per liter}$$

The degree of hydrolysis is the fractional amount of the Ac^- ion hydrolyzed. The amount of Ac^- ion which hydrolyzed was X or 0.75×10^{-5} M. Therefore the degree of hydrolysis is X divided by the total amount of Ac^- ion.

$$\text{Degree of hydrolysis} = \frac{X}{0.1} = \frac{0.75 \times 10^{-5}}{0.1} = 7.5 \times 10^{-5}$$

The percent hydrolysis is equal to the degree of hydrolysis multiplied by 100.

$$\text{Percent hydrolysis} = 7.5 \times 10^{-5} \times 100 = .0075 \text{ percent}$$

Example 2.

To 250 ml. of a 0.4 M HCN solution is added 250 ml. of a 0.4 M NaOH solution to give 500 ml. of the mixture. What will be the value of the (H^+) when the acid and base exactly neutralize each other? $K_I(HCN) = 4 \times 10^{-10}$

Due to the fact that both the HCN and the NaOH solutions have been diluted to 500 ml., the resulting solution would contain these two substances each at a concentration of 0.2 M assuming no reaction to take place. After the reaction takes place and when equilibrium is reached a solution is obtained which would be the same as that produced by adding 0.2 mole of NaCN to a liter of water, or 0.1 mole NaCN to 500 ml. of water. Therefore, the concentration of the CN^- ion in this solution is approximately 0.2 M, but it will be slightly less than this value due to the hydrolysis, as the following equation indicates.

$$CN^- + H_2O = HCN + OH^-$$

Concentrations: $\quad (0.2 - X) \qquad\qquad X \qquad X$

Then

$$\frac{(HCN)(OH^-)}{(CN^-)} = \frac{X^2}{0.2 - X} = \frac{K_w}{K_{I(acid)}} = \frac{1 \times 10^{-14}}{4 \times 10^{-10}} = 2.5 \times 10^{-5}$$

Neglecting X in comparison with 0.2

$$\frac{X^2}{0.2 - X} \cong \frac{X^2}{0.2} = 2.5 \times 10^{-5}$$

$$X^2 = 5 \times 10^{-6}$$

$$X = 2.2 \times 10^{-3} \text{ mole per liter} = (OH^-)$$

Since

$$(H^+)(OH^-) = 1 \times 10^{-14}$$

$$(H^+) = \frac{1 \times 10^{-14}}{(OH^-)} = \frac{1 \times 10^{-14}}{2.2 \times 10^{-3}}$$

$$(H^+) = 4.5 \times 10^{-12} \text{ mole per liter}$$

Example 3.

(a) Calculate the concentration of the S^{--} ion in a 0.1 M Na$_2$S solution.

(b) Calculate the degree of hydrolysis of the S^{--} ion.

The hydrolysis of the HS^- ion (second step) is negligible as compared with the hydrolysis of the S^{--} ion (first step).

The reaction is

$$S^{--} + H_2O = HS^- + OH^-$$

Let X be the number of moles of S^{--} ion undergoing hydrolysis. Then, at equilibrium, $(HS^-) = X$, $(OH^-) = X$, and $(S^{--}) = (0.1 - X)$. We then have

$$\frac{(HS^-)(OH^-)}{(S^{--})} = \frac{X^2}{0.1 - X} = K_H = \frac{K_w}{K_{I_2}} = \frac{1 \times 10^{-14}}{1.3 \times 10^{-13}} = 7.7 \times 10^{-2}$$

Since the value of K_H is large, X will be large as compared with 0.1 and we cannot neglect X in the expression $(0.1 - X)$. Accordingly, we must solve this equation by the use of the quadratic solution. Clearing of fractions, we have

$$X^2 = 7.7 \times 10^{-3} - 7.7 \times 10^{-2}X$$

Transposing,

$$X^2 + 7.7 \times 10^{-2}X - 7.7 \times 10^{-3} = 0$$

$$X = .058 \text{ mole per liter} = (HS^-) = (OH^-)$$

$$(0.1 - X) = (S^{--}) = .042 \text{ mole per liter}$$

(See Appendix for the solution of the quadratic equation.)

The degree of hydrolysis is the amount of S^{--} ion hydrolyzed divided by the total amount of S^{--} ion originally present. Therefore

$$\text{Degree of hydrolysis} = \frac{.058}{0.1} = 0.58$$

The percent hydrolysis is 0.58×100 or 58 percent.

Example 4.

What is the pH of a solution which contains 0.535 g. of NH_4Cl in 250 ml. of solution?

0.535 g. NH_4Cl is equal to $\frac{0.535}{53.5}$ or .01 mole. .01 mole of NH_4Cl in 250 ml. of solution is equivalent to .04 mole of NH_4Cl per liter. Thus, the concentration of the NH_4^+ ion is .04 M. The NH_4^+ ion undergoes hydrolysis to produce the H^+ ion according to the following equation.

$$NH_4^+ + H_2O = NH_4OH + H^+$$

Let X be the number of moles of NH_4^+ ion undergoing hydrolysis; then, at equilibrium, $(NH_4^+) = (.04 - X)$, $(NH_4OH) = X$, and $(H^+) = X$. Then we have

$$\frac{(NH_4OH)(H^+)}{(NH_4^+)} = \frac{X^2}{.04 - X} = K_H = \frac{K_W}{K_{I(base)}} = \frac{1 \times 10^{-14}}{1.8 \times 10^{-5}}$$

and

$$\frac{X^2}{.04 - X} = 5.6 \times 10^{-10}$$

Neglecting X as compared with .04 we have

$$\frac{X^2}{.04} = 5.6 \times 10^{-10}$$

$$X^2 = 22.4 \times 10^{-12}$$

$$X = 4.7 \times 10^{-6} \text{ mole per liter} = (H^+) = (NH_4OH)$$

$$pH = \log \frac{1}{(H^+)} = - \log (H^+)$$

$$\log (H^+) = \log (4.7 \times 10^{-6}) = \log 4.7 + \log 10^{-6}$$
$$= 0.67 + (-6) = -5.33$$

Therefore

$$pH = - \log (H^+) = - (-5.33) = 5.33$$

Example 5.

How many grams of NaAc must be added to 500 ml. of water to give a solution having a pH of 8.52? (Neglect the volume change due to the addition of the salt.)

The reaction is

$$Ac^- + H_2O = HAc + OH^-$$

From the value given for the pH of the solution, the (H^+) may be calculated. Then (OH^-) may be obtained from $K_W = (H^+)(OH^-) = 1 \times 10^{-14}$. In the NaAc solution $(HAc) = (OH^-)$. Having this information, the (Ac^-) in equilibrium with HAc and OH^- ion may be determined from the hydrolysis equilibrium.

$$pH = - \log (H^+) = 8.52$$
$$\log (H^+) = - 8.52 = - 9.00 + 0.48$$
$$\text{antilog } (-9) = 10^{-9} \text{ and antilog } 0.48 = 3.1$$

Therefore $(H^+) = 3.1 \times 10^{-9} \ M$

$$(H^+)(OH^-) = 1 \times 10^{-14}$$

$$(OH^-) = \frac{1 \times 10^{-14}}{(H^+)} = \frac{1 \times 10^{-14}}{3.1 \times 10^{-9}} = 3.2 \times 10^{-6} \ M$$

If $(OH^-) = 3.2 \times 10^{-6}$ M, then (HAc) has the same value. The equilibrium expression for the hydrolysis reaction is

$$\frac{(HAc)(OH^-)}{(Ac^-)} = K_H = \frac{K_W}{K_I} = \frac{1 \times 10^{-14}}{1.85 \times 10^{-5}} = 5.4 \times 10^{-10}$$

Then

$$\frac{(HAc)(OH^-)}{(Ac^-)} = \frac{(3.2 \times 10^{-6})(3.2 \times 10^{-6})}{(Ac^-)} = 5.4 \times 10^{-10}$$

$$(Ac^-) = \frac{(3.2 \times 10^{-6})^2}{5.4 \times 10^{-10}} = \frac{10.2 \times 10^{-12}}{5.4 \times 10^{-10}} = 1.9 \times 10^{-2} \text{ mole per liter}$$

$.019$ mole per liter $= \dfrac{.019}{2}$ mole per 500 ml. $= .0095$ mole per 500 ml.

The molecular weight of NaAc is 82. Therefore, .0095 mole per 500 ml. is equivalent to $.0095 \times 82$ or 0.78 g. NaAc per 500 ml.

Example 6.

(a) What is the concentration of the H^+ ion and of the OH^- ion in a solution which is .05 M with respect to NH_4CN?

(b) What is the degree of hydrolysis of the NH_4CN?

Ammonium cyanide is a salt of a weak acid and of a weak base. Both ions undergo hydrolysis in accordance with the equation

$$NH_4^+ + CN^- + H_2O = NH_4OH + HCN$$

The equilibrium expression is

$$\frac{(NH_4OH)(HCN)}{(NH_4^+)(CN^-)} = K_H = \frac{K_W}{K_{I(base)} K_{I(acid)}} = \frac{1 \times 10^{-14}}{1.8 \times 10^{-5} \times 4 \times 10^{-10}}$$

$$K_H = \frac{1 \times 10^{-14}}{7.2 \times 10^{-15}} = 1.4$$

We shall assume that for every NH_4^+ ion which hydrolyzes, a CN^- ion also hydrolyzes. It can be shown readily that this assumption is a justifiable one provided the concentration of the NH_4CN is not exceedingly low. Let X be the number of moles of NH_4^+ ion undergoing hydrolysis; then X is also the number of moles of CN^- ion hydrolyzed. Since the initial concentration of the NH_4CN is .05 M and since the salt is completely ionized, the initial concentration of NH_4^+ ion and of CN^- ion is each .05 M. But at equilibrium, $(NH_4^+) = (.05 - X)$, and $(CN^-) = (.05 - X)$. Then

$$\frac{(NH_4OH)(HCN)}{(NH_4^+)(CN^-)} = \frac{X \times X}{(.05 - X)(.05 - X)} = \frac{X^2}{(.05 - X)^2} = 1.4$$

Taking the square root of both sides of the equation, we have

$$\frac{X}{.05 - X} = 1.18$$

$$X = .059 - 1.18X$$

$$2.18X = .059$$

$$X = .027 \text{ mole per liter} = (NH_4OH) = (HCN)$$

The value for the (H^+) may be calculated from the known amount of HCN produced and from the amount of CN^- ion remaining unhydrolyzed. The (HCN) was found to be .027 M; while the value for (CN^-) is $(.05 - X)$ or $(.05 - .027)$ or .023 M. The equation for the ionization of HCN is

$$HCN = H^+ + CN^-$$

while the equilibrium expression is

$$\frac{(H^+)(CN^-)}{(HCN)} = K_I = 4 \times 10^{-10}$$

Substituting in this expression the known values of (HCN) and (CN^-), we have

$$\frac{(H^+)(.023)}{.027} = 4 \times 10^{-10}$$

$$(H^+) = \frac{.027 \times 4 \times 10^{-10}}{.023}$$

$$(H^+) = 4.7 \times 10^{-10} \text{ mole per liter}$$

The (OH^-) then must be

$$(OH^-) = \frac{1 \times 10^{-14}}{4.7 \times 10^{-10}} = 2.1 \times 10^{-5} \text{ mole per liter}$$

The value for (OH^-) could have been calculated from the known amounts of NH_4OH and NH_4^+ ion present in the solution.

$$NH_4OH = NH_4^+ + OH^-$$

and
$$\frac{(NH_4^+)(OH^-)}{(NH_4OH)} = K_I = 1.8 \times 10^{-5}$$

Since (NH_4OH) has a value of .027 M and the (NH_4^+) a value of .023 M, then

$$\frac{.023(OH^-)}{.027} = 1.8 \times 10^{-5}$$

$$(OH^-) = \frac{.027 \times 1.8 \times 10^{-5}}{.023} = 2.1 \times 10^{-5} \text{ mole per liter}$$

This value is the same as that obtained in the first calculation.

The degree of hydrolysis is the number of moles of NH_4CN hydrolyzed divided by the total amount of NH_4CN originally present.

$$\text{Degree of hydrolysis} = \frac{X}{.05} = \frac{.027}{.05} = 0.54$$

$$\text{The percent hydrolysis} = 0.54 \times 100 = 54 \text{ percent}$$

Experiments show that the concentration of the H^+ ion in a solution of NH_4CN is the same for all concentrations of the salt, provided the concentration is not too high, in which case the Law of Mass Action fails to hold, and provided that the concentration of the salt is not excessively low, in which case the degree of hydrolysis of the NH_4^+ ion cannot be regarded as the same as that of the CN^- ion. At intermediate concentrations of NH_4CN the (H^+) is independent of the salt concentration and has a value which is determined by the values of the three equilibrium constants, namely, K_w, $K_{I(base)}$, and $K_{I(acid)}$. This relationship is

$$(H^+) = \sqrt{\frac{K_w \cdot K_{I(acid)}}{K_{I(base)}}}$$

We may arrive at this conclusion in the following manner. From the equilibrium expression for the ionization of HCN

$$\frac{(H^+)}{K_{I(acid)}} = \frac{(HCN)}{(CN^-)}$$

From the hydrolysis equilibrium we have

$$\frac{(NH_4OH)(HCN)}{(NH_4^+)(CN^-)} = \frac{K_w}{K_{I(base)} K_{I(acid)}}$$

But since $\dfrac{(NH_4OH)}{(NH_4^+)} = \dfrac{(HCN)}{(CN^-)}$, and since the latter expression $= \dfrac{(H^+)}{K_{I(acid)}}$, we have $\qquad \left(\dfrac{HCN}{CN^-}\right)^2 = \left(\dfrac{H^+}{K_{I(acid)}}\right)^2 = \dfrac{K_W}{K_{I(base)} \, K_{I(acid)}}$

Then $\qquad\qquad (H^+)^2 = \dfrac{K_W (K_{I(acid)})^2}{K_{I(base)} \, K_{I(acid)}}$

$\qquad\qquad\qquad (H^+)^2 = \dfrac{K_W K_{I(acid)}}{K_{I(base)}}$

and $\qquad\qquad (H^+) = \sqrt{\dfrac{K_W K_{I(acid)}}{K_{I(base)}}}$

Substituting into this expression the values for the constants, we have

$$(H^+) = \sqrt{\frac{1 \times 10^{-14} \times 4 \times 10^{-10}}{1.8 \times 10^{-5}}} = 4.7 \times 10^{-10} \text{ mole per liter}$$

This value for the (H^+) is the same as that originally obtained directly from the hydrolysis equilibrium. It may be advantageous, as the occasion arises, to make use of this expression for calculating the concentration of the H^+ ion in a solution containing the salt of a weak acid and of a weak base.

Example 7.

Calculate the solubility of PbS in water:
(a) Neglecting the hydrolysis of the S^{--} ion.
(b) Considering the hydrolysis of the S^{--} ion.

The hydrolysis of the S^{--} ion becomes a very important factor in calculating the solubilities of sulfides from their solubility product constants and, conversely, in calculating the solubility product constants from solubility data. When hydrolysis is taken into account the solubility of any slightly soluble sulfide is about one thousand times greater than that calculated by neglecting hydrolysis.

(a) First calculate the solubility of PbS neglecting hydrolysis. ($K_{S.P.}$ for PbS $= 4 \times 10^{-26}$.)

$$PbS_{(s)} = Pb^{++} + S^{--}$$

Let X equal the number of moles of PbS dissolved in 1 liter of solution. Then X will be equal to (S^{--}) and (Pb^{++}).

$$(Pb^{++})(S^{--}) = X^2 = 4 \times 10^{-26}$$

$$X = 2 \times 10^{-13} \text{ mole per liter}$$

Therefore, the calculated solubility of PbS in water is 2×10^{-13} M if the hydrolysis of the S^{--} ion is neglected.

(b) In considering the hydrolysis of the S^{--} ion we can assume that only the first step of hydrolysis is important, since the second step is negligibly small.

$$S^{--} + H_2O = HS^- + OH^-$$

The value for K_H for this reaction as calculated previously in *Example 3* is .077, and we found the S^{--} ion to be hydrolyzed to the extent of 58 percent in 0.1 M Na_2S solution. At lower concentrations the hydrolysis of the S^{--} ion is even greater than this. If the concentration of the S^{--} ion were extremely small, of the order of magnitude of the concentration of the OH^- ion in water, then the hydrolysis would be reduced somewhat due to the common ion effect of the OH^- ion. Nevertheless, the S^{--} ion at a concentration of 1×10^{-13} M would be practically completely hydrolyzed. In such an event the concentration of the OH^- ion produced by the hydrolysis would be only 1×10^{-13} M. This value is small compared with the concentration of the OH^- ion already present in water, namely, 1×10^{-7} M. Therefore, though the hydrolysis of the S^{--} ion in a saturated solution of PbS may be complete, the (OH^-) in the solution will still have a value of 1×10^{-7} M. Accordingly,

$$\frac{(HS^-)(OH^-)}{(S^{--})} = \frac{(HS^-) \times 1 \times 10^{-7}}{(S^{--})} = K_H = .077$$

$$\frac{(HS^-)}{(S^{--})} = 7.7 \times 10^5 \quad \text{or} \quad (S^{--}) = \frac{(HS^-)}{7.7 \times 10^5}$$

From this ratio we see that there are almost one million times as many HS^- ions as S^{--} ions in solution and that the hydrolysis is almost complete. From the two equilibria involved here

$$PbS_{(s)} = Pb^{++} + S^{--}$$
$$S^{--} + H_2O = HS^- + OH^-$$

it is evident that for every S^{--} ion which is removed by hydrolysis, one Pb^{++} ion and one HS^- ion are produced. Therefore, the concentration of the Pb^{++} ion will be practically the same as the concentration of the HS^- ion in solution.

Substituting the value for the S^{--} ion concentration in the solubility product expression, we have

$$(Pb^{++})(S^{--}) = (Pb^{++})\frac{(HS^-)}{7.7 \times 10^5} = K_{S.P.} = 4 \times 10^{-26}$$

Since $\qquad (Pb^{++}) = (HS^-),$

$$\frac{(Pb^{++})^2}{7.7 \times 10^5} = 4 \times 10^{-26}$$

$$(Pb^{++})^2 = 3.1 \times 10^{-20}$$

$$(Pb^{++}) = 1.8 \times 10^{-10} \text{ mole per liter}$$

Therefore, the solubility of PbS in 1 liter of solution is also 1.8×10^{-10} mole per liter, which value is approximately one thousand times greater than that obtained $(2 \times 10^{-13} M)$ when hydrolysis is neglected.

If we were to consider the second step of hydrolysis,

$$HS^- + H_2O = H_2S + OH^-$$

the calculated solubility would be further increased but the order of magnitude of the solubility would not be appreciably changed. In addition, the Pb^{++} ion undoubtedly hydrolyzes to give $Pb(OH)^+$ ion and $Pb(OH)_2$, and these effects would also increase the solubility of PbS.

Example 8.

Calculate the concentration of (a) the H^+ ion, (b) the OH^- ion, (c) the HCO_3^- ion, and (d) the CO_3^{--} ion in a solution which contains 0.1 mole of $NaHCO_3$ per liter.

Since $NaHCO_3$ is a salt it is completely ionized to give Na^+ and HCO_3^- ions. The HCO_3^- ion is not only a weak acid itself but it is also an ion of another weak acid, H_2CO_3. Therefore, the HCO_3^- ion takes part in two reactions in water solution,

$$HCO_3^- + H_2O = H_2CO_3 + OH^- \qquad (1)$$

and

$$HCO_3^- = CO_3^{--} + H^+ \qquad (2)$$

Reaction (1), the hydrolysis of the HCO_3^- ion, produces OH^- ion, while reaction (2), the ionization of the HCO_3^- ion, produces H^+ ion. As both reactions proceed, the H^+ and OH^- ions formed are practically all used up in the formation of water,

$$H^+ + OH^- = H_2O \qquad (3)$$

Adding equations (1), (2), and (3), we have

$$2HCO_3^- = H_2CO_3 + CO_3^{--} \tag{4}$$

The equilibrium expression for (4) is

$$\frac{(H_2CO_3)(CO_3^{--})}{(HCO_3^-)^2} = K_{(4)}$$

When equations are added, the corresponding equilibrium expressions are multiplied. Therefore the numerical value for $K_{(4)}$ is

$$\frac{(H_2CO_3)(OH^-)}{(HCO_3^-)} \times \frac{(CO_3^{--})(H^+)}{(HCO_3^-)} \times \frac{1}{(H^+)(OH^-)} = K_{(1)} \times K_{(2)} \times K_{(3)}$$

Cancelling (H^+) and (OH^-) in the numerator and denominator,

$$\frac{(H_2CO_3)(CO_3^{--})}{(HCO_3^-)^2} = K_{(1)} \times K_{(2)} \times K_{(3)} = K_{(4)}$$

$K_{(1)}$ is the hydrolysis constant for the HCO_3^- ion and has a value of $\dfrac{1 \times 10^{-14}}{4.2 \times 10^{-7}}$; $K_{(2)}$ is the ionization constant for the second stage of ionization of carbonic acid and is equal to 4.8×10^{-11}; and $K_{(3)}$ equals $\dfrac{1}{K_W}$ or $\dfrac{1}{1 \times 10^{-14}}$. Substituting these values in the above expression, we have

$$\frac{(H_2CO_3)(CO_3^{--})}{(HCO_3^-)^2} = \frac{1 \times 10^{-14}}{4.2 \times 10^{-7}} \times \frac{4.8 \times 10^{-11}}{1} \times \frac{1}{1 \times 10^{-14}}$$

$$= 1.14 \times 10^{-4} = K_{(4)} \tag{5}$$

Referring to equations (1), (2), and (3), it is seen that for every OH^- ion which reacts with H^+ ion to form water, one H_2CO_3 molecule and one CO_3^{--} ion are produced. Therefore, for practical purposes we are justified in making the assumption that at equilibrium the (H_2CO_3) will be the same as the (CO_3^{--}). We can also assume that since reactions (1) and (2) take place to a limited extent, the (HCO_3^-) remains practically unchanged; therefore, in this case the value for (HCO_3^-) will be for all practical purposes $0.1\ M$.

Making use of equation (5) and letting (H_2CO_3) and (CO_3^{--}) each be X, we have

$$\frac{X^2}{(0.1)^2} = 1.14 \times 10^{-4}$$

$$X^2 = 1.14 \times 10^{-6}$$

$$X = 1.06 \times 10^{-3} \text{ mole per liter} = (H_2CO_3) = (CO_3^{--})$$

Having obtained the values for (H_2CO_3) and (CO_3^{--}), (H^+) and (OH^-) may then be calculated from the equilibrium expressions of (1) and (2). Taking reaction (2), we have

$$\frac{(H^+)(CO_3^{--})}{(HCO_3^-)} = \frac{(H^+) \times 1.06 \times 10^{-3}}{0.1} = K_{(2)} = 4.8 \times 10^{-11}$$

$$(H^+) = \frac{0.1 \times 4.8 \times 10^{-11}}{1.06 \times 10^{-3}} = 4.5 \times 10^{-9} \text{ mole per liter}$$

The value for (OH^-) may then be obtained from the water equilibrium as follows.

$$(OH^-) = \frac{1 \times 10^{-14}}{4.5 \times 10^{-9}} = 2.2 \times 10^{-6} \text{ mole per liter}$$

The $NaHCO_3$ solution is found to be basic.

The value for the concentration of the hydrogen ion in this solution may be obtained more conveniently by making use of a general rule which can readily be shown to hold for acid salts of the type $NaHCO_3$. The rule states that the (H^+) is equal to the square root of the product of the two ionization constants for the dibasic acid. Thus, in the present case,

$$(H^+) = \sqrt{K_{I_1} \times K_{I_2}}$$

$$(H^+) = \sqrt{4.2 \times 10^{-7} \times 4.8 \times 10^{-11}}$$

$$(H^+) = \sqrt{20 \times 10^{-18}}$$

$$(H^+) = 4.5 \times 10^{-9} \text{ mole per liter}$$

This value is the same as that obtained in the previous calculation. Since the latter calculation does not involve the concentration of the dissolved $NaHCO_3$, the value obtained for (H^+) must be the same for all concentrations of the salt.

The rule, in this case, may be derived from the first and second ionization constants for carbonic acid.

$$\frac{(H^+)^2(CO_3^{--})}{(H_2CO_3)} = K_1 \times K_2$$

Remembering that for all practical purposes (CO_3^{--}) and (H_2CO_3) are essentially the same, we therefore cancel them in the above expression, and

$$(H^+) = \sqrt{K_1 \times K_2}$$

At intermediate concentrations, this relationship applies to such ions of weak acids as $HC_2O_4^-$, $H_2PO_4^-$, $H_2PO_3^-$, HSO_3^-, and HS^-.

Questions and Problems

1. Write the equation representing the dissociation of water into H^+ and OH^- ions. Explain why the addition of more water will not shift this equilibrium. How may it be shifted?

2. Why is the equilibrium expression for the dissociation of water written $(H^+) \times (OH^-)$ and not $\dfrac{(H^+) \times (OH^-)}{(H_2O)}$?

3. When solid sodium acetate is added to water why do not all of the Ac^- ions combine with H^+ ions to form acetic acid?

4. Does (a) the salt of a weak acid and a strong base, (b) the salt of a strong acid and a weak base, (c) the salt of a strong acid and a strong base, produce an acidic, basic or neutral solution?

5. Show that the hydrolysis constant for a salt of a strong base and a weak acid is equal to the ionization constant for water divided by the dissociation constant for the acid.

6. Show that the hydrolysis constant for the *first* step of hydrolysis for the salt of a strong base and a weak dibasic acid is equal to the ionization constant for water divided by the second dissociation constant for the acid.

7. Explain why aluminum hydroxide and not aluminum carbonate is precipitated from solution when a solution of sodium carbonate is added to one of aluminum sulfate.

8. Why is BaS not stable when added to water?

9. Why is the carbonate ion concentration in a solution of ammonium carbonate less than it is in a sodium carbonate solution of the same molarity?

10. Explain by the Rule of Le Chatelier why the degree of hydrolysis of sodium acetate increases as the solution is diluted.

11. Write equations for the hydrolysis reactions occurring when sodium carbonate is dissolved in water.

12. If a 0.1 molar solution of HCN is neutralized by a 0.1 molar solution of NaOH the two solutions do not neutralize each other when the H^+ ion concentration is 10^{-7} molar but rather when the H^+ concentration is about 10^{-11} molar. Explain.

13. What is a buffer solution? Explain its action.

14. Write the ionic equations for the reaction representing the hydrolysis of each of the following salts:
    (a) Ammonium chloride — NH_4Cl
    (b) Sodium acetate — $NaC_2H_3O_2$

    (c) Methyl ammonium chloride — CH_3NH_3Cl
    (d) Sodium benzoate — $NaC_6H_5CO_2$
    (e) Potassium cyanide — KCN
    (f) Sodium phenolate — NaC_6H_5O
    (g) Barium nitrite — $Ba(NO_2)_2$
    (h) Lithium formate — $LiCHO_2$
    (i) Dimethyl ammonium chloride — $(CH_3)_2NH_2Cl$
    (j) Potassium propionate — $KC_3H_5O_2$

15. Calculate the hydrolysis constant for each of the salts listed in problem 14. (K_I for the corresponding acids or bases are given in tables in the Appendix.)

16. Calculate the (H^+) for (A) a 0.1 molar, (B) a .01 molar solution of each of the salts listed in problem 14.

17. What is the pH value for each of the solutions in problem 16?

18. What is the degree of hydrolysis for each salt in problem 16?

19. How many grams of sodium acetate must be added to 1 liter of water to give an OH^- ion concentration of 1×10^{-5} mole per liter?

20. How many grams of NH_4Cl must be added to 1 liter of water to give an OH^- ion concentration of 10^{-9} mole per liter?

21. How many moles of NH_4Cl must be added to 1 liter of water to give the same pH value as a 0.1 molar solution of HCN?

22. (a) Using only $K_I(HAc)$, calculate the H^+ concentration in a solution containing 0.1 mole sodium acetate and 0.1 mole acetic acid. (b) Repeat the calculation using K_H.

23. What is the concentration of the undissociated HAc in a solution containing 1 mole NaAc per liter?

24. A .01 molar solution of NaCN is found to be hydrolyzed to the extent of 5 percent. What is the value of the ionization constant for HCN?

25. Show by calculation whether it is possible to make a solution of sodium formate concentrated enough to produce the same OH^- concentration as that of a .001 molar solution of KCN. (In this case assume the Law of Mass Action to hold for concentrated solutions.)

26. Calculate (a) the hydrolysis constant, (b) the H^+ ion concentration, and (c) the degree of hydrolysis for a 0.1 M Na_2CO_3 solution. (Neglect the second hydrolysis step.)

27. What will be the minimum concentration of a NaAc solution necessary to begin the precipitation of $Mg(OH)_2$ if equal quantities of this solution and one containing 0.2 mole Mg^{++} ion per liter are mixed?

28. Solid Na_2S is added slowly to a .01 M $FeSO_4$ solution. Which will be precipitated first, $Fe(OH)_2$ or FeS?

29. Calculate the H^+ ion concentration in the resulting solution when equal amounts of the following are mixed:

(a) 0.1 M HCl and 0.1 M NH_4OH

(b) 0.1 M HCl and 0.1 M NaOH

(c) 0.1 M H_2SO_4 and 0.1 M NaOH (see p. 181)

(d) .02 M HAc and .02 M NaOH

(e) 0.1 M H_2S and 0.2 M NaOH

30. Calculate the CO_3^{--} ion concentration and the OH^- ion concentration in a .01 M solution of $NaHCO_3$. (See *Example 8*, page 184.)

31. If $MgCl_2$ is added slowly to a solution which is 0.1 M with respect to $NaHCO_3$, which will begin to precipitate first, $Mg(OH)_2$ or $MgCO_3$? (See *Example 8*, page 238.)

32. Calculate the solubility in moles per liter of the following sulfides in water, (A) neglecting the hydrolysis of the S^{--} ion, (B) considering the hydrolysis of the S^{--} ion.

(a) CdS   (b) CuS   (c) PbS   (d) Ag_2S (e) CoS

33. What must be the ratio of (Ac^-) to (HAc) in a buffer solution made up of acetic acid and sodium acetate if the H^+ ion concentration is to be maintained at 10^{-5} M?

34. What is the concentration of the H^+ ion in a solution which is .01 M with respect to $ZnCl_2$? $(K_I(Zn(OH)^+$ has a value of 4×10^{-5}.)

35. Calculate the ratio of the (HPO_4^{--}) to $(H_2PO_4^-)$ in a solution in which these two ions are used as a buffer, if the pH of the solution is to be maintained at (a) 6.0, (b) 7.0, and (c) 8.0. Assume that the H^+ ion concentration is controlled entirely by the reaction $H_2PO_4^- = H^+ + HPO_4^{--}$.

CHAPTER 8

Complex
Ions

For the sake of simplicity and because of a lack of definite information we designate an ion in solution merely by the symbol of the element or radical and by the charge which the ion carries. Thus, hydrogen ion is written as H^+; sodium ion, Na^+; chloride ion, Cl^-; sulfate ion, SO_4^{--}, etc. There is sufficient evidence for the argument that no ion exists in solution as a simple charged atom or group as its chemical symbol might imply. It has been shown by experiments designed to determine the relative amounts of electricity carried by various ions in solution that ions carry with them relatively large quantities of water. Although it is not possible as yet to determine the absolute amount of water carried by each, these experiments do allow calculations to be made concerning the amount of water carried by an ion of one element or group, relative to that transported by an ion of another element or group. For example, if we arbitrarily assume that the fastest moving ion, the hydrogen ion, carries a minimum amount of water, one molecule, then the potassium ion carries on the average about five; the sodium ion, eight; the lithium ion, fourteen; while the chloride ion carries about four molecules of water. These numbers are known as the *hydration numbers* of the ions. These hydration numbers vary with the concentration of the solution. They are related to the speeds of the ions, in that an ion carrying a large amount of water moves slowly in comparison with an ion which carries a relatively small amount of water.

From what has been said in earlier chapters regarding the attractive forces between ions of opposite charge, it would seem reasonable to expect that these attractive forces also exist between ions and water molecules to give rise to hydrated ions, since the water molecule is a dipole having separated positive and negative centralizations of charge. Polar molecules tend to attract each other to form aggregates of molecules and, similarly, we might conclude that polar water molecules are attracted to charged ions in solution. Accordingly, we may look upon all ions as solvated in solution, i.e., having molecules of solvent attached to them.

The union between most ions and water is not a very firm or stable one, and the law of definite proportions does not apply in the cases cited, namely, the hydration of such ions as Li^+, Na^+, and Cl^-. The binding force between water molecules and these ions is of the dipole moment type. The sodium ion, for example, attracts the negative end of the water molecule, thus binding the water molecule to it. If one were able to see these hydrated molecules with a sub-microscopic eye, he would find that some sodium ions have six H_2O molecules associated with them; some, seven; some, eight; others, nine; etc. The average number would be about eight.

In the case of the cobalt ion, however, a definite number of water molecules are associated with each metallic cobalt ion. This definiteness in the number of water molecules associated with the cobalt ion indicates that the bonding is primarily of the covalent type, i.e., by shared electrons. When we speak of complex ions we usually are referring to the coordinately bonded, exactly defined type of ion. Examples of such complex ions involving other than H_2O molecules are: $Zn(NH_3)_4^{++}$, $Fe(CN)_6^{---}$, $AgCl_2^-$, and $Co(NH_3)_6^{+++}$.

It is possible to produce complex ions which are made up of a positively charged metallic ion and more than one kind of negative ion or neutral molecule associated with it. For example, the following complex molecules or ions are known: $[Co(NH_3)_3 Cl_3]$, $[Co(NH_3)_2 Cl_4]^-$, $[Co(NH_3)_4 Cl_2]^+$, etc. (in all combinations). Note that, for the first example given, the charge on the ion is zero; it is a neutral molecule. The charge on the next ion is -1 (it is an anion), and for the third, $+1$ (a cation). Thus complex ions made up from positively charged metallic ion cores are not necessarily positively charged. They may be neutral molecules, anions, or cations.

The Hydronium Ion. Since the hydrogen ion moves much faster than any other ion in solution when subjected to an electric field, we believe that it has associated with it less water than other ions. If we assume that it combines with one molecule of water, we may write its formula as $H^+(H_2O)$ or H_3O^+.

$$H^+ + H_2O = H_3O^+ \tag{1}$$

The latter ion is known as the **hydronium ion** and is believed by many to represent the condition of the hydrogen ion in water.

One argument for this structure for the H^+ ion in water is that the H_2O molecule possesses an extra pair of bonding p electrons which are available to combine with the H^+ ion. This process is illustrated schematically in Figure 8.1.

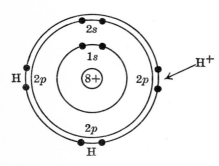

The H_3O^+ ion thus formed can have other H_2O molecules attached to it through the action of dipole forces. Only one H_2O molecule is associated with the H^+ ion in the form

FIG. 8.1 The electronic concept of the formation of the H_3O^+ ion.

of a covalent bond. Other arguments for believing that the H^+ ion exists in water solution as H_3O^+ are given in the following paragraphs.

When two substances react with each other to form a third

substance, an energy change takes place which usually manifests itself in the form of heat; heat is either liberated or absorbed. The former is the more usual case. This heat effect is usually large when the substance formed possesses great stability. In general, the smaller the heat effect the less stable is the product. When one substance dissolves in another, an energy change likewise results. Heat is usually, not always, absorbed in the process of solution, but the magnitude of the energy change is usually very small compared with that involved in a chemical reaction. When HCl, H_2SO_4, HBr, HNO_3, and similar substances are placed in water a very large amount of heat is liberated, much more than one would expect from the simple process of solution. On the contrary, when sodium chloride is placed in water, a small amount of heat is absorbed. Many other salts behave similarly. Where the hydrogen ion is involved in the process of solution, the amount of heat liberated is comparable with that of many chemical reactions. This behavior may be ascribed to the formation of the hydronium ion.

If we assume that one molecule of water is associated with the hydrogen ion, the resulting hydronium ion may be represented structurally as being similar to the ammonium ion. The hydronium ion is a complex ion and is the fundamental particle used in the Brønsted definitions for the explanation of acid-base reactions.

The Ammonium Ion. Pure liquid ammonia, boiling point $-33.5°$ C, is a poorer conductor of electricity than is pure water; the conductivity of water is at least 10,000 times greater than that of ammonia. When hydrogen chloride is placed in pure ammonia the resulting solution is found to be an excellent conductor of electricity; the value of its conductivity is of the same order of magnitude as that of hydrogen chloride in water. In this case a reaction takes place which involves the formation of a new ion. The ion produced is quite familiar to us, the ammonium ion, and its formation may be expressed by the equation,

$$H^+ + NH_3 = NH_4^+ \tag{2}$$

The ammonium ion is a complex ion and may be looked upon as an analogue of the hydronium ion. It differs from the hydronium ion in that it forms salts with negative ions which possess considerable stability. When the excess ammonia from the solution just considered is allowed to evaporate, a solid remains which upon examination is found to be ammonium chloride. It is known that solid ammonium chloride may be heated to several hundred degrees before it noticeably dissociates to give ammonia and hydrogen chloride. Ammonia reacts in a similar manner with many other hydrogen compounds; thus HBr, HI, H_2SO_4, and HNO_3 form ammonium salts with ammonia, all of which are highly stable in that they may be crystallized from solution.

Pure ammonia ionizes very slightly in accordance with the equation,

$$NH_3 = H^+ + NH_2^- \tag{3}$$

The hydrogen ion formed in this process combines with ammonia, as expressed in equation (2). The NH_2^- (amide) ion in liquid ammonia corresponds to the OH^- ion in water, and metal ions in combination with the NH_2^- ion behave as bases.

Like hydrogen chloride in water (hydronium chloride), ammonium chloride behaves as an acid in liquid ammonia. It will react with ammono bases such as potassium amide, KNH_2, sodium amide, $NaNH_2$, etc., to form salts and ammonia. These reactions are analogous to those between hydrochloric acid and hydroxides in water. Typical reactions in the two solvents may be written:

$$H_3O^+ + OH^- = 2H_2O \tag{4}$$

$$NH_4^+ + NH_2^- = 2NH_3 \tag{5}$$

One of the characteristic properties of an acid in an aqueous medium is its ability to react with certain metals with the displacement of hydrogen. Thus,

$$Zn + 2H^+ = Zn^{++} + H_2 \qquad (6)$$

or, using hydronium chloride,

$$Zn + 2H_3O^+ = Zn^{++} + H_2 + 2H_2O \qquad (7)$$

Ammonium chloride in liquid ammonia behaves in a similar manner,

$$Zn + 2NH_4^+ = Zn^{++} + H_2 + 2NH_3 \qquad (8)$$

Like the hydronium ion in water, the ammonium ion in ammonia is an acid. The only essential difference between the two is that the ammonium ion possesses a far greater stability at ordinary temperatures than does the hydronium ion. The similarity of water to ammonia leads to the assumption of the hydronium ion as the analogue of the ammonium ion. However, for most purposes it is immaterial which formula we use. Simplicity recommends the use of the symbol H^+ rather than H_3O^+ for the hydrogen ion in water solution.

Solid Hydrates and Ammonates. The ability of ions to combine with water and ammonia molecules is not limited to the hydrogen ion. As we previously stated, attractive forces exist between ions and polar water molecules, and all ions are more or less associated with water in this medium. In most cases the resulting combination, which is not a definite one, is capable of existence only in solution. Sometimes a crystalline product containing water may be obtained from solution. The number of such compounds is relatively large; only a few familiar examples may be mentioned here, such as $CuSO_4 \cdot 5H_2O$, $CaCl_2 \cdot 6H_2O$, $Na_2SO_4 \cdot 10H_2O$, and $CrCl_3 \cdot 6H_2O$. These addition compounds, made up of salts and water molecules, are commonly called *hydrates*. The fact that these solids contain water in definite proportions is no assurance that definite proportions hold true in solution. The crystal lattice, i.e., the space distribution in the crystal, allows a definite number of water molecules to be associated or trapped with each particle (ion or atom) in the crystal. Such restrictions do not prevail in solution.

Ammonia shows an even greater tendency to combine with ions both in water and in liquid ammonia to form analogous solid compounds, called **ammonates.** Characteristic examples of such combinations are $CuSO_4 \cdot 4NH_3$, $CaCl_2 \cdot 8NH_3$, $CrCl_3 \cdot 6NH_3$, and $CoCl_3 \cdot 6NH_3$. All of these ammonates may be crystallized from solution and upon analysis they have been shown to be definite compounds. In general, the ammonates are more stable, both in solution and. in the solid state, than are the analogous combinations containing water molecules. This property of ions or molecules to combine with solvent molecules is not confined entirely to water and ammonia. Molecules of many other solvents show the same tendency to a greater or lesser degree. This fact is demonstrated clearly when one considers that there are known in well-crystallized form several thousand combinations similar to those mentioned above, in which water, ammonia, alcohols, amines, and many other solvent molecules assume a definite part in the crystalline solid complex.

Valence and Complex Molecules. An examination of complex molecules reveals that the valence relationships among their atoms cannot be explained by the ordinary concepts which apply fairly well to other types of molecules. It appears that in each instance the ion in the complex molecule exhibits a combining capacity which exceeds the primary or ordinary valence. Thus in $[Cu(NH_3)_4]^{++}$ the copper ion displays the ability to acquire four additional molecules of ammonia. On the other hand, the cobalt ion takes on six molecules of water or ammonia. A similar situation exists in many other known compounds. This additional combining capacity is usually spoken of as the **auxiliary** or **secondary valence,** which for the copper ion is four and for the cobalt ion, six. What is the nature of this auxiliary valence and what explanation can be offered to account for it?

When the periodic table is followed into the third series of elements (beginning with argon), scandium appears in the third group. This element is not very closely related to the preceding elements in the same group. Since it is in the first long series, between argon and krypton, which series is composed of 18 elements, a shell of 18 electrons must be taken into consideration. In the case of scandium one electron falls back into a shell which already possesses a stable grouping of eight electrons; this shell then contains nine electrons. This thus becomes the first step in the formation of an inner shell of 18 electrons. The same shell for the element titanium (atomic number 22, one greater than that of scandium) contains 10 electrons, for vanadium it contains 11 electrons, etc., until zinc (atomic number 30) is reached, which has 18 electrons. This number persists in this shell as far as the next rare gas, krypton (atomic number 36). The fourth series of the periodic table is likewise a long series and contains 18 elements, while the fifth series contains 32 elements, due to the 14 rare earth elements which occupy a single position in the table. The elements in these long series have more than 8 electrons in the next to the outermost shell. The outermost shell contains the normal valence electrons. In the long series we find the elements which make up the sub-groups of the table and, in addition, the transition elements, such as iron, cobalt and nickel.

Ions which show no auxiliary valence have a completed group of eight electrons in the outermost shell. Those displaying secondary valence have in their outermost shells either a completed or partially completed group of 18 electrons. Thus, the magnesium ion (magnesium atom minus 2 electrons) has an outer group of 8 electrons while the zinc ion has an outer group of 18.

The secondary valence which is displayed in the formation of complex molecules is undoubtedly due to forces which result from the electrons of that shell immediately within the one containing the valence electrons of the atoms, i.e., the outermost shell of the ions. The binding between the metal ion and the peripherally attached molecules or ions is probably of the coordinately bonded type. This fact is strongly suggested when one considers the properties of these complexes.

The Coordination Theory of Werner. About the beginning of the century, Alfred Werner, a German chemist, made a thorough study of complex molecules and proposed a theory which fits their observed properties in a remarkable manner. He first introduced the concept of auxiliary or secondary valence, thus explaining the behavior of these compounds. Let us examine this theory in order to explain the properties of a typical complex molecule such as $CoCl_3 \cdot 6NH_3$. This molecule is a salt, a good conductor of electricity in water solution, and its anion may readily be identified as the chloride ion by the precipitation of silver chloride when silver nitrate is added to its solution. All the chlorine is found in the anion form, and sulfuric acid converts the complex into the corresponding sulfate salt. Contrary to what might be expected, sulfuric acid fails to remove ammonia molecules very rapidly from the complex, even though ammonia and hydrogen ion have a great tendency to combine with each other to form the ammonium ion, NH_4^+.

This complex ion is not as stable as one might think. The dissociation constant for the equilibrium, $Co(NH_3)_6^{+++} = Co^{+++} + 6NH_3$, has a value of 2.2×10^{-34}; however, the Co^{+++} ion appears to the first power and the concentration of NH_3 to the sixth power. (These high powers or exponents make the equilibrium constant seem inordinately small.) On standing, dissociation becomes appreciable; it so happens that the rate of dissociation is low, which effect makes it appear that the complex is much more stable than it actually is. On the basis of these properties and according to the theory of Werner the molecule is represented as $[Co(NH_3)_6]Cl_3$, or

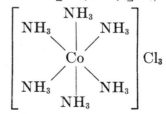

It is assumed that the addition of the six molecules of ammonia takes place through the secondary valencies. The complex grouping contains only a cobalt atom and ammonia molecules, and as a unit it does not possess properties characteristic of either constituent. The chlorine atoms, however, retain their characteristic properties, in that all three are readily removed by silver ions with the formation of silver chloride. Consequently, all three chlorine atoms must exist in solution as chloride ions. The conductivity of this complex in water solution has a value similar to that of a typical tri-univalent electrolyte such as ferric chloride, $FeCl_3$; hence the complex must produce four ions. Accordingly, we may indicate its structure in solution as

$$\begin{bmatrix} & & NH_3 & & \\ NH_3 & & | & & NH_3 \\ & \diagdown & | & \diagup & \\ & & Co & & \\ & \diagup & | & \diagdown & \\ NH_3 & & | & & NH_3 \\ & & NH_3 & & \end{bmatrix}^{+++} + 3Cl^-$$

One molecule of ammonia may be easily removed from the cobalt complex discussed above by heating the solid to 250° C. This procedure produces the compound $CoCl_3 \cdot 5NH_3$. When this molecule is treated with silver ion in water solution, only two chlorine atoms are readily removed through the precipitation of silver chloride. In addition, the conductivity of this salt shows it to be a bi-univalent electrolyte, producing only three ions. Its structure may be represented as

$$\begin{bmatrix} & & Cl & & \\ NH_3 & & | & & NH_3 \\ & \diagdown & | & \diagup & \\ & & Co & & \\ & \diagup & | & \diagdown & \\ NH_3 & & | & & NH_3 \\ & & NH_3 & & \end{bmatrix}^{++} + 2Cl^-$$

In like manner $[Co(NH_3)_4Cl_2]Cl$ is found to be a uni-univalent electrolyte, because of its conductivity and because silver ion reacts rapidly with only one chloride ion per molecule. $[Co(NH_3)_3Cl_3]$ is quite insoluble in water and is a nonconductor of the electric current. Silver ion fails to precipitate silver chloride rapidly when added to a solution of this compound. Continued removal of ammonia and the addition of potassium nitrite produces $K[Co(NH_3)_2(NO_2)_4]$, which is found to be a uni-univalent electrolyte and to ionize as

$$K[Co(NH_3)_2(NO_2)_4] = K^+ + [Co(NH_3)_2(NO_2)_4]^- \qquad (9)$$

The resulting charge on the complex ion is negative because the nitrite ions replacing the ammonia molecules in the complex are themselves negatively charged. By this process a neutral molecular complex is changed into a negatively charged ion.

The resulting charge on any complex ion can easily be determined by taking the algebraic sum of the charges on the constituent parts of the complex ion. Thus, in this case,

$$
\begin{aligned}
&Co^{+++} \text{ contributes } 3\ + \\
&2NH_3 \text{ contribute }\ \ 0 \\
&\underline{4NO_2^- \text{ contribute }\ \ 4\ -} \\
&\ \ \ \text{resultant charge } 1\ -
\end{aligned}
$$

The next member of the series is not known, but its formula would be $K_2[Co(NH_3)(NO_2)_5]$, a uni-bivalent electrolyte. The last member of the series is well known as potassium cobaltinitrite which is only slightly soluble in water. In one of the analytical tests for potassium ion, the sodium salt, $Na_3[Co(NO_2)_6]$, is added to a solution of the unknown. In dilute solution $NaK_2[Co(NO_2)_6]$ is precipitated if potassium ion is present; in concentrated solution $K_3[Co(NO_2)_6]$ may be formed. The latter is a uni-trivalent electrolyte, as shown by the magnitude of its conductivity, and ionizes in solution to produce four ions,

$$K_3[Co(NO_2)_6] = 3K^+ + [Co(NO_2)_6]^{---} \qquad (10)$$

The following series of platinum compounds is also well established: $[Pt(NH_3)_6]Cl_4$, $[Pt(NH_3)_5Cl]Cl_3$, $[Pt(NH_3)_4Cl_2]Cl_2$, $[Pt(NH_3)_3Cl_3]Cl$, $[Pt(NH_3)_2Cl_4]$, $[Pt(NH_3)Cl_5]K$, and

$[PtCl_6]K_2$. It will be observed that the number of single constituents associated with the central atom in the complex cation or anion, as the case may be, in both the cobalt and platinum series, is always six. This number is known as the *coordination number,* which for most ions is usually 4 or 6. In the case of the well-known copper-ammonia complex ion, $[Cu(NH_3)_4]^{++}$, the coordination number of the copper is 4.

The coordination number of an ion in many instances is equal to twice the charge on the ion. Thus the coordination number of Cu^{++} is 4; that of Zn^{++}, 4; that of Ag^+, 2; that of Cu^+, 2; and that of Co^{+++}, 6. This rule is not a rigid one; the most common exception is the coordination number of 6 for Fe^{++} in the ferrocyanides.

The complex anion or cation or molecule is sometimes designated as the *coordination sphere.* Thus the coordination sphere of the compound $[Co(NH_3)_5Cl]Cl_2$ contains one cobalt atom, five molecules of ammonia and one chlorine atom. Polyvalent acid radicals, such as SO_4^{--}, CO_3^{--}, $C_2O_4^{--}$ (oxalate) ions, may be taken up by the central atom and occupy two positions in the coordination sphere; for example, in the complex $[Co(NH_3)_4SO_4]Cl$, the coordination number of the cobalt ion remains as 6. Although the examples given above for the cobalt and platinum series contain only ammonia molecules, it must be remembered that water and other solvent molecules can occupy positions within the coordination sphere. The ammonia complexes are chosen here since they are well defined and relatively simple.

The following list includes some of the molecules and ions which form complexes with metallic cations:

NH_3, RNH_2, R_2NH, R_3N
H_2O, ROH, R_2O
CO, NO
CN^-, SCN^-, F^-, OH^-, Cl^-, Br^-, I^-

(The symbol R refers to an organic radical)

The student is very probably familiar with some of the complexes formed with negative ions, such as: ferricyanide ion,

$Fe(CN)_6^{---}$; ferrocyanide ion, $Fe(CN)_6^{----}$; aurous cyanide ion, $Au(CN)_2^-$, formed in the extraction of gold by the cyanide process; nickel carbonyl, $Ni(CO)_4$, an intermediate compound in the extraction and purification of nickel; and $Ag(Cl_2)^-$.

The Geometrical Configurations of Complex Ions. Previously we indicated schematically the structure of the

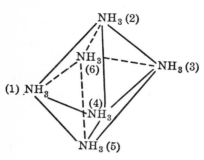

$[Co(NH_3)_6]^{+++}$ ion as lying in one plane. Actually the distribution of the NH_3 molecules about the (Co^{+++}) core is that of an octahedron. In fact, all complex ions with a coordination number of 6 have octahedral structures. The octahedral structure of $[Co(NH_3)_6]^{+++}$ is that given in Figure 8.2.

FIG. 8.2 The octahedral structure of the $Co(NH_3)_6^{+++}$ ion.

The Co^{+++} core lies within the octahedron. All edges of the octahedron have equal lengths. Suppose that we substitute two of the NH_3 groups by Cl^- ions. It will be apparent that substituting the Cl^- ions in positions 1 and 2 will result in the same configuration as in 1 and 4, 1 and 5, 1 and 6, 2 and 3, 2 and 4, 2 and 6, 3 and 4, 3 and 5, 3 and 6, 4 and 5, and 5 and 6. In each of the above cases one gets the same configuration by twisting the molecule around.* However, if the two Cl^- ions occupy positions 1 and 3, they are different from those cited above, but exactly like those configurations in which the Cl^- ions occupy positions 4 and 6, and 2 and 5. There are therefore two kinds of $[Co(NH_3)_4(Cl_2)]^+$ ions. The former are known as the *cis* and the latter as *trans* forms. These two different kinds of compounds have been isolated and shown to be different. The fact that two different compounds and no more than two are known confirms the octahedral structure of cobalt complexes and, in fact, all complexes with a coordination number of 6. These complex ions or compounds having

* This is a good example of three-dimensional visualization which the student in chemistry will often encounter and which he must master.

the same empirical formulae, i.e., built up of exactly the same constituents, but having different configurations and different properties, are known as *geometrical isomers* (compounds which differ only in the geometrical location of the different components).

Let us now consider the complex ions having a coordination number of 4 (four molecules or ions about the central core). In this case two possibilities present themselves. Let us consider the generalized compound or ion $[A(X)_4]$ where A represents a metallic atom or ion and X the peripheral groups.

The first case to consider is that in which all the X groups lie in a plane, at the corners of a square. This condition is illustrated in Figure 8.3. If two of the X groups are substituted by Y groups, giving

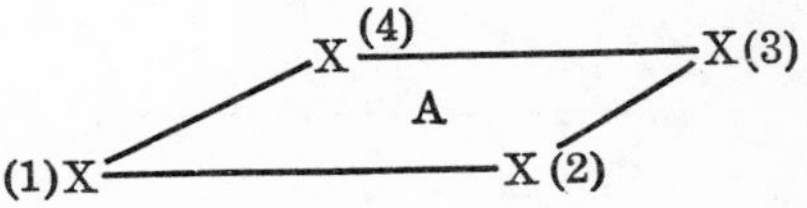

FIG. 8.3 Planar structure of complex ions with coordination number of four.

the compound or ion $[A(X)_2(Y)_2]$, then if the Y groups are in positions 1 and 2, 2 and 3, 3 and 4, and 1 and 4, they are equivalent. But if the Y groups are in positions 1 and 3 or in 2 and 4, the compound is different from that formed when the Y groups are in the positions previously cited. Again, geometrical isomers are formed. An example of such geometric isomers is found in the compound $[Pt(NH_3)_2Cl_2]Cl_2$.

The other case to consider is that in which the peripheral groups are located at the corners of a tetrahedron as illustrated in Figure 8.4. In this case, if two Y groups are substituted for two of the X groups, all configurations are alike and no geometrical isomers are formed. This is one criterion in determining the geometrical shapes of the complex ions with coordination number of four.

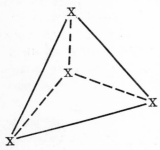

FIG. 8.4 Tetrahedral structure of complex ions with coordination number of four.

Only if all four outer groups in the tetrahedral configuration are different can isomers be formed. This condition is illustrated in Figure 8.5. Configuration I cannot be twisted around in any way to be the same as II. This type of isomerism is treated very fully in the study of organic chemistry.

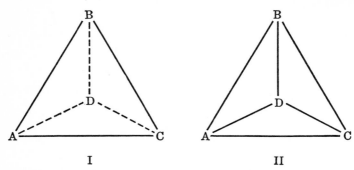

I   II

FIG. 8.5 The two kinds of isomers formed when all four groups in a tetrahedral structure are different.

Equilibria Involving Complex Ions. When ammonium hydroxide is slowly added to a solution of silver nitrate, there is first observed a brown precipitate of silver hydroxide (or silver oxide). In the presence of a large number of silver ions, there are sufficient hydroxide ions from the ionization of the ammonium hydroxide to exceed the solubility product constant of silver hydroxide. However, the continued addition of ammonium hydroxide to this same solution is found to dissolve the silver hydroxide with the formation of the complex silver ion.

Experiments show that the ammonia molecule is responsible for the dissolving of the silver hydroxide. The original solution of silver nitrate contains only silver and nitrate ions, while the ammonium hydroxide solution introduces four new constituents, ammonium ions, hydroxide ions, free ammonia, and ammonium hydroxide molecules, all of which are in equilibrium with each other:

$$NH_3 + H_2O = NH_4OH = NH_4^+ + OH^- \tag{11}$$

Neither the ammonium ion nor the hydroxide ion is responsible for the dissolving of silver hydroxide by an excess of ammonium hydroxide. The only two constituents left are free ammonia and ammonium hydroxide molecules. We are not able to distinguish between the two, the equilibrium between them never having been determined with any degree of certainty. We may consider ammonia in water as consisting entirely of free ammonia, NH_3, or of ammonium hydroxide, NH_4OH, molecules, whichever is more convenient. For our purposes it matters little which we choose. The silver-ammonia complex ion, $Ag(NH_3)_2{}^+$, is the substance formed. (It is to be noted that the names of these complexes are *ammonia* complexes and not *ammonium* complexes. Ammonia refers to the molecule NH_3; ammonium to the radical NH_4.) The coordination number of the silver ion in the silver-ammonia complex is 2. The original experiment may now be expressed in the form of two equations,

$$Ag^+ + NH_4OH = AgOH(\text{solid}) + NH_4{}^+ \qquad (12)$$

$$AgOH(\text{solid}) + 2NH_3 = Ag(NH_3)_2{}^+ + OH^- \qquad (13)$$

Since silver ion and ammonia combine to form the silver-ammonia ion, we would also expect this ion to dissociate somewhat into its constituents,

$$Ag(NH_3)_2{}^+ = Ag^+ + 2NH_3 \qquad (14)$$

The dissociation process is in a general way like the dissociation of weak acids and bases. Lacking sufficient information, the dissociation is expressed by the over-all reaction (equation 14), rather than by steps. According to the equation three kinds of particles are in equilibrium with each other, the silver-ammonia complex ion, silver ion, and ammonia molecules. If an additional amount of silver ions was added to this system, the equilibrium would shift to the left, with the formation of more silver-ammonia ions. The addition of ammonia molecules would have the same effect. Dilution with water would favor the dissociation of the complex to produce more ions. We may write an equilibrium constant for this reaction in the usual way, with the products appearing in the numerator and the reactants in the denominator as follows:

$$\frac{(Ag^+)(NH_3)^2}{(Ag(NH_3)_2^+)} = K = 6 \times 10^{-8} \tag{15}$$

The dissociation constant has a value of 6×10^{-8} which is sufficiently low to signify that the dissociation of the complex ion is slight. What then is the amount of dissociation of this complex ion in a solution in which it is present at moderate concentration?

Let us take, for example, a solution which is 0.1 molar with respect to silver-ammonia and nitrate ions, $Ag(NH_3)_2^+$ and NO_3^-. The concentration of the silver-ammonia ion would be very nearly 0.1 molar provided it were not appreciably dissociated. Since we know from the small value of the equilibrium constant that its dissociation must be very low, we can assume that the concentration of the silver-ammonia ion is practically 0.1 molar at equilibrium. Let X be the number of moles of the complex which dissociate, then the concentration of the silver ion at equilibrium will be X and the concentration of the ammonia molecules, $2X$. Therefore,

$$\frac{(Ag^+)(NH_3)^2}{(Ag(NH_3)_2^+)} = \frac{X(2X)^2}{0.1} = \frac{4X^3}{0.1} = 6 \times 10^{-8}$$

$$4X^3 = 6 \times 10^{-9} \quad \text{and} \quad X^3 = 1.5 \times 10^{-9}$$

$$X = 1.15 \times 10^{-3} \quad \text{and} \quad 2X = 2.3 \times 10^{-3} \text{ mole per liter}$$

In a 0.1 molar solution of the silver-ammonia nitrate, the concentration of the silver ion is then 1.15×10^{-3} mole per liter and the concentration of the free ammonia is twice as great. These values appear to be quite large, larger than one would expect for a highly stable complex. As a matter of fact the silver-ammonia complex is about the least stable of the known ammonia complexes. It will be recalled that in the case of the cobalt-ammonia complexes the addition of sulfuric acid merely converted the original salt to the sulfate and failed to remove readily any ammonia from the complex ion. However, in the case of the silver-ammonia complex the situation is entirely different. When a strong acid is added to a solution of the latter the complex is destroyed due to the combination of the ammonia with hydrogen ion. In this process the equilibrium (equation 14) shifts to the right. Addition of sulfide ion, iodide ion, and other ions which form very insoluble salts with silver ion will also destroy the complex.

But now consider the situation in the presence of the chloride ion. Suppose we attempted to make a solution 0.1 molar with respect to silver-ammonia and chloride ions. What would the concentration of the silver ion be in this solution? It is obvious that the concentration of the silver ion could not be 1.15×10^{-3} mole per liter as it was in the case of the silver-ammonia complex nitrate solution, for with a concentration of chloride ion in the solution as high as 0.1 mole per liter, the solubility product constant would be exceeded for silver chloride ($K_{\text{s.p.}} = 2.8 \times 10^{-10}$) by more than one millionfold. Hence, silver chloride would precipitate from solution and the concentration of the silver ion would be greatly reduced. It is apparent that in such a case the silver ion concentration must satisfy both equilibria, the complex ion equilibrium and the solubility product equilibrium of silver chloride. In order to prevent the precipitation of silver chloride in this solution, it is evident that the concentration of the Ag^+ ion must be less than 2.8×10^{-9}, for

$$(Ag^+)(Cl^-) = (Ag^+)(0.1) = 2.8 \times 10^{-10}$$
or $$(Ag^+) = 2.8 \times 10^{-9} \; M$$

This amount of silver ion must likewise be in equilibrium with the silver-ammonia complex ion, which in turn requires a fairly high concentration of ammonia in solution to prevent the dissociation of the complex ion. In other words, a relatively high concentration of ammonia is required to dissolve silver chloride, the quantitative calculation of which is to be found in the following examples and problems.

Examples of Problems Involving Complex Ions

Example 1.

How many moles of NH_3 must be added to 1 liter of water to enable this solution to dissolve .001 mole of solid silver bromide? The solubility product constant for AgBr has a value of 5×10^{-13}, and the value for the dissociation constant for the silver-ammonia complex ion is 6×10^{-8}.

The reaction which takes place when the solid AgBr dissolves is

$$AgBr_{(s)} + 2NH_3 = Ag(NH_3)_2^+ + Br^- \qquad (1)$$

Two equilibria are involved in this process,

$$AgBr_{(s)} = Ag^+ + Br^- \qquad (2)$$

and

$$Ag(NH_3)_2^+ = Ag^+ + 2NH_3 \qquad (3)$$

The concentration of the Ag^+ ion must be the same for both equilibria as long as solid AgBr and $Ag(NH_3)_2^+$ ion are present. From the equation for the reaction we see that .001 mole of AgBr, when it has just dissolved, produces .001 mole of $Ag(NH_3)_2^+$ ion and .001 mole of Br^- ion. From equation (2) we have

$$(Ag^+)(Br^-) = 5 \times 10^{-13}$$

When (Br^-) becomes .001 M, then

$$(Ag^+) = \frac{5 \times 10^{-13}}{.001} = 5 \times 10^{-10} \text{ mole per liter}$$

This latter value will also be the concentration of the Ag^+ ion which is in equilibrium with the complex ion when the AgBr has just dissolved, since both equilibria are confined to the same solution. Practically all of the silver in the solution is in the form of $Ag(NH_3)_2^+$ ion. Therefore, we may assume that the concentration of the $Ag(NH_3)_2^+$ ion is .001 M. Then, from the equilibrium expression for reaction (3), we have

$$\frac{(Ag^+)(NH_3)^2}{(Ag(NH_3)_2^+)} = \frac{5 \times 10^{-10} \times (NH_3)^2}{.001} = 6 \times 10^{-8}$$

$$(NH_3)^2 = \frac{6 \times 10^{-8} \times 10^{-3}}{5 \times 10^{-10}} = 12 \times 10^{-2}$$

$$(NH_3) = 3.2 \times 10^{-1} = 0.3 \; M \;\text{(approximately)}$$

In this calculation the amount of ammonia consumed in forming the complex ion is .002 mole, which is negligible compared with 0.3 mole. However, it should be emphasized that the total amount of ammonia required to dissolve the AgBr is the sum of the combined and free amounts; in other words, it is $0.320 + 0.002$ or 0.322 mole. Since the application of the Law of Mass Action is not valid when the solutions become too concentrated, the value of 0.3 M is sufficient, though approximate.

Example 2.

What is the concentration of the Zn^{++} ion in a solution made by adding 0.1 mole of $ZnCl_2$ and 0.4 mole of NH_3 to water to make 1 liter of solution?

Since the formula for the zinc-ammonia complex ion is $Zn(NH_3)_4{}^{++}$, the amounts of Zn^{++} ion and NH_3 given here are just sufficient to form 0.1 mole of the complex ion. Let us assume that this amount of the complex ion is formed and that it dissociates until equilibrium is reached, in accordance with the equation

$$Zn(NH_3)_4{}^{++} = Zn^{++} + 4NH_3$$

The dissociation constant for this complex ion has a value of 3.4×10^{-10}. If X moles of the complex ion dissociate, then, at equilibrium, $(Zn^{++}) = X$, $(NH_3) = 4X$, and $(Zn(NH_3)_4{}^{++}) = 0.1 - X$. We then have

$$\frac{(Zn^{++})(NH_3)^4}{(Zn(NH_3)_4{}^{++})} = \frac{X(4X)^4}{0.1 - X} = \frac{(4)^4 X^5}{0.1 - X} = \frac{256 X^5}{0.1 - X} = 3.4 \times 10^{-10}$$

Neglecting X as compared with 0.1, the expression becomes

$$\frac{256 X^5}{0.1} = 3.4 \times 10^{-10}$$

$$X^5 = \frac{3.4 \times 10^{-10} \times 0.1}{2.56 \times 10^2}$$

$$= \frac{3.4 \times 10^{-11}}{2.56 \times 10^2} = 1.33 \times 10^{-13}$$

$$= 133 \times 10^{-15}$$

$$X = 2.7 \times 10^{-3} = .0027 \text{ mole per liter} = (Zn^{++})$$

$$(NH_3) = 4X \cong .01 \text{ mole per liter}$$

The student might encounter some difficulty in finding the fifth root of 133. All that is necessary to do in this case is to obtain the logarithm of 133 which is 2.124. Dividing this by 5 we have 0.425 and the antilog of 0.425 is very nearly 2.7.

Example 3.

(a) How many moles of AgI will dissolve in 1 liter of 1 M NH$_4$OH solution?

Silver iodide is very slightly soluble in pure water ($K_{\text{S.P.}}$ = 8.5 $\times$ 10^{-17}), but in NH$_4$OH solution there is some tendency for the Ag$^+$ ion to combine with the NH$_3$ to form the Ag(NH$_3$)$_2$$^+$ ion, according to the equation

$$AgI_{(s)} + 2NH_3 = Ag(NH_3)_2 + I^- \tag{1}$$

However, the amount of complex ion formed will be very small since AgI is so insoluble. From the equilibrium expression for the complex ion we have

$$\frac{(Ag^+)(NH_3)^2}{(Ag(NH_3)_2{}^+)} = 6 \times 10^{-8}$$

Since such a small amount of the complex ion is formed it may be assumed that practically all of the ammonia exists in the free condition in solution and has a value of 1 M. Then

$$(Ag^+) = 6 \times 10^{-8}(Ag(NH_3)_2{}^+)$$

From this expression it is seen that the concentration of the Ag(NH$_3$)$_2$$^+$ ion is very much larger than the concentration of the free Ag$^+$ ion. This means that practically all of the silver in solution is in the form of the complex ion. Also the concentration of the I$^-$ ion in solution must be practically the same as the concentration of the complex ion.

$$(I^-) = (Ag(NH_3)_2{}^+)$$

From the solubility product expression, we have

$$(Ag^+)(I^-) = (Ag^+)(Ag(NH_3)_2{}^+) = 8.5 \times 10^{-17}$$

Substituting in the second expression the value for the $(Ag(NH_3)_2{}^+)$ above,

$$(Ag^+) \frac{(Ag^+)}{6 \times 10^{-8}} = 8.5 \times 10^{-17}$$

$$(Ag^+)^2 = 8.5 \times 10^{-17} \times 6 \times 10^{-8} = 5 \times 10^{-24}$$

$$(Ag^+) = 2.2 \times 10^{-12}$$

$$(Ag(NH_3)_2{}^+) = (I^-) = \frac{2.2 \times 10^{-12}}{6 \times 10^{-8}} = 3.7 \times 10^{-5} \text{ mole per liter}$$

Thus the concentration of the I^- ion is 3.7×10^{-5} M; this value is also the solubility of the AgI in the 1 M NH_4OH solution.

The same result could have been obtained in the following manner. Since two equilibria are involved in this system, let us divide one equilibrium expression by the other. Then

$$\frac{(Ag^+)(I^-)}{\dfrac{(Ag^+)(NH_3)^2}{(Ag(NH_3)_2{}^+)}} = \frac{(Ag(NH_3)_2{}^+)(I^-)}{(NH_3)^2} = \frac{8.5 \times 10^{-17}}{6 \times 10^{-8}} = 14 \times 10^{-10}$$

This is the equilibrium constant for reaction (1). But since (NH_3) has a value of 1 M and $(Ag(NH_3)_2{}^+)$ equals (I^-),

$$(Ag(NH_3)_2{}^+) \times (I^-) = (I^-)^2 = 14 \times 10^{-10}$$

$$(I^-) = 3.7 \times 10^{-5} \ M = (Ag(NH_3)_2{}^+)$$

$$= \text{solubility of AgI}$$

(b) What concentration of NH_4OH would be necessary to dissolve .01 M of AgI in 1 liter of solution?

Using the value obtained in (a) we have

$$\frac{(Ag(NH_3)_2{}^+)(I^-)}{(NH_3)^2} = 14 \times 10^{-10}$$

If .01 mole of AgI were to dissolve, (I^-) and $(Ag(NH_3)_2{}^+)$ would each have a value of .01 M. Then

$$\frac{(.01)(.01)}{(NH_3)^2} = 14 \times 10^{-10}$$

$$(NH_3)^2 = \frac{1 \times 10^{-4}}{14 \times 10^{-10}} = 7 \times 10^4$$

$$(NH_3) = 2.6 \times 10^2 = 260 \ M \text{ (impossible)}$$

This value of 260 M is obtained on the assumption that the Law of Mass Action holds in very concentrated solutions. Evidently, the AgI will not completely dissolve, since it is not possible to obtain at room temperature a solution of ammonia in water of higher concentration than about 18 M.

The method used in (b) could also have been applied in *Example 1*.

Example 4.

A given solution contains .01 mole of Cl$^-$ ion and .07 mole of NH$_3$ per liter. If .01 mole of solid AgNO$_3$ is added to 1 liter of this solution will AgCl precipitate? The solution of this problem involves two equilibria,

$$AgCl_{(s)} = Ag^+ + Cl^-$$

and

$$Ag(NH_3)_2^+ = Ag^+ + 2NH_3$$

The equilibrium expressions are

$$(Ag^+)(Cl^-) = 2.8 \times 10^{-10}$$

and

$$\frac{(Ag^+)(NH_3)^2}{(Ag(NH_3)_2^+)} = 6 \times 10^{-8}$$

Due to the great stability of the complex ion we shall first assume that .01 mole of this ion is formed from .01 mole of Ag$^+$ ion. This process would consume .02 mole of NH$_3$; then .05 mole of NH$_3$ would be left in solution. Under these conditions, we can calculate the concentration of the free Ag$^+$ ion in solution.

$$\frac{(Ag^+)(.05)^2}{.01} = 6 \times 10^{-8}$$

$$(Ag^+) = \frac{6 \times 10^{-8} \times .01}{2.5 \times 10^{-3}} = 2.4 \times 10^{-7} \text{ mole per liter}$$

Since .01 mole of Cl$^-$ ion is present per liter of solution, the product of the ion concentrations is $(2.4 \times 10^{-7})(.01)$ or 2.4×10^{-9}. This value is greater than the solubility product constant; therefore, AgCl precipitates.

This problem could be solved in another manner. Let us calculate the amount of Ag$^+$ ion necessary to start the precipitation of AgCl when .01 M Cl$^-$ ion is present. This would be

$$(Ag^+) = \frac{2.8 \times 10^{-10}}{.01} = 2.8 \times 10^{-8} \ M$$

With this amount of free Ag^+ ion in solution and making the assumption that .01 mole of $Ag(NH_3)_2^+$ is formed, we can then calculate the amount of free NH_3 which would be required to maintain these conditions. Then

$$\frac{(2.8 \times 10^{-8})(NH_3)^2}{.01} = 6 \times 10^{-8}$$

$$(NH_3)^2 = \frac{6 \times 10^{-8} \times .01}{2.8 \times 10^{-8}} = 2.1 \times 10^{-2}$$

$$(NH_3) = 1.4 \times 10^{-1} = 0.14 \ M.$$

This value for the amount of free ammonia necessary to maintain .01 mole of the complex in solution is much larger than the available ammonia; therefore, AgCl precipitates.

Questions and Problems

1. Is there any definite experimental evidence for the existence of the hydronium ion?
2. Compare the properties of water and ammonia. What is the water analogue of the ammonium ion?
3. What is the ammonia analogue of the hydroxide ion?
4. What are hydrates and ammonates?
5. On the basis of the coordination theory of Werner, give the structures (not electronic) of the respective complex ions formed when the following salts are dissolved in water: $CoCl_3 \cdot 4NH_3$, $CoCl_3 \cdot 6NH_3$, $Cu(NO_3)_2 \cdot 4NH_3$, $K_3Fe(CN)_6$, and $PtCl_4 \cdot 5NH_3$.
6. Give examples of four complex anions.
7. Why does ammonium polysulfide dissolve SnS readily while ammonium sulfide will not?
8. What experiments could be designed to show that the ammonia molecule and not the NH_4^+ nor the OH^- ions is responsible for the solution of silver oxide by excess ammonium hydroxide?
9. If 0.1 mole $AgNO_3$, 0.1 mole NaCl, and 0.2 mole NH_3 were added to 1 liter of water, show by calculation whether AgCl would precipitate.
10. If it were possible to prepare solid $Ag(NH_3)_2Cl$ and if 0.1 mole of this were added to 1 liter of water, would AgCl precipitate? Explain.
11. What is the Zn^{++} concentration in a solution that has been made by adding 0.1 mole $ZnCl_2$ and 1 mole of NH_3 to enough water to give 1 liter of solution?

12. Which gives the greater concentration of Ag^+; a solution made by adding 1 mole $AgNO_3$ and 2 moles KCN to 1 liter of water or a solution made by adding 0.1 mole $AgNO_3$ and 1 mole NH_3? (Note: In the first solution neglect hydrolysis of CN^- ion. In the second solution 0.2 mole NH_3 is used in making $Ag(NH_3)_2^+$. Assume the Law of Mass Action for these more concentrated solutions.)

13. Will 0.1 g. AgBr dissolve in 100 ml. of 1 M NH_4OH solution?

14. Will 0.1 g. AgI dissolve in 100 ml. of 1 M NH_4OH solution?

15. How much ammonia (expressed in grams) is necessary to dissolve 1 g. AgCl in 100 ml. of water?

16. Calculate the concentration of Ag^+ ion in a solution which is .05 M with respect to $Ag(NH_3)_2NO_3$.

17. Calculate the Cu^+ ion concentration in a solution which contains .02 mole $K_3Cu(CN)_4$ per liter.

18. What is the CN^- ion concentration in a solution 0.1 M with respect to $K_2Cd(CN)_4$?

19. What is the concentration of NH_3 in a solution which contains .04 mole $Ag(NH_3)_2NO_3$ per liter?

20. (a) Which solution furnishes the higher concentration of Cd^{++} ion, a 0.1 M solution of $Cd(NH_3)_4Cl_2$ or a 0.1 M solution of $K_2Cd(CN)_4$?

    (b) Give the ratio of the Cd^{++} ion concentrations in these two solutions.

21. If to a liter of a solution, which is .06 M with respect to $K_3Cu(CN)_4$ and .06 M with respect to $K_2Cd(CN)_4$, CN^- ion is added to increase its concentration to .005 M, what will be the concentration of (a) the Cu^+ ion, and (b) the Cd^{++} ion?

22. One liter of a solution contains 0.1 mole of Cl^- ion and 0.1 mole of CN^- ion. To this solution solid silver nitrate is added little by little.

    (a) What happens?

    (b) How many moles of $AgNO_3$ must be added before a precipitate begins to appear?

    (c) When a precipitate first appears, what will be the concentration of the Cl^- ion, of the CN^- ion, and of the Ag^+ ion? (Note: AgCN does not precipitate in this solution.)

CHAPTER 9

Amphoteric
Substances

The metals of the alkali and alkaline earth groups of the periodic table are often classified as highly electropositive elements. They exhibit a pronounced tendency to lose electrons and thereby form positive ions. Sodium in its reactions with other elements loses one electron readily to give sodium ion, Na^+, while calcium of the alkaline earth group loses two electrons with the formation of a positive calcium ion, Ca^{++}. These elements are among the first few of the electromotive force (E.M.F.) series of the elements, since this series is one in which the elements are arranged according to the decreasing tendency to lose electrons and form positive ions. In contrast to the alkali metals, sulfur and chlorine of the sixth and seventh groups respectively show a decided tendency to acquire electrons in their reactions with other elements and thereby form negative ions. The latter elements are accordingly termed electronegative; e.g., chlorine can acquire one electron and sulfur two electrons to give ions bearing one and two negative charges, respectively.

Sodium and calcium on the one hand, and sulfur and chlorine on the other, represent extreme types in the classification of the elements according to their tendencies to lose or gain electrons. A large proportion of the elements of the periodic table show dual properties which are characteristic of both sodium and chlorine. They may react with some elements to lose electrons and with other elements to gain them. Hydrogen under favorable conditions reacts with chlorine to form hydrogen chloride. In this reaction we regard the hydrogen atom as partially giving up an electron to the chlorine atom, and we may regard the hydrogen chloride molecule as one containing hydrogen in the more electropositive condition and chlorine in the more electronegative condition. Likewise, hydrogen reacts directly with lithium to form lithium hydride, LiH. This substance is an excellent conductor of electricity in the fused state in which it must be ionized as positive lithium ions and negative hydrogen or hydride ions, H^-, since upon electrolysis hydrogen is liberated at the anode. In this reaction the hydrogen atom acquires an extra electron to form a negative hydrogen ion. Apparently the hydrogen atom has a greater tendency to acquire an electron and a smaller tendency to lose an electron than has the lithium atom. So far as chemical evidence goes, the lithium atom shows no tendency to form negative ions. Thus, hydrogen may behave in a dual manner, it may gain or lose electrons depending upon its environment. If it is in the presence of a strongly electronegative element such as chlorine it will behave electropositively, while in the presence of a strongly electropositive element, for example lithium, it will behave electronegatively. Such elements lie in an intermediate position in the E.M.F. series and are sometimes spoken of as *amphoteric* elements, a designation which implies this dual character.

Many other elements show amphoteric properties in their reactions. Thus, sulfur, selenium, and tellurium of the sixth group of the periodic table react with chlorine and oxygen to form chlorides and oxides. They likewise react with sodium, potassium, and other electropositive elements to form sulfides, selenides, and tellurides which are salts. Examples of such compounds are: Na_2S, Na_2Se, Na_2Te, K_2S, K_2Se, and K_2Te. Phosphorus, arsenic, antimony, and bismuth of the fifth group of the periodic table behave in a similar manner, while germanium, tin, and lead may be mentioned as typical examples of the fourth-group elements. Even elements in the second and third groups such as zinc, cadmium, mercury, gallium, indium, and thallium will combine with sodium and other strongly electropositive elements to form definite compounds. This dual behavior is the general case rather than the exceptional one.

Amphoteric Hydroxides. Many of the elements which show this dual behavior in the ability to acquire and to lose electrons in their reactions show another, but somewhat different, type of duality in the reactions of their hydroxides. It is well known that the oxides of strongly electropositive elements such as Na_2O, K_2O, CaO, and MgO form strong bases in water solution, $NaOH$, KOH, $Ca(OH)_2$, and $Mg(OH)_2$, respectively. However, oxides of strongly electronegative elements such as SO_3, N_2O_5, and Cl_2O_7 in water solution are decidedly acidic in character; they are the anhydrides of the acids, H_2SO_4, HNO_3, and $HClO_4$, respectively.

Oxides of most of the elements which lie in an intermediate position in the E.M.F. series of elements, which are neither strongly electropositive nor strongly electronegative, show both acidic and basic properties in water. As would be predicted, such acids and bases are extremely weak. Thus lead oxide, PbO; aluminum oxide, Al_2O_3; chromic oxide, Cr_2O_3; zinc oxide, ZnO; stannous oxide, SnO; and antimonous oxide, Sb_2O_3, are the anhydrides of the very weak hydroxides, $Pb(OH)_2$, $Al(OH)_3$, $Cr(OH)_3$, $Zn(OH)_2$, $Sn(OH)_2$, and $Sb(OH)_3$, respectively, which hydroxides may also be regarded as very weak acids. To emphasize the acidic properties of these hydroxides their formulae could be written H_2PbO_2, H_3AlO_3 (or $HAlO_2 + H_2O$), H_3CrO_3 (or $HCrO_2 + H_2O$), H_2ZnO_2, H_2SnO_2, and H_3SbO_3 (or $HSbO_2 + H_2O$). In the cases of H_3AlO_3, H_3CrO_3, and H_3SbO_3 only one hydrogen is replaceable in water solution, the simpler and more informative formulae $HAlO_2$, $HCrO_2$, and $HSbO_2$, respectively, are usually used. In each of these cases the same substance may be represented by two differently arranged formulae; by convention, one emphasizes the basic properties and the other, the acidic properties.

All of these hydroxides are very slightly soluble in water but dissolve readily when either a strong acid such as hydrochloric acid or a strong base such as sodium hydroxide is present. Taking $Al(OH)_3$ as an example, we may write,

$$Al(OH)_3 + 3HCl \text{ (in solution)} = AlCl_3 \text{(in solution)} + 3H_2O \quad (1)$$

and

$$Al(OH)_3 + NaOH \text{ (in solution)} = NaAlO_2 \text{(in solution)} + 2H_2O \quad (2)$$

Both of these reactions appear familiar in that the products in each case are a salt and the solvent, water; in other words, they are neutralization reactions. Since both HCl, an acid, and NaOH, a base, are used, it must necessarily follow that the aluminum hydroxide is functioning in equation (1) as a base and in equation (2) as an acid. Hydroxides which show properties characteristic of both acids and bases are known as *amphoteric hydroxides.*

The ionization of aluminum hydroxide when acting both as a weak acid and a weak base is expressed in the following equation:

$$Al^{+++} + 3OH^- = \left\{ \begin{array}{l} Al(OH)_3 \\ H_3AlO_3 \end{array} \right\} = AlO_2^- + H^+ + H_2O \quad (3)$$
$$\text{(solid)}$$

For lack of definite information regarding the ionization of aluminum hydroxide as a base we have expressed the reaction as one producing $3OH^-$ ions. It is a weak polyacid base and undoubtedly would not be expected to ionize highly even in the first stage, let alone in the two successive stages. However, at present it is not experimentally feasible to determine the exact extent of ionization of aluminum hydroxide for each of the three steps. Equation (3) also shows the aluminate ion, AlO_2^-, a product of the ionization of aluminum hydroxide as an acid.

We may now predict, with the aid of Le Chatelier's Rule, the effect of strong acids and of strong bases upon the equilibrium. If a strong acid, such as hydrochloric acid, is added to a suspension of aluminum hydroxide in water, the hydrogen ions which are in excess combine with some of the hydroxide ions to form water. According to the Rule of Le Chatelier, we would predict a shift in the equilibrium to the left. The tendency is for the equilibrium to shift in such a way as to attempt to retrieve the loss of hydroxide ions. This can be done only by the further dissociation of aluminum hydroxide from the solid phase. As fast as hydroxide ions are produced by this process, they are removed by hydrogen ions. Finally, all the solid dissolves and the concentration of the hydroxide ions in solution still remains at a very small value due to the continued removal of the hydroxide by hydrogen ions. Although the hydroxide ions are depleted as fast as they are produced by the ionization of the aluminum hydroxide, the latter reaction also yields large amounts of aluminum ions which remain as such in solution. Therefore, when hydrochloric acid is used as a source of hydrogen ions, the final result is that the solid aluminum hydroxide dissolves and the solution contains aluminum and chloride ions. Hydrogen and hydroxide ions will also be present in concentrations which must satisfy the water equilibrium, $(H^+)(OH^-) = 1 \times 10^{-14}$.

The addition of a strong base such as sodium hydroxide furnishes a large concentration of hydroxide ions. According to Le Chatelier's Rule the equilibrium should shift in such a direction as to use up hydroxide ions; that is, it should shift to the right as equation (3) is written. Naturally, hydrogen ions will be removed from the reaction medium by their combination with hydroxide ions to form water. When this happens more aluminum hydroxide will dissolve to give hydrogen ions and aluminate ions in an attempt to retrieve the loss of hydrogen ions. The hydrogen ions are removed as fast as they are produced and finally, when all of the solid aluminum hydroxide has dissolved, sodium ions and aluminate ions will be left in solution in large quantities, and the hydrogen ion and hydroxide ion concentrations will be in accord with that demanded by the water equilibrium.

Aluminum hydroxide has been taken here as a typical example of an amphoteric hydroxide. Others previously mentioned, $Pb(OH)_2$, $Cr(OH)_3$, $Zn(OH)_2$, $Sn(OH)_2$, and $Sb(OH)_3$ behave similarly in that they dissolve and function as bases in the presence of a strong acid, and also dissolve and function as acids in the presence of a strong base. The latter reaction is the more unfamiliar one and in the presence of sodium hydroxide the following ions are produced: $HPbO_2^-$, CrO_2^-, ZnO_2^{--}, $HSnO_2^-$, and SbO_2^-, namely, biplumbite, chromite, zincate, bistannite, and antimonite ions.

As was previously stated the amphoteric hydroxides are derived from elements occupying an intermediate position in the E.M.F. series. They must necessarily occupy a similar intermediate position in a given series of the periodic table since the elements of the main groups to the left are strongly electropositive, while those of the main groups to the right are strongly electronegative. Those elements which show both properties lie in between these two extremes. As one passes from one extreme position of the table to the other, the change in properties is not an abrupt one; on the contrary, it is very gradual. As an example, let us choose the series of the table beginning with the inert gas argon, atomic number 18 (see back cover); the next element, potassium, forms a very strong base, potassium hydroxide. Under ordinary conditions of temperature it acts only as a base in water solution. Calcium hydroxide, representative of the second group, likewise possesses only basic properties in water. Scandium hydroxide is also a strong base, but titanium hydroxide, vanadium hydroxide, and chromium hydroxide, hydroxides of the fourth, fifth, and sixth groups, respectively, in the series under consideration, show amphoteric properties in that they form titanates, vanadites, and chromites with strong bases. Vanadates and chromates are also known, being derived from the higher valence hydroxides, which, however, are distinctly more acidic than basic in nature. In the seventh group manganous hydroxide, $Mn(OH)_2$, is a moderately strong base and possesses very little acid properties; while H_2MnO_4, manganic acid, is a weak acid and $HMnO_4$, permanganic acid, is a very strong acid. In general, the higher the valence of the metal in any two or more similarly derived acids the more acidic properties it will display. Thus, stannic acid is a stronger acid than stannous acid, arsenic is stronger than arsenous, chromic stronger than chromous, etc. Ferric, ferrous, cobaltous, nickelous, and cuprous hydroxides are distinctly basic in aqueous solutions and acid properties are almost entirely lacking. The next element of the series, zinc, atomic number 30, forms a hydroxide, $Zn(OH)_2$, which is well known for its amphoteric properties. Following zinc hydroxide are $Ga(OH)_3$, $Ge(OH)_4$, and $AsO(OH)_3$, all of which dissolve in sodium hydroxide solution to produce gallate, germanate, and arsenate ions. H_2SeO_4, selenic acid, and $HBrO_3$, bromic acid, are decidedly acidic in water. Thus, in this series of eighteen elements, many of their hydroxides are amphoteric.

Within a given group, occupying an intermediate position in the periodic table, the amphoteric properties change as one proceeds from the element of lower to one of higher atomic weight. Thus HNO_2 shows only acid properties; H_3PO_3 likewise is acidic; H_3AsO_3 or $As(OH)_3$ and H_3SbO_3 or $Sb(OH)_3$ are amphoteric, while $Bi(OH)_3$ is basic in its reactions. Thus, in passing from nitrogen to bismuth in the main fifth group, the hydroxides change from strong acids to weak acids and moderately strong bases, but the change is a gradual one.

Amphoteric Sulfides. Sulfur occupies a position in the sixth group of the periodic table just below oxygen. Hence, many of the compounds of sulfur contain the sulfur atom in a position similar to that occupied by oxygen in the more familiar oxygen compounds. In qualitative analysis we are particularly interested in the amphoteric nature of analogous sulfides and oxides. Since hydrogen sulfide is the analogue of water, the bisulfide ion of the hydrogen sulfide system corresponds to the hydroxide ion of the water system, as the following equations readily demonstrate:

$$H_2O = H^+ + OH^- \tag{4}$$

$$H_2S = H^+ + SH^- \tag{5}$$

Likewise, the metal sulfides are analogues of the metal oxides; K_2S, CaS, As_2S_5, and Sb_2S_3 in the hydrogen sulfide system correspond to K_2O, CaO, As_2O_5, and Sb_2O_3, respectively, in the water or oxygen system. On the basis of these analogies, one might expect sulfides to dissolve in the presence of bisulfide ions in the same way that oxides or hydroxides, in an aqueous medium, dissolve in the presence of hydroxide ions. When the sulfides behave in this manner, they are exhibiting acid properties. A few examples will serve to illustrate this type of reaction.

$$As_2S_5 + 6HS^- = 2AsS_4^{---} + 3H_2S \tag{6}$$

or
$$As_2S_5 + 2HS^- = 2AsS_3^- + H_2S \tag{7}$$

$$Sb_2S_5 + 6HS^- = 2SbS_4^{---} + 3H_2S \tag{8}$$

Actually the H_2S produced in the above equations reacts with the OH^- ions to produce HS^- ions and water. Therefore the equation for the process of the solution of As_2S_5 by HS^- ions in alkaline solution is

$$As_2S_5 + 3HS^- + 3OH^- = 2AsS_4^{---} + 3H_2O \tag{9}$$

rather than that given by equation (6). The same would be true for the reactions represented by equations (7) and (8).

Another explanation may be given for the fact that arsenic and antimony sulfides dissolve in alkaline sulfide solution. In such a solution, the concentration of the sulfide ion is certainly appreciable and much larger than the concentration of the oxide ion, O^{--}, in solutions containing alkali hydroxides, since the bisulfide ion is dissociated to a much greater extent to give hydrogen and sulfide ions than is the hydroxide ion to give hydrogen and oxide ions. As a matter of fact, it has not been possible through experiment to determine the concentration of the oxide ion. Due to the presence of sulfide ions in alkaline sulfide solutions, it is possible, however, to explain the solubility of arsenic and antimony sulfides as follows:

$$As_2S_5 + 3S^{--} = 2AsS_4^{---} \tag{10}$$

$$As_2S_3 + 3S^{--} = 2AsS_3^{---} \tag{11}$$

$$As_2S_5 + S^{--} = 2AsS_3^- \tag{12}$$

$$Sb_2S_5 + 3S^{--} = 2SbS_4^{---} \tag{13}$$

Antimony and tin in the lower valence states are much more strongly basic or more weakly acidic than in the higher valence states. Accordingly, antimonous sulfide dissolves with difficulty in ammonium sulfide solution and stannous sulfide is practically insoluble in this medium. However, antimonic and stannic sulfides are readily soluble in this same solvent.

Just as oxygen can oxidize a lower valence oxide to a higher valence one, so sulfur can oxidize a lower to a higher valence sulfide. Ammonium polysulfide is ammonium sulfide containing dissolved sulfur (chemically combined with the sulfide ion). When the lower sulfides are treated with ammonium polysulfide they are oxidized to the higher valence state in which they are readily soluble. This process of solution has already been discussed in the previous chapter, as an illustration of complex ion formation. The process of solution of the amphoteric sulfides may be explained on the basis of the amphoteric properties of the sulfides and on the basis of sulfur in sulfide solution acting as an oxidizing agent.

Application of Amphoteric Substances to Analysis. Suppose we consider a solution which has been obtained as a hydrochloric acid extraction of an ore known to contain iron, zinc, and aluminum. We wish to separate these elements from each other in solution by methods which will reduce the difficulties to a minimum. The solution contains all three elements in the form of their chlorides and is slightly acidic. We might first add sodium hydroxide to the solution to the point of neutralization and obtain a precipitate containing all three substances in the form of hydroxides, $Fe(OH)_3$, $Al(OH)_3$, and $Zn(OH)_2$. Knowing that both zinc and aluminum hydroxides are decidedly amphoteric in nature, let us continue the addition of the sodium hydroxide solution. Both $Al(OH)_3$ and $Zn(OH)_2$ dissolve immediately with the formation of aluminate and zincate ions, respectively; however, ferric hydroxide is not amphoteric and does not dissolve in the presence of excess hydroxide ion. Accordingly, the ferric hydroxide can be separated at this point by filtration. Ammonium hydroxide would not behave in the same way as the sodium hydroxide since the former does not furnish sufficient hydroxide ions to dissolve aluminum hydroxide.

If it should appear desirable to separate the aluminum from the zinc, the filtrate could be treated with hydrochloric acid until the zinc and aluminum hydroxides dissolve, and to this solution could be added excess ammonium hydroxide. Under these conditions the aluminum hydroxide would precipitate and the zinc would stay in solution in the form of the zinc-ammonia ion, $Zn(NH_3)_4^{++}$.

Thus, through the application of the amphoteric properties of the aluminum and zinc hydroxides and the subsequent use of the ability of the zinc ion to form complex ions, it is possible to readily separate these three elements from each other. The hydroxides, $Fe(OH)_3$, $Al(OH)_3$, and $Cr(OH)_3$ may also be separated from each other by the same general procedure; $Al(OH)_3$ and $Cr(OH)_3$ are amphoteric while $Fe(OH)_3$ is not. Chromium and aluminum may be subsequently separated from each other by the oxidation of the chromite ion, CrO_2^-, to the chromate ion, CrO_4^{--}. Chromium ion combining with other elements displays two principal valences of $+3$ and $+6$, while aluminum has only the one valence of $+3$. Other examples to illustrate the behavior of amphoteric hydroxides and sulfides in the separation and identification of ions are too numerous to mention here. However, several illustrations will be given in Part II of this text relating to the separation of the analytical groups and the properties of individual ions.

Amphoteric Hydroxides as Coordinated Complexes. To illustrate the application of the Brønsted definitions to problems involving amphoteric hydroxides, let us choose aluminum hydroxide as the example for consideration.

Many hydroxides do not have a constant and definite composition. Nevertheless we use definite formulae to designate them. In our previous discussions, for the sake of convenience we designated aluminum hydroxide by the formula $Al(OH)_3$. According to this formula this substance should consist of 34.58 percent aluminum, 61.55 percent oxygen, and 3.87 percent hydrogen. Under most circumstances an analysis of aluminum hydroxide would not give these percentages but other rather widely different values. The reason for this discrepancy is that aluminum hydroxide when freshly precipitated contains additional water not indicated in the formula, $Al(OH)_3$. This additional water may be chemically bound to the aluminum atom or it may merely be adsorbed. When the aluminum hydroxide is dried it loses water, and upon continued drying the loss of water does not stop when the composition corresponds to the formula $Al(OH)_3$, but rather when its composition is such as to correspond more nearly to the formula $AlO(OH)$ or $Al_2O_3 \cdot H_2O$. Upon excessive drying (by heating) all the water is lost and only the oxide Al_2O_3 remains. The formula for aluminum hydroxide is therefore often written as $Al_2O_3 \cdot XH_2O$. But for convenience, most chemists have adopted the formula $Al(OH)_3$ for this substance.

To explain the hydrolysis of the aluminum ion by the Brønsted definitions we may write its formula as $Al(H_2O)_6^{+++}$, assuming a coordination number of six for the aluminum ion. In keeping with this same concept we can also write an analogous formula for aluminum hydroxide in the hydrated form, again using the coordination number of six. Its formula would then be $Al(H_2O)_3(OH)_3$. Using this formula let us explain the amphoteric nature of aluminum hydroxide as we have done with the older definitions. As an amphoteric hydroxide this substance is both a proton donor and a proton acceptor. When dissolved in water it may be regarded as accepting protons from and donating them to water molecules.

$$\underset{\text{Acid}_1}{Al(H_2O)_3(OH)_{3(s)}} + \underset{\text{Base}_2}{H_2O} = \underset{\text{Base}_1}{Al(H_2O)_2(OH)_4^-} + \underset{\text{Acid}_2}{H_3O^+} \qquad (14)$$

$$\underset{\text{Base}_2}{3H_2O} + \underset{\text{Acid}_1}{Al(H_2O)_6^{+++}} = \underset{\text{Acid}_2}{3H_3O^+} + \underset{\text{Base}_1}{Al(H_2O)_3(OH)_{3(s)}} \qquad (15)$$

In the first equilibrium (14) aluminum hydroxide is represented as a weak acid, i.e., as a proton donor. In equation (15) reading right to left, it is represented as a proton acceptor or as a base. This latter process could be expressed in three stages, i.e., aluminum hydroxide is a tri-acid base, but for convenience we have combined all three steps in this single equation. Both reactions (14) and (15) are acid-base reactions. If aluminum hydroxide is treated with a strong acid the equilibrium (15) is shifted to the left; the solid is dissolved and the aluminum ion, $Al(H_2O)_6^{+++}$ is formed. If a sodium hydroxide solution is added to a suspension of aluminum hydroxide, the OH^- ion of the solution combines with the H_3O^+ ion, shifting the equilibrium reaction (14) to the right, and aluminate ion $Al(H_2O)_2(OH)_4^-$ is formed. The over-all reaction for this latter process is

$$Al(H_2O)_3(OH)_{3(s)} + OH^- = Al(H_2O)_2(OH)_4^- + H_2O \quad (16)$$

The amphoteric nature of zinc hydroxide can be explained in an analogous way. In this case the formula of zinc hydroxide can be written as $Zn(H_2O)_2(OH)_2$; the coordination number of zinc is assumed to be four. Then the equilibrium reactions representing the amphoteric nature of zinc hydroxide are

$$\underset{\text{Acid}_1}{Zn(H_2O)_2(OH)_{2(s)}} + \underset{\text{Base}_2}{2H_2O} = \underset{\text{Base}_1}{Zn(OH)_4^{--}} + \underset{\text{Acid}_2}{2H_3O^+} \quad (17)$$

$$\underset{\text{Acid}_1}{Zn(H_2O)_4^{++}} + \underset{\text{Base}_2}{2H_2O} = \underset{\text{Acid}_2}{2H_3O^+} + \underset{\text{Base}_1}{Zn(H_2O)_2(OH)_{2(s)}} \quad (18)$$

In acid solution the equilibrium of the lower equation is shifted to the left; $Zn(H_2O)_2(OH)_{2(s)}$ dissolves and $Zn(H_2O)_4^{++}$ is formed. In alkaline solution the OH^- ion combines with the H_3O^+ ion and the equilibrium of reaction (17) is shifted to the right. The over-all reaction for the dissolving of solid zinc hydroxide by a solution of sodium hydroxide is then

$$Zn(H_2O)_2(OH)_{2(s)} + 2OH^- = Zn(OH)_4^{--} + 2H_2O \quad (19)$$

All amphoteric hydroxides may be treated in the same way. In each case the accepted coordination number of the metal ion should be used.

The structural form of zinc hydroxide in solution is similar to that given for zinc ammonia complex except that two of the NH_3 groups are replaced by OH^- ions and two by water molecules. Structurally, equation (19) may be represented by the equation

$$\begin{matrix} H & & H \\ H:\ddot{O}:H & & :\ddot{O}: \\ :\ddot{O}:Zn:\ddot{O}: + 2:\ddot{O}:H = H:\ddot{O}:Zn:\ddot{O}:H + 2H:\ddot{O}:H \\ H:\ddot{O}:H & & :\ddot{O}: \\ \ddot{H} & & \ddot{H} \end{matrix} \qquad (20)$$

In this reaction each of the two water molecules in the complex may be thought of as losing a hydrogen ion, which combines with the OH^- ion to produce water. As a result $Zn(OH)_4]^{--}$ complex ion is formed. The latter ion is essentially hydrated zincate ion.

Examples of Problems Involving Amphoteric Substances

Example 1.

How many moles of NaOH must be added to 1 liter of water to dissolve completely .001 mole of zinc hydroxide?

The reaction is expressed by the equation

$$Zn(OH)_{2(s)} + 2OH^- = ZnO_2^{--} + 2H_2O$$

Zinc hydroxide is a weak acid and ionizes to give H^+ and ZnO_2^{--} ions.

$$Zn(OH)_{2(s)} = ZnO_2^{--} + 2H^+$$

The equilibrium expression for the ionization of $Zn(OH)_2$ as an acid is

$$(ZnO_2^{--})(H^+)^2 = 1 \times 10^{-29}$$

If .001 mole of $Zn(OH)_2$ dissolves, then .001 mole of ZnO_2^{--} ion will be produced.

$$(ZnO_2^{--})(H^+)^2 = (.001)(H^+)^2 = 1 \times 10^{-29}$$
$$(H^+)^2 = 1 \times 10^{-26}$$
$$(H^+) = 1 \times 10^{-13} \text{ mole per liter}$$

From the water equilibrium (OH^-) may be calculated.

$$(OH^-) = \frac{1 \times 10^{-14}}{(H^+)} = \frac{1 \times 10^{-14}}{1 \times 10^{-13}} = 0.1 \text{ mole per liter}$$

This value for (OH⁻) is the amount in solution at equilibrium after the .001 mole of $Zn(OH)_2$ has dissolved. But to dissolve the $Zn(OH)_2$ an additional amount (.002 mole) of OH^- ion was required. Therefore the total amount of OH^- ion needed to dissolve .001 mole of $Zn(OH)_2$ and to maintain it in solution as ZnO_2^{--} ion is 0.1 + .002 or 0.102 mole.

(The constant used in this calculation is not accurate enough nor is the Law of Mass Action sufficiently valid to warrant taking into account the amount of OH^- ion consumed in the reaction. Therefore the answer 0.1 mole, instead of 0.102 mole, is more appropriate.)

Example 2.

A solution is .05 M with respect to OH^- ion and is in equilibrium with solid $Pb(OH)_2$. What is the concentration of (a) the Pb^{++} ion, (b) the $HPbO_2^-$ ion, and (c) the H^+ ion in the solution? (Disregard the second step of ionization of $Pb(OH)_2$ as an acid.)

In this solution the following equilibria are present.

$$Pb(OH)_{2(s)} = Pb^{++} + 2OH^- \tag{1}$$

$$Pb(OH)_{2(s)} = HPbO_2^- + H^+ \tag{2}$$

Since (OH⁻) has a value of .05 M and the value for the solubility product constant for $Pb(OH)_2$ is 4×10^{-15}, we have from equation (1)

$$(Pb^{++})(OH^-)^2 = (Pb^{++})(.05)^2 = 4 \times 10^{-15}$$

Therefore

$$(Pb^{++}) = \frac{4 \times 10^{-15}}{2.5 \times 10^{-3}} = 1.6 \times 10^{-12} \ M$$

From equation (2) we may write

$$(HPbO_2^-)(H^+) = 2 \times 10^{-16}$$

Since the value for (OH⁻) is .05 M, (H⁺) must be

$$\frac{1 \times 10^{-14}}{(OH^-)} = \frac{1 \times 10^{-14}}{5 \times 10^{-2}} = 2 \times 10^{-13} \ M$$

Then

$$(HPbO_2^-)(2 \times 10^{-13}) = 2 \times 10^{-16}$$

$$(HPbO_2^-) = \frac{2 \times 10^{-16}}{2 \times 10^{-13}} = 1 \times 10^{-3} \ M$$

QUESTIONS AND PROBLEMS

Example 3.

How many moles of $Cr(OH)_3$ will dissolve in 1 liter of 0.2 M NaOH solution? The equation for the reaction is

$$Cr(OH)_{3(s)} + OH^- = CrO_2^- + 2H_2O$$

According to this equation the number of moles of $Cr(OH)_3$ which dissolves will be equivalent to the number of moles of CrO_2^- ion in solution.

As an acid $Cr(OH)_3$ ionizes as follows:

$$Cr(OH)_{3(s)} = CrO_2^- + H^+ + H_2O$$

The ionization constant has a value of 1×10^{-16}; therefore

$$(CrO_2^-)(H^+) = 1 \times 10^{-16}$$

Since (OH^-) has a value of 0.2 M, (H^+) is $\dfrac{1 \times 10^{-14}}{0.2}$ or 5×10^{-14} M.

Then

$$(CrO_2^-)(5 \times 10^{-14}) = 1 \times 10^{-16}$$

$$(CrO_2^-) = \frac{1 \times 10^{-16}}{5 \times 10^{-14}} = 2 \times 10^{-3} \text{ mole per liter}$$

Therefore .002 mole of $Cr(OH)_3$ dissolves in 1 liter of 0.2 M NaOH solution.

Questions and Problems

1. What are the anhydrides of the following substances: (a) HNO_3, (b) $Ca(OH)_2$, (c) NaOH, (d) H_2SO_4, (e) $Mg(OH)_2$, and (f) $HClO_4$?
2. Give the formulae of the hydroxides of which the following are the anhydrides: ZnO, Cr_2O_3, PbO, Al_2O_3, and Sb_2O_3.
3. Rearrange the formulae of the hydroxides given in question 2 in such a way as to emphasize their acidic properties.
4. Write the equations for the equilibrium involved when aluminum hydroxide acts both as an acid and as a base.
5. How may the equilibrium in problem (4) be shifted so as to produce (a) a large concentration of Al^{+++} ions, (b) a large concentration of AlO_2^- ions?
6. Are the elements in the first main group of the periodic system more electronegative than those of the fourth group or vice versa?

7. In the series of 18 elements of the periodic table beginning with argon, name those the hydroxides of which are not amphoteric.
8. Which hydroxide acts as a stronger acid, $Sn(OH)_2$ or $Sn(OH)_4$?
9. Predict which hydroxide would act as the stronger acid, $Ge(OH)_2$ or $Ge(OH)_4$. Explain the basis of your prediction.
10. Write the formula for the sulfur analogue of each one of the following oxygen compounds: (a) H_2O, (b) SnO, (c) K_2O, (d) CO_2, (e) OH^-.
11. Give equations for the reactions involved when As_2O_5 is dissolved by a solution containing OH^- and when As_2S_5 is dissolved by a solution containing HS^- ions.
12. Why will SnS dissolve readily in ammonium polysulfide while in ammonium sulfide it is soluble only to a very small extent?
13. Making use of the amphoterism of $Zn(OH)_2$ and $Al(OH)_3$ and the complex-forming properties of Zn^{++} show how $Zn(OH)_2$, $Al(OH)_3$, and $Fe(OH)_3$ may be separated from each other.
14. How many moles of NaOH must be added to 100 ml. of water to dissolve completely .001 mole of $Zn(OH)_2$?
15. A saturated solution of $Zn(OH)_2$ in water contains the following ions in equilibrium with each other: Zn^{++}, ZnO_2^{--}, H^+, and OH^-. Calculate the concentration of each ion in such a solution. (Note: from the solubility product constant for $Zn(OH)_2$ calculate (Zn^{++}) and (OH^-), then obtain (H^+) from the water equilibrium, and finally calculate (ZnO_2^{--}) from the equilibrium for the ionization of $Zn(OH)_2$ as an acid.)
16. What is the concentration of the Zn^{++} ion and of the ZnO_2^{--} ion in a solution which is .01 molar with respect to OH^- ion and which is in equilibrium with solid $Zn(OH)_2$?
17. A solution is 0.1 molar with respect to OH^- ion and is in equilibrium with solid $Pb(OH)_2$. What is the concentration of (a) the Pb^{++} ion, (b) the $HPbO_2^-$ ion, and (c) the H^+ ion in this solution?
18. Will .002 mole of $Cr(OH)_3$ dissolve in 1 liter of 0.1 molar NaOH?
19. Excess $Al(OH)_3$ is added to 1 liter of a solution of NaOH. After equilibrium is reached .01 mole of $Al(OH)_3$ is dissolved. What is the final concentration of the OH^- ion?
20. Write equations (17) and (18) in structural form, similar to equation (20).
21. Calculate the concentrations of the Cu^{++}, $HCuO_2^-$, and CuO_2^{--} ions in equilibrium with solid $Cu(OH)_2$ and with a NaOH solution for which the OH^- ion concentration is 0.1 M.

PART
II

CHAPTER 10

Laboratory
Techniques

Before undertaking any work in the laboratory it will be necessary for the student to construct a few simple pieces of apparatus and to become acquainted with laboratory manipulations. This section deals with this introductory work. As his work in the course develops, the student will find it profitable to refer to this section for information when new problems of technique arise.

Apparatus To Be Constructed and Assembled

Wash-Bottle. Figure 10.1 shows a sketch of a wash-bottle. Obtain a 250 ml. flask of the type shown in the sketch and fit it with a two-hole rubber stopper. The pieces to be inserted into the stopper are constructed in the following way. The nozzle is made by drawing out a piece of 6 mm. glass tubing after it has been heated in the flame of a Bunsen burner to the softening point. After it has cooled scratch it with a file to allow the tube to be broken at the proper place. To bend a glass tube rotate it in a horizontal position in the flame of a burner equipped with a wing-top. Continue the heating with rotation of the tube until the glass is soft enough to bend without kinking. This procedure necessitates the heating of at least a two-inch portion of the glass tubing. Heat very slowly to allow a uniform distribution of the heat. The angles of bending of the two pieces should be such that the upper end of the exit tube, which connects with the nozzle, is parallel with the upper end of the delivery tube. The ends of all tubes should be heated just to the softening point (fire-polishing) to remove all sharp edges. After they have cooled they should be lubri-

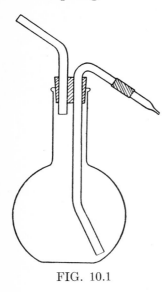

cated with water, saliva, or preferably alcohol, and then inserted in the rubber stopper. *Be careful!* Hold the tube in a towel to protect the hand in case the glass tube should break. Grasp the tube near the end that is to be inserted into the stopper. Push the tube through the hole until it protrudes about two inches. Then grasp the protruding end of the tube and *pull* it into position. The moistened surface of glass allows this operation to be carried out with greater ease and safety. Finally assemble the apparatus and introduce about 100 ml. of water. Test the wash-bottle for leaks by blowing into

FIG. 10.1

the inlet tube, observing whether the column of water maintains its position in the outlet tube when the finger is placed over the end of the mouthpiece. When full pressure is applied the nozzle should deliver a fine, even, unscattered stream of water.

Stirring Rods. It is convenient to have at hand several glass stirring rods, each 4–6 mm. in diameter and approximately 15 cm. in length. Obtain glass rods from the storeroom and cut them to the proper length. Fire-polish each end of rod in the flame.

Capillary Syringes. Two types of medicine droppers are needed in the course; one for adding reagent solutions on a small scale and a second type for washing small quantities of precipitates (see Figure 10.2). The first type is the standard medicine dropper of approximately 1 ml. capacity (1 ml. capacity refers to that of the glass tube only) and which delivers about twenty drops per ml. For the second type ("capillary syringe") it is necessary to draw out the tip of the ordinary dropper to a very small nozzle in a flame so as to obtain a fine stream of water when the bulb is subjected to pressure. To draw out the tip of the capillary, remove the rubber bulb and weld the end of the medicine dropper to a small piece of glass tubing or glass rod in the Bunsen flame. This extra piece of tubing or rod acts as a handle in making the syringe. To pull out the end of the dropper, rotate it with both hands well above the luminous flame of the Bunsen burner. Allow it to just reach the softening point and then pull it out. Break the capillary at a point such that the orifice formed is very small. If it is too small the end may be broken off to obtain the desired opening. The tip should be so small that at least 15 seconds are required to fill the syringe. Each student should have six medicine droppers, two of which should be converted into syringes.

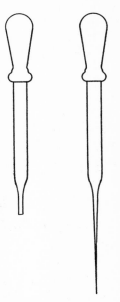

Apparatus for Saturation with H₂S. This apparatus is depicted in Figure 10.3. The wash-bottle B may be a permanent piece of apparatus which remains connected to the H₂S generator. In such a case the student

FIG. 10.2 Dropper and capillary syringe.

need not construct it. If it is to be constructed use a bottle of about 200–300 ml. capacity. The flask D is a 25 ml. Erlenmeyer flask. The instructions for bending the glass tubing are given in the description of the assembly of the wash-bottle.

To saturate a solution contained in a test tube use the tube illustrated in Figure 10.4. The rubber stopper should fit a 10 ml. test tube and is meant to slide along the tube to the proper distance from the end. The stopper is provided to cap the test tube after the air has been displaced thus preventing excessive escape of the H₂S. This apparatus should be connected to the wash-bottle at C (Figure 10.3).

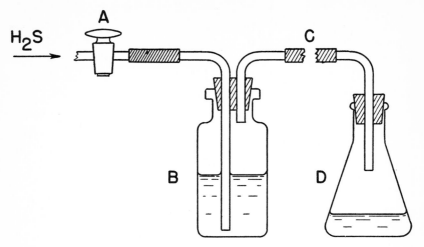

FIG. 10.3   Apparatus for saturating a solution with hydrogen sulfide.

General Manipulative Procedures

Precipitation.   Whenever a reagent is added to a solution to bring about the precipitation of a desired compound conditions most favorable for its complete precipitation and subsequent separation should be employed.   In the first place an excess of the reagent must be used to insure completeness of precipitation.   Although in no instance may any given ion be completely removed from solution, nevertheless its concentration in the solution after precipitation may be reduced to a negligible value.   For example, suppose we have a solution containing .01 mole of Ag^+ ion per liter and a solution of NaCl is added to it to precipitate AgCl.   The problem is to remove the silver from the solution as completely as possible. When solid silver chloride is present in equilibrium with its ions in solution the following expression must hold.

$$(Ag^+)(Cl^-) = K_{s.p.} = 2.8 \times 10^{-10}$$

If the concentration of the Cl^- ion is made .01 M, then the concentration of the Ag^+ ion left in solution will be only 2.8×10^{-8} M, which value is so small as to be negligible.

Under these conditions the precipitation is regarded as complete for the purpose of separation of Ag^+ ion from the remaining ions in the solution. On the other hand, if the concentration of the Cl^- ion in the solution were only 10^{-7} M, then the concentration of the Ag^+ ion remaining in solution would be 2.8×10^{-3} M, which value is 28 percent of the total amount of Ag^+ ion originally present. Under the latter conditions the precipitation is far from complete. It is apparent from the equilibrium expression given above that as the concentration of the Cl^- ion in the solution is increased, the concentration of the Ag^+ ion is decreased by a corresponding amount. A reasonable amount of Cl^- ion must be maintained in the solution to remove from it all but a negligible quantity of Ag^+ ion. On the other hand a very large excess of Cl^- ion will bring about the formation of the complex, $AgCl_2^-$ ion, and thereby increase the solubility of $AgCl$. Many ions form complexes of this type. In most cases an estimation can be made as to what is an adequate but not an excessive amount of reagent to be added. For example, if a 0.1 M solution of any particular ion is ample, it is obviously undesirable to increase the concentration to 1 M. All precipitations should be carried out with this point in mind. The directions given in the procedures which follow in this text are based upon a consideration of the optimum conditions for precipitation and should be adhered to closely. Nevertheless, the student should check the completeness of precipitation by adding a drop of the reagent to the filtrate or centrifugate collected in the separation of the precipitate. If the filtrate shows precipitation is incomplete, more of the reagent should be added, the solution again filtered or centrifuged and the second filtrate tested with the reagent. This procedure should be continued until the filtrate fails to give a precipitate.

There are other factors to be considered in precipitation procedures. Precipitation should be carried out in such a manner as to favor the formation of large crystals, the coagulation of colloids, and the reduction of the adsorption of other ions. These conditions are favored by heating the solution and adding the reagent slowly with constant stirring. In certain cases, the hydrogen ion concentration must be adjusted so as to favor these conditions. In other cases, salts are added to the solution to prevent the formation of colloids. For this purpose the addition of solutions of ammonium salts or the addition of the solid salts themselves may be used conveniently.

Saturation of a Solution with a Gas. Precipitation with Hydrogen Sulfide. In the precipitation of insoluble sulfides by hydrogen sulfide either in acidic or basic solutions the apparatus shown in Figure 10.3 should be used. Hydrogen sulfide gas from a generator or from a gasometer (storage tank, if cylinders of liquid hydrogen sulfide are used) enters the apparatus at the point indicated in the sketch. A stopcock *A* controls the flow of the gas into the wash-bottle *B* which contains water. Wash-bottle *B* may be a permanent piece of apparatus which remains connected to the supply of hydrogen sulfide at all times. It serves to remove any hydrochloric acid that might be carried over from the generator in the gas stream. It is in turn connected by means of soft rubber tubing *C* (longer than shown in figure) to the flask *D* (25 ml. capacity) which contains the unknown solution to be saturated with hydrogen sulfide. The inlet tube to *D* projects below the rubber stopper to a point which is about 2 cm. above the liquid to be saturated. After the solution has been placed in *D* the inlet tube is attached to *C*. Be sure that the inlet tube is clean.

Insert the inlet tube into the Erlenmeyer flask but do not stopper it tightly. Partly open the stop-cock *A* and allow the H₂S to sweep out the air in *D*. This will require only a few seconds. With the gas flowing, stopper the flask *D* with the stopper of the inlet tube and shake or rotate *D*. Loosen the stopper in *D* to again sweep out the gas and stopper tightly. Again rotate or shake the flask.

As shaking continues, the solution in *D* absorbs the hydrogen sulfide, thereby causing the precipitation. Shaking should be continued until the bubbling of the gas through the water in *B* is almost completely retarded. At this point the solution in *D* should be saturated with hydrogen sulfide and the precipitation of the sulfides should be complete. Only 2 to 3 minutes are required for saturation of the unknown solution, provided the flask D contains the normal amount of solution, 3 ml. To insure complete precipitation this procedure should be repeated with the filtrate until hydrogen sulfide fails to produce a precipitate.

If the solution to be saturated is contained in a 10 ml. test tube use the tube illustrated in Figure 10.4. This procedure should only be used for small quantites of solution. The inlet tube should be very clean and may be inserted below the surface of the liquid. If prolonged saturation is necessary stopper the test tube and saturate in a manner similar to that described above. In fact, the procedure illustrated in Figure 10.3 is the preferable one.

Thioacetamide as a Source of Hydrogen Sulfide. Hydrogen sulfide gas in the laboratory, as generated from the reaction of iron sulfide with hydrochloric acid or liberated from tanks or gasometers, if not controlled, can be dangerous, due to its high toxicity. Semi-micro procedures reduce the amount of

FIG. 10.4. Saturation tube.

hydrogen sulfide and consequently its hazard, to a negligible level. Recently, it has been found that an organic compound, thioacetamide, CH_3CSNH_2, hydrolyzes in aqueous solution with the liberation of hydrogen sulfide. The rate of hydrolysis is low at room temperature, but it increases rapidly as the solution is warmed.

$$CH_3CSNH_2 + H_2O = CH_3CONH_2 + H_2S$$
(Thioacetamide) (Acetamide)

When thioacetamide is added to the solution to be analyzed, the liberated hydrogen sulfide is in a position to react immediately with ions of the copper-arsenic group and of the zinc group, in addition to ferrous iron, to precipitate to corresponding sulfides. In this manner very little hydrogen sulfide es-

capes from the solution into the atmosphere. The thioacetamide is very soluble in water. For the purpose of the procedures described in this text a one molar solution of the
reagent is used; about 15 to 20 drops of this solution are usually
adequate for complete precipitation. Even in quite hot solution the rate of hydrolysis of the thioacetamide is not high,
and as long as 10 to 15 minutes may be required for complete
precipitation. The reagent is effective in acid or alkaline
media.

In acid solution the acetamide formed in the reaction undergoes hydrolysis with the production of acetic acid and ammonium ion,

$$H^+ + CH_3CONH_2 + H_2O = CH_3COOH + NH_4^+$$

In basic solution the reaction is as follows,

$$OH^- + CH_3CONH_2 + H_2O = CH_3COO^- + NH_4OH$$

Heating of Solutions. All solutions must be heated carefully to avoid bumping and spattering. Not only will bumping cause a serious loss of the test solution but it may often
be dangerous. The spattering of hot solutions may give rise
to painful burns. These burns may be serious if the solution
contains strong acids or hydroxides.

All solutions contained in very small test tubes should be
heated in a water bath or in a small beaker of boiling water.
This procedure also applies to solutions contained in 10 ml.
test tubes if these tubes are more than one-third full. With
the larger amounts of solution (more than 3 ml.) it is advisable
to pour the solution into a casserole and to heat it in this
container. The solution, reduced in volume, may be returned
to the test tube if desired.

Solutions contained in a 10 ml. test tube and occupying less
than one-third the capacity of the tube may be heated directly
by the flame of the Bunsen burner. Use a test tube holder
and *in all cases point the mouth of the test tube away from your-*

self or any other person nearby. When heating a solution directly in a flame, bring the bottom of the test tube to the edge of the flame and after allowing it to remain there for about one second, withdraw it and gently shake the test tube. Continue this procedure until the solution is heated. This operation may also be carried out by repeatedly flicking the end of the test tube into the flame, i.e., by not allowing the test tube to remain in the flame for more than a fraction of a second at a time. The flicking operation also shakes the solution. Quickly withdraw the test tube from the flame completely as soon as there is any sign of boiling and then proceed very gently using only the edge of the flame. If the 10 ml. test tube contains only a very small amount of solution (not strongly acidic or alkaline) the test tube may be held with the fingers instead of the test tube holder. Practice this operation with varying amounts of water.

Evaporation. The analytical procedures may specify evaporation of a solution to a definite volume or evaporation to dryness. In addition, it may be advisable at some points in the procedure to concentrate a solution by evaporation in order to have a smaller volume with which to deal, thereby saving time in subsequent filtrations and other manipulations. A small casserole or porcelain evaporating dish is suitable for this operation. However, the container should be as small as possible for the amount of liquid prepared. For many purposes a water bath will suffice as a source of heat. When corrosive fumes are evolved during the process of evaporation, the hood should be used unless the quantity of material is very small. If evaporation does not take place rapidly on a water bath, an open flame may be used. For this purpose the liquid is placed in a small casserole which is then rotated horizontally in the flame. This motion allows the liquid to come in contact with the hot walls of the casserole, thereby facilitating evaporation. Too hot a flame must not be used, otherwise bumping and spattering will take place.

In heating to dryness remove the casserole or evaporating dish while there is still some liquid left. The heat capacity of the dish is sufficient to complete the operation without further heating.

Testing Acidity or Alkalinity of Solutions. To test the acidity or alkalinity of a solution place a piece of litmus (or test) paper on the towel or paper on the desk, or on a watch glass, and then dip the end of a stirring rod into the solution and apply it to the paper. In this way several tests may be made with a single strip of paper. Sometimes it is possible to tear off a small fragment of the test paper and place it in the solution, but the former method is preferable.

Cleaning Glassware. All reaction vessels should be thoroughly clean before they are to be used. Small traces of contaminants in any test solution may give rise to spurious results.

All apparatus should be cleaned as soon after use as possible. Test tubes should be cleaned with a test tube brush. Use ground pumice or some cleaning powder if necessary. If these agents fail it may be advisable to use a strong concentrated acid such as HNO_3. (Do not use the test tube brush with acids.) Test tubes containing sulfur and some sulfides can be easily cleaned with a few drops of commercial ammonium sulfide or yellow ammonium sulfide. The test tubes should be rinsed with distilled water. The same procedure applies to casseroles, evaporating dishes, and beakers except that the test tube brush may be omitted.

When medicine droppers or capillary syringes are used for solutions, they should be rinsed several times in a beaker containing distilled water immediately after use. They should then be placed in another beaker containing distilled water for storage. The beaker containing the wash water should be refilled with distilled water at frequent intervals.

Flame Tests. Two wires should always be used for a flame test; one for the unknown solution and the other for a solution known to contain the ion in question at a concentration of about that to be expected in the unknown. Prepare two pieces of Chromel wire, both looped at the end and each inserted into a cork as a handle as shown in Figure 10.5.

Never rely upon memory to judge the characteristics of the flame. Alternately apply the two wires to the flame; one for the unknown and the other for the comparison solution.

The nitrate and sulfate salts of the unknown do not give good flame tests. In the flame these break down into the corresponding oxides which do not volatilize readily. Therefore a drop or two of 6 *M* HCl should be added to the solution (comparison as well as unknown) or solid, on a watch glass, and the looped end of the wire should be dipped into it. The loop should be small enough to retain a drop of the liquid within it.

Do not use the hottest portion of the flame but rather bring the looped end containing the solution slowly up to its edge. Some flame colors last a relatively long time; some are very ephemeral, disappearing quickly. Do not lay the wires on the table top. Use the towel or paper spread on the desk for this purpose.

FIG. 10.5
Wire for flame tests.

Procedures When Centrifugation Operations are Used

The Centrifuge and Its Operation. There are two general types of centrifuges used for analytical purposes — the hand-driven and the motor-driven types. The hand-driven are not recommended but may be used.

The motor-driven centrifuge consists of the driving motor, a shaft, and an attached head, which is known as the rotor, in which the test tubes that are to be spun are placed. When the rotor is spinning a centrifugal force is developed which like gravity brings about the settling of the precipitate. The difference in the time required for settling and centrifugation lies in the fact that the centrifugal force is much greater than the gravitational force at the earth's surface. There is a simple formula which relates the characteristics of the centrifuge to the force of gravity.

Centrifugal force (number of times greater than gravity) =

$$\frac{\text{diameter (in feet)} \times (\text{R.P.M.})^2}{6000}$$

R.P.M. refers to revolutions per minute. Thus if the centrifuge operates at 1600 R.P.M. and the effective diameter is 6 inches ($\frac{1}{2}$ foot) the centrifugal force is equal to

$$\frac{.5 \times (1600)^2}{6000} = 210 \text{ times that of gravity.}$$

The rate of sedimentation or settling depends upon (1) the centrifugal force; (2) the size of the particle; the larger the particle the quicker it settles; (3) the difference in density between the solid and that of the solution; the greater this difference the faster the settling, and (4) the viscosity of the solution; the greater the viscosity the slower the settling. With these factors in mind it is easy to understand the following considerations.

FIG. 10.6 The centrifuge.

(Courtesy Wilkens-Anderson Company, Chicago)

(a) The greater the density of the salt, the greater is the sedimentation rate. $BaSO_4$ is very dense, as are the sulfides; hence, they settle quickly if the particles are not too small. Sulfur has a much smaller density than a sulfide and for this reason it should be possible to separate sulfur from sulfides by controlling the speed of the rotor or the time of centrifugation.

(b) The greater the concentration of the salts in the solution, the slower is the rate of sedimentation. The addition of salts to a solution increases its density and decreases the difference in density between the precipitate and the solution; hence, the slower rate.

(c) The smaller the amount of solution in a test tube the

faster the sedimentation. With a larger amount of solution more of the precipitate is nearer the center of rotation and therefore this portion of it is subjected to a smaller centrifugal force.

(d) Colloids need much longer time for spinning. Due to the small size of the particles the sedimentation is slow.

In operating the centrifuge always balance it symmetrically. See to it that approximately equal amounts of liquid are in the two opposite test tubes. An unbalanced centrifuge vibrates and may become dangerous if it is subjected to this vibration continuously. The vibration wears the bearings supporting the rotor, usually identical with those of the motor.

Do not usurp the centrifuge by spinning it an undue length of time. Two minutes time is usually ample, except for the finer and lighter precipitates.

Before beginning a centrifugation see to it that particles are not floating on the surface of the liquid or are adhering to the side of the test tube. Surface tension effects prevent surface particles from settling. Agitate the surface with a stirring rod if necessary, and wash down the side of the test tube, using the capillary syringe and a very small amount of water or appropriate solution.

Under no circumstances use test tubes with broken or cracked lips. When spinning in the centrifuge these broken ends which protrude above the surface of the rotor may cause serious injury to the operators.

Do not attempt to retard the speed of the centrifuge with the hand until the electric current has been turned off and until the rotor has lost its full speed. Under no circumstances brake the rotor with the hand if it does not have a smooth outside surface.

If the centrifuge should become unduly hot, notify the instructor. Do not abuse the mechanism in any way. It should be well cared for at all times. Above all, do not let it come in direct contact with corrosive chemical reagents. Test tubes should not be too full of liquid since spilling may corrode and produce an unbalanced rotor.

Washing of Precipitates. Before the precipitate which has already been centrifuged is washed, it should be separated as completely as possible from the supernatant liquid. In pouring off the supernatant liquid a few drops are often held behind by the surface tension of the liquid. To remove these last drops tip the test tube upside down and drain the test tube with the aid of a piece of filter paper. Making contact between the liquid and the stirring rod often suffices to accomplish this end. It is important that these last drops be removed in as much as they may contain more dissolved salt than is held in the precipitate.

Add the required amount of distilled water or wash solution to the test tube containing the centrifuged precipitate and then with the aid of the stirring rod agitate the precipitate until it is in suspension. Then centrifuge and pour off the wash water. In almost all cases this operation should be carried out at least twice.

It sometimes happens that the removal of the ions in the solution by washing causes the precipitate to become dispersed, i.e., to form a colloid, which then cannot be easily centrifuged. In such a case add some ammonium salt which will not interfere with subsequent tests.

Transferring Precipitates. In semi-micro procedure it is usually not necessary to transfer precipitates from one test tube to another. If the precipitate is to be treated with some reagent in a casserole or evaporating dish, the reagent is first added to the precipitate in the test tube. It is brought into suspension by agitation with the stirring rod and the suspension is then poured into the open receptacle. The test tube may be washed by tipping it into an almost vertical (upside down) position and while holding the mouth of the test tube over the receptacle, the sides of the test tube may be subjected to the very fine stream of solution from a capillary syringe.

The transferring of a part or the whole of the precipitate to another test tube is accomplished by suspending the precipitate in distilled water (or in a suitable reagent) and by withdrawing the suspension with a medicine dropper, from which it is ejected into the second container.

Precipitates can sometimes be transferred with a spatula but this operation is usually quite difficult, especially when the containers are test tubes.

Procedures When Filtration Operations Are Used

Filtration. Filtration is one of the most time-consuming operations of the laboratory work. It will be used in this text only in a few operations where it has a distinct advantage over

FIG. 10.7

the centrifuge. For most purposes only the centrifuge is recommended. Filtration is greatly expedited if the volume of the liquid is maintained at a reasonable minimum and if the filtration procedures are carried out in an efficient manner. For the purpose of this course, the procedures are so devised that at no time should the volume of the liquid exceed 10 ml.

The funnel used for filtration should be about 4 cm. in diameter and should have a short stem. The filter paper (55 mm. in diameter) should be folded in exact halves and then not quite into quarters as shown in Figure 10.7. A small corner is torn off as indicated by the dotted line in the figure. This tear seals the paper when wet against an inflow of air to the underside of the filter paper. The folding angle here is greater than 90° and depends upon the shape of the particular funnel with which it is used. This may readily be determined by making a few tests using different angles of fold and noting roughly which angle gives the greatest rate of flow of water. The filter prepared in this manner is then inserted into the funnel, moistened with distilled water and then pressed with the fingers against the top part of the funnel to make a tight fit. This particular technique is an important one in speeding up filtration, since it insures the support of a column of liquid in the stem of the funnel and thereby leads to a small but an appreciable suction on the filter paper.

The precipitate should be allowed to settle before filtration so that a greater portion of the supernatant liquid may be poured through the filter paper in the funnel before it becomes clogged. The precipitate is then washed in the test tube with a small quantity of distilled water which is likewise transferred to the filter paper. This procedure is repeated two or three times and then the bulk of the precipitate and the remaining liquid is introduced to the filter. For the latter operation it is essential that in the process of transfer a small stirring rod be placed across the mouth of the test tube so that the liquid will follow the rod to the funnel. A rubber "policeman" (a stirring rod with one end covered by a short piece of rubber tubing) may be used to detach the last traces of solid precipitate which adhere to the glass walls of the test tube or flask.

In many instances it is advisable to heat the tube or flask, containing the liquid and the precipitate, in a beaker of hot water before filtration is attempted. The hot liquid flows faster through the filter and heating also coagulates the precipitate with the production of larger particles, thereby facilitating filtration. It is evident that this procedure cannot be used if the precipitate is appreciably soluble at the higher temperatures.

The speed of filtration may also be increased by the application of suction. For this purpose a side-arm test tube or a side-arm 25 ml. filter flask may be conveniently used to catch the filtrate. The side-arm of the apparatus is connected through a safety-trap to the aspirator pump and the funnel is inserted through a rubber stopper which fits tightly in the mouth of the flask as shown in Figure 10.8. For this operation it is necessary to use a hardened filter paper or a retaining cone in the funnel to prevent rupture of the paper when suction is applied.

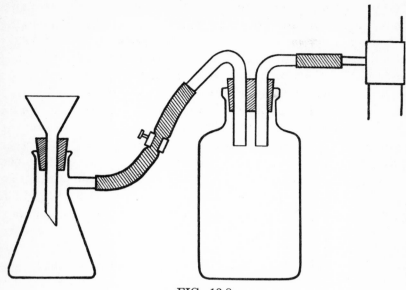

FIG. 10.8

Washing of Precipitate on Filter Paper. To wash a precipitate on a filter paper use the fine capillary syringe and
with it spray the distilled water or washing solution around
the outer edge of the paper thus washing the precipitate down
into the apex of the cone. If the capillary syringe delivers a
fine stream of water, the precipitate is loosened from the
paper and is suspended in the wash water. Allow the filter
to drain thoroughly before adding more wash water or solution, and with each successive washing bring the precipitate
more toward the apex of the cone.

Removing and Transferring the Precipitate from the
Filter Paper. Several different procedures may be used to
remove the precipitate from the filter paper. The selection
of one of these methods depends upon the intended use of the
precipitate and its subsequent treatment. A common procedure is that of punching a small hole through the apex of
the filter paper with a small pointed glass rod and then washing
the precipitate into the receiving vessel with a fine stream of
water from the wash-bottle or capillary syringe. Another

method is that of removing the filter paper and its contents from the funnel, unfolding the paper over a small evaporating dish or casserole and then washing the precipitate with water into the receiving dish while holding the paper in an inclined position. If the precipitate is sufficiently dry and present in an appreciable quantity, the bulk of it may be scraped with a spatula from the unfolded paper into the desired container. In this case the small amount retained by the paper may be removed by washing as previously described. Still another method for removing the precipitate is that of soaking the unfolded filter paper and its contents in a dish containing water. This latter method is applicable to precipitates which are held to the filter paper loosely and which are not too dry.

If the amount of precipitate is very small, it is advisable to place the entire filter paper and its contents in a dish containing water or solution to dissolve it. The filter paper may then be removed by filtration.

Reagents

Each student is provided with 13 small reagent bottles most of which are similar to the medicine bottles used by pharmacists; shown in Figure 10.9. These may be kept in a tray provided for this purpose or they may be stored each as a separate unit, and when used they are to be placed in a definite order in a row at the back of the laboratory desk. These bottles are for the following common reagents.

6 *M* Acetic Acid	18 *M* Sulfuric Acid
12 *M* Hydrochloric Acid	6 *M* Sulfuric Acid
6 *M* Hydrochloric Acid	15 *M* Ammonium Hydroxide
3 *M* Hydrochloric Acid	6 *M* Ammonium Hydroxide
15 *M* Nitric Acid	3 *M* Ammonium Hydroxide
6 *M* Nitric Acid	6 *M* Sodium Hydroxide

1 *M* Thioacetamide

The stoppers for these bottles are usually made of a hard rubber or plastic composition, and this as well as the rubber cap of the dropper is attacked rapidly by concentrated HNO_3

and more slowly by concentrated H_2SO_4 and HCl. Therefore the bottle containing the 15 M HNO_3 must be glass-stoppered. It is also desirable to use glass-stoppered bottles for the 18 M H_2SO_4, the 12 M HCl, and the 15 M NH_4OH. However these latter reagents may be kept in the composition or rubber-capped bottles provided the cap and the rubber bulb of the medicine dropper are renewed periodically (every semester).

FIG. 10.9   Student
reagent bottle.

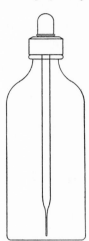

FIG. 10.10   Large
reagent bottle.

These bottles are to be refilled from the larger supply bottles (500 ml.) kept on the general reagent shelf.

The other reagents which are used less frequently are kept in 250 ml. bottles on the reagent shelf. These bottles (Figure 10.10) are also provided with droppers. In using these be very careful that the tips of the droppers do not come in contact with the test solutions, thus contaminating the reagents. *Never dip the end of the droppers into any foreign solution.*

The Notebook

The keeping of a good notebook for scientific work is an accomplishment that often requires much experience to learn. Most beginners either write too much or too little. This essential task should take up as little of the student's time as possible and yet the notebook should be sufficiently complete to contain all of the important information in an easily obtainable form. The student should obtain specific advice from his instructor on the notebook, its form and contents. However, some general suggestions on this subject might be made here.

Bear in mind that the instructor may want to review or inspect the notebook; therefore, do not be too verbose. Do not copy passages of instructions from the laboratory directions; refer to these by page, paragraph, or test number. Tabulate as many of the results as possible and record all observations in the form of short, concise statements. When an experiment or a significant part of an experiment is completed, record the results immediately.

In keeping notes on an analysis, make a list in a vertical column of all of the ions for which tests are to be made. This table can be used to advantage as a rough index to the specific tests which follow later. The conclusions reached regarding the presence or absence of ions can be inserted into this table after sufficient information has been obtained. Make certain to note all phenomena which seem to be irregular, since it is often possible for the instructor as well as the student to locate difficulties in an analysis by examining such notations. Record the date of the experiment.

General Instructions

The qualities which make for excellence in laboratory technique are orderliness, neatness, and cleanliness. These qualities are inherent in some people who naturally become good technicians. Others must develop them by making a special effort to overcome careless habits. Eventually their application becomes a habit and no further special effort is then required. Such a habit the laboratory worker in science should strive to acquire.

Orderliness is largely a state of mind. The orderly mind thinks ahead to the next operation when carrying out the operation at hand. What one does now very often depends upon what one is to do next. *Do not read only one step at a time in the laboratory directions.* Look ahead, to get the general picture of the procedure well in mind.

Neatness and cleanliness have more to do with the appearance of the student's desk and the condition of his apparatus and equipment with which he is to work. Do not allow dirty test tubes and flasks to accumulate. Place them in some definite place and wash them at the first opportunity. Replace the stoppers of the reagent bottles as soon as the reagent has been poured out, and then return the bottles to their specified places, either to the reagent racks or to the shelves. Always have those pieces of equipment at hand which are most often used.

The following suggestions should be adopted by the student when working in the laboratory.

(1) Upon beginning work spread a clean towel or paper on the top of the desk. The more common and frequently used apparatus should be arranged on the desk in an orderly fashion. All apparatus should have been cleaned during the previous laboratory period.

(2) Make certain that the reagent bottles at the desk are clean.

(3) Place several medicine droppers and capillary syringes in a beaker of distilled water. This water is to be used for diluting solutions and for washing precipitates. Never place a dropper on the bare desk; use the towel or paper, or a watch glass.

(4) Read the laboratory directions carefully and then plan a program of work for the day.

(5) During the course of the work place dirty test tubes and flasks in a definite place, preferably in a beaker, and wash them at convenient intervals. This task can often be done while waiting for a solution to evaporate, to filter, or to be centrifuged.

(6) In pouring a reagent from a bottle hold the stopper between the third and fourth finger of the hand holding the

bottle. The solution should be poured from the back side of the bottle, i.e., the bottle is to be held with the label side up.

(7) While the student is expected to adhere closely to directions, he should not work blindly. Some bit of information may show a certain test to be unnecessary. If, for example, he observes that an ammoniacal solution of his unknown is colorless he can be sure that Cu^{++} ion is absent. Specific tests for this ion may therefore be omitted.

(8) A blank test should always be made whenever an unknown test is doubtful. The blank test serves as a basis for comparison. In addition, if the test for a given ion is found to be negative, the student can determine whether the conditions for obtaining the test were satisfactory by adding to the final solution one drop of a solution containing the ion in question.

The Unknown

The analytical procedures described in this text have been devised so as to reduce to a minimum the time required for their successful operation. This is done in part by specifying the amount of unknown sample. The minimum amount of a given salt present in an unknown solution is from 1 to 8 mg. per ml., depending upon the atomic weight of the ion under consideration. This amount is sufficient for the success of all the tests to be applied. The volume of the solution containing the unknown ions is 3 ml. Accordingly each ion should be present at a concentration of about .02 M.* For solid unknowns the amounts used are of the same order of magnitude.

Introduction to the Positive Ions

The elements may be classified in two distinctly different ways: (1) according to their atomic numbers as in the familiar periodic classification and (2) according to the reactions and

---

* Most of the tests in the procedures used in this text are sufficiently sensitive to allow detection at one-fifth the concentrations here specified or lower. However, a moderate "factor of safety" has been allowed the student.

properties of their ions which lend themselves to analytical separation and detection. The latter classification includes, in addition to the simple ions, compound and complex ions such as the ammonium (NH_4^+) and sulfate (SO_4^{--}) ions, and the silver-ammonia $[Ag(NH_3)_2^+]$ and chloro-platinate ($PtCl_6^{--}$) ions. In this classification ions which form compounds having similar properties are placed in a single group. For example, only Ag^+, Hg_2^{++} and Pb^{++} ions react with Cl^- ion in solution to form relatively insoluble chlorides. These three elements then constitute one group in the analytical classification. Likewise, those sulfides which can be precipitated in acid solution of sufficient strength constitute another group. The latter includes the sulfides of Hg^{++}, Pb^{++}, Bi^{+++}, Cu^{++}, Cd^{++}, As^{+++}, Sb^{+++} and Sn^{++} ions. A third group is made up of positive ions, the hydroxides or sulfides of which are precipitated by a solution containing NH_4OH, NH_4Cl and $(NH_4)_2S$. It includes Al^{+++}, Cr^{+++}, Fe^{+++}, Ni^{++}, Co^{++}, Mn^{++} and Zn^{++} ions. A fourth group consists of Ca^{++}, Ba^{++}, Sr^{++} and Mg^{++} ions which, with the exception of the latter, form relatively insoluble carbonates, while a fifth group is made up of K^+, Na^+ and NH_4^+ ions, the chlorides, sulfides, hydroxides, and carbonates of which are soluble. Such a grouping of the positive ions allows for the separation of most of the common elements.

This method of separating the different ions from each other is not a unique one. Small variations in procedure may shift one ion from one group to another but in the main the different methods of separation are very much alike.

Since the compounds of elements in a given main group of the periodic table have similar properties it is to be expected that these elements will also appear in the same analytical group. In some cases this expectation is realized. Thus Ca^{++}, Ba^{++}, and Sr^{++} ions are precipitated together as carbonates, while Na^+, K^+, and NH_4^+ ions constitute another group. However, the compounds of elements in the sub-groups of the periodic system do not show the same close similarity in chemical and physical properties exhibited by the compounds of the main group elements, and since many of the more common elements belong to the sub-groups, this parallelism between the periodic table classification and the analytical classification is not very marked.

The five groups of positive ions in the analytical procedure are presented in the following order:

(1) The alkali group; Na^+, K^+, and NH_4^+.

(2) The silver group; Ag^+, Pb^{++}, and Hg_2^{++}.

(3) The copper-arsenic group; Hg^{++}, Pb^{++}, Bi^{+++}, Cu^{++}, Cd^{++}, As^{+++}, Sb^{+++}, Sn^{++}, and Sn^{++++}.

(4) The aluminum–zinc group; Al^{+++}, Cr^{+++}, Fe^{+++}, Co^{++}, Ni^{++}, Fe^{++}, Mn^{++}, and Zn^{++}.

(5) The alkaline earth group; Ba^{++}, Ca^{++}, Sr^{++}, and Mg^{++}.

In each chapter the general chemical properties of the group are discussed first. This is followed by the specific properties of the different ions within the group, the preliminary experiments, and finally by the analytical procedure.

CHAPTER 11

The Alkali Metal Group of Ions

Na+, K+, and NH₄+ Ions

The alkali metals are characterized by the solubility in water of practically all salts formed by the ions of these metals and negative ions. Therefore the presence of this group of ions is detected, not by the insolubility of any particular compound, but, rather, by flame tests.

The ammonium ion is included with those of the alkali metals in the analytical procedures, since this ion is like the alkali metal ions with respect to solubility. However, the ammonium ion is not analyzed by flame test.

Sodium salts impart a yellow color to the flame while those of potassium give a violet color. In making these tests *it is essential that a comparison be made with a known sample.* In addition, for the identification of potassium by the flame test, it is advisable to use *two thicknesses of cobalt glass* in order to eliminate more completely the colors due to the presence of other ions, in particular Na^+ and Ca^{++} ions.

The presence of NH_4^+ ion in solution may be readily detected through the addition of a strong base, such as NaOH or $Ca(OH)_2$, with subsequent heating of the solution to liberate NH_3, and finally through the detection of NH_3 by moist red litmus paper. The odor of NH_3 may be sufficiently strong to be detected. An examination of the equilibria involved in a solution containing NH_3 and NH_4^+ ion explains this test.

$$NH_3 + H_2O = NH_4OH = NH_4^+ + OH^- \qquad (1)$$

The strong base furnishes a high concentration of OH^- ions which drives the reaction to the left with the production of free NH_3. At higher temperatures the solubility of NH_3 in water is considerably less than at room temperature. Consequently, when the solution is heated more NH_3 gas is liberated. When it comes in contact with moistened litmus paper, OH^- ion is produced according to equation (1) and a basic reaction is observed.

Preliminary Experiments

1. Add 10 drops (0.5 ml.) of 0.1 M NH_4NO_3 solution to 2.5 ml. of water in a 30 ml. beaker or small evaporating dish and determine the presence of the NH_4^+ ion in the following manner. Add 6 M NaOH solution dropwise until the solution is just alkaline (see directions page 242). Add 1 ml. of 6 M NaOH solution in excess. Have ready a moistened strip of red litmus paper adhering to the under side of a watch glass just large enough to cover the container. Place the watch glass over the container and heat the solution gently. The ammonia generated from the hot solution will react with the litmus paper turning it blue.[1] When NH_4^+ ion is present in sufficient concentration, the odor of ammonia can be easily detected. Try this same experiment using only 1 drop of 0.1 M NH_4NO_3 solution and 1 ml. of water.

NOTE 1. *If the heating is too vigorous, some of the boiling NaOH solution may spatter onto the litmus paper. Do not confuse scattered blue spots on the litmus paper caused by spattering with the even change to blue brought about by the NH_3.*

---

2. Prepare a .02 M solution of $NaNO_3$ by adding 0.5 ml. of the 0.1 M $NaNO_3$ solution to 2 ml. of water. Add 1 ml. of 6 M HCl.[2]

    Bend one end of an iron, platinum, Nichrome, or Chromel wire into a very small loop so that it will retain a drop of the solution to be tested. The other end of the wire may be inserted into a cork for a handle (see page 242). Dip the loop end of the wire into the solution containing the Na^+ ion and insert it into the edge of the blue flame of the Bunsen burner. Note the intense yellow flame characteristic of sodium. To clean the wire heat it in the flame and while it is hot, dip it into a drop of $6M$ HCl placed on a watch glass, and again heat. Now using a clean wire, test various reagents in the laboratory which are not supposed to contain Na⁺ ion. Note that a weak sodium flame is obtained. This is to be distinguished from the very strong positive test.

Make a solution which is .002 M in Na⁺ ion, i.e., take one part of the solution previously used and add to it 9 parts of water. Again note the strong sodium flame. With experience it is possible to distinguish between sodium present in small traces and that present as an essential constituent of the solution. Save the original solution containing the Na⁺ ion as a comparison for later tests.

NOTE 2. *In making any flame test always add HCl to the solution. If nitrates alone are present, these upon heating will be converted to the oxides which are relatively non-volatile. Chlorides are not as easily converted to the oxides and are usually volatile at high temperatures.*

---

3. Prepare 2.5 ml. of a .02 M KNO_3 solution. Add 1 ml. 6 M HCl and (as described in Exper. 2) make a flame test for potassium. Note the light violet color of the flame. This color is easily obscured by the presence of other ions, particularly sodium. To distinguish the K⁺ ion in the presence of other ions the light emitted by the other ions is filtered out by means of a cobalt glass. One thickness of the cobalt glass is not sufficient to extinguish all the extraneous light, therefore two are necessary. Now view the potassium flame through two thicknesses of cobalt glass. Note the deep red color. The flames of some other ions are visible through this filter yet none of them give this characteristic color of potassium.

Prepare a solution which is .002 M with respect to the K⁺ ion by diluting one part of the former solution with 9 parts of water and again test for potassium. Save the original solution for later tests.

4. ***Test for K⁺ and Na⁺ Ions in the Presence of Each Other.***
Add 5 drops of 0.1 M $NaNO_3$ solution and 5 drops of 0.1 M KNO_3 solution to 1.5 ml. of water. Add 1 ml. of 6 M HCl. Test for both Na⁺ and K⁺ ions by the method outlined in the previous experiments.

5. *Test for K+ and Na+ Ions in the Presence of Other Ions.*
Prepare a solution containing a number of ions selected *ad lib*
from the reagent shelf. Divide the solution into two parts and
make one of these .02 M with respect to both Na^+ and K^+ ions.
Add $6M$ HCl to each part, as directed before, and perform tests
for the sodium and potassium ions on both these solutions.

Analysis of the Alkali Metal Group

Obtain from the laboratory instructor a sample of an unknown
solution which is to be tested for the Na^+, K^+, and NH_4^+ ions.

A–1. Test for NH₄+ Ion. To 1 ml. of this solution in a casserole,
an evaporating dish, or a 30 ml. beaker add 6 M NaOH dropwise
until alkaline, and then add 1 ml. of the solution in excess. Moisten
a strip of red litmus paper and place it on the under side of a watch
glass just large enough to cover the container. Place the watch glass
over the container and heat gently. If ammonia is present the
litmus paper will turn blue. If the concentration of ammonia is
high, its odor may be easily detected.

A–2. Test for Na+ Ion. Make 10 drops of the original solution
acidic with 6 M HCl, added dropwise, and add 10 drops of 6 M HCl
in excess. (If the original solution is already acidic, merely add 10
drops of 6 M HCl.) Dip the loop end of an iron, platinum, Ni-
chrome, or Chromel wire into the above solution and then insert it
into the edge of the blue flame of the Bunsen burner. An intense
yellow color in the flame shows the presence of sodium. Compare
the color of this flame with that imparted by a solution known to
contain sodium. (See Preliminary Experiment 2, page 258, for instructions for maintaining a clean wire.)

A–3. Test for K+ Ion. Dip the loop end of a clean wire into
the acidified unknown solution prepared for A–2 above, and then
place the wire in the blue flame of the Bunsen Burner. View the
color of the flame through two thicknesses of cobalt glass. If potassium is present a deep red color will be seen in the flame when viewed
with the cobalt glass. Make certain to compare the color imparted
by the unknown with that obtained from a solution known to contain K^+ ion.

CHAPTER 12

The Silver Group

Ag⁺, Pb⁺⁺, and Hg₂⁺⁺ Ions

Silver, lead, and mercurous ions differ from the other ions considered in our general scheme of analysis in that the chlorides of these ions are relatively insoluble. If, under the right conditions, chloride ion is added to a solution containing these ions, among others, the chlorides of the silver, lead, and mercurous ions will precipitate, leaving the remaining positive ions in solution.

Silver chloride differs from the other two chlorides of this group in that it is soluble in NH_4OH. Upon dissolving it forms the silver-ammonia complex ion, $Ag(NH_3)_2^+$. (See Chapter 8.)

Lead chloride differs from the other two chlorides of this group in that it is relatively soluble in hot water, whereas the other two are not. Furthermore, $PbCl_2$ is soluble in NaOH solution with the formation of the plumbite ion, $HPbO_2^-$. (See Chapter 9.) The presence of mercurous chloride is detected by the addition of NH_4OH to it. The Hg_2Cl_2 with NH_4OH solution forms the precipitate $Hg(NH_2)Cl$ and free mercury, which in this finely divided state appears to be black.

Preliminary Experiments

1. To 2 ml. of water add 2 drops of 0.1 M AgNO₃ solution, and to this solution add 5 drops of 0.1 M NaCl. Now add 6 M NH₄OH dropwise and note that the precipitate dissolves.

(a) Devise an experiment to show that the NH_4^+ ion is not responsible for dissolving the AgCl.

(b) Devise an experiment to show that the OH^- ion is not responsible for this effect.

(c) What substance in NH_4OH is responsible for this effect?

2. Add 1 M NH_4OH dropwise to 1 ml. of 0.1 M $AgNO_3$ solution and note that the precipitate of Ag_2O first formed dissolves in excess of NH_4OH.

Now add a few crystals of NH_4NO_3 to 1 ml. of 0.1 M $AgNO_3$ solution and then add an excess of 1 M NH_4OH solution drop by drop. No precipitate of Ag_2O is produced in this experiment.

(a) How does the addition of NH_4^+ ion (NH_4NO_3) effect the concentration of the OH^- ion?

(b) Explain why Ag_2O is not precipitated, whereas it was when NH_4NO_3 had not been added.

3. Devise and try an experiment to show that $Pb(OH)_2$ is amphoteric.

4. (a) Add 1 ml. 0.1 M $Pb(NO_3)_2$ solution to 2 ml. water and to this solution add 20 drops of 3 M HCl to precipitate $PbCl_2$. Filter the solution and by means of the capillary syringe wash the crystals with 1 ml. of boiling water. Collect the washings and cool by placing the test tube in cold water. Explain.

(b) To the latter mixture (crystals and solution) add 2 drops 1 M K_2CrO_4 solution. Write an equation for the reaction. Which is the more soluble, $PbCl_2$ or $PbCrO_4$?

5. (a) To about 1 ml. of 0.1 M $Hg_2(NO_3)_2$ solution add 10 drops of 6 M HCl solution.

(b) To about 1 ml. of 0.1 M $Hg(NO_3)_2$ solution add 10 drops of 6 M HCl solution. Note the difference in the two experiments.

6. (a) Add 1 small drop of metallic mercury to 1 ml. of 0.1 M $Hg(NO_3)_2$ solution and heat.

(b) Add a few drops of HCl solution to solution (a). What is the evidence that a reaction took place between Hg and Hg^{++} in (a)?

(c) Filter solution obtained (b) and to the filtrate add a few drops of $SnCl_2$ solution. What is the evidence that the reaction in (a) was not complete?

(d) Write equations to express the reactions of (a) and (b) and (c).

7. Add a few drops of 1 M NH_4OH to 1 ml. of 0.1 M $HgCl_2$ solution and observe the precipitate. Write an equation for the reaction.

8. Prepare a small quantity of freshly precipitated Hg_2Cl_2 and to

its suspension in water add a few drops of 1 M NH_4OH solution. Observe any changes which take place. Give an equation for the reaction.

The Analysis of the Silver Group

SCHEMATIC OUTLINE

Add 6 M HCl — Precipitate: $PbCl_2$, Hg_2Cl_2, AgCl (Filtrate may contains ions of subsequent groups) Treat with hot water $\quad\quad\quad\quad$ ***(B)***		
Solution: Pb^{++} Add 6 M HAc and 1 M K_2CrO_4	Residue: AgCl, Hg_2Cl_2 Pour 6 M NH_4OH through the filter	
Precipitate: $PbCrO_4$ (yellow) $\quad\quad$ ***(B–1)***	Black residue on filter: $Hg + Hg(NH_2)Cl$ (black)$\quad$(white) ***(B–2)***	Solution: $Ag(NH_3)_2^+$ and Cl^- Add 6 M HNO_3
		Precipitate: AgCl $\quad\quad$ ***(B–3)*** (white)

NOTE 1. *In the analysis of the silver group it is not advisable to use the centrifuge. Filtering is more convenient for the required operations.*

B. Precipitation of the Silver Group. Obtain a sample of a solution of an unknown from the laboratory instructor and to 3 ml. of it add 10 drops of 6 M HCl from a medicine dropper, with constant shaking. If no precipitate appears, it is evident that Ag^+, Pb^{++}, and Hg_2^{++} ions are absent. (Small amounts of Pb^{++} ion may be present owing to the relatively high solubility of $PbCl_2$.) In the event of the formation of a precipitate, pour the contents on a filter supported by a 40 mm. funnel. Test the filtrate for completeness of precipitation by adding 1 drop of 6 M HCl. If a precipitate appears add 2 more drops of 6 M HCl[2] and pour through the filter containing the precipitates.[3]

NOTE 2. *A slight excess of HCl is added for the following reasons:*
(a) the common ion effect insures more complete precipitation,
(b) the precipitation of BiOCl and SbOCl is prevented, and
(c) the possibility of colloidal suspensions of the chlorides is lessened.

NOTE 3. *The addition of a very large excess of HCl is to be avoided. With a large excess or a high concentration of Cl^- ion, soluble complex chloride ions of silver and lead, namely, $AgCl_2^-$ and $PbCl_4^{--}$, will be formed.*

B–1. Test for Pb⁺⁺ Ion. Place about 25 ml. of distilled water in a beaker and heat to boiling. Gently lift out of the funnel the filter paper cone which contains the precipitates. Slowly pour about one-half of the water through the funnel in order to heat it, then discard the water. Quickly place the filter paper back into the funnel. Place a test tube under the stem of the funnel and with the aid of the capillary syringe, add 2 ml. of hot water to the precipitate. (The capillary syringe should also be hot.)

Add to the solution first 1 drop of 6 *M* acetic acid and then 1 drop of 1 *M* K_2CrO_4 solution. A yellow precipitate of $PbCrO_4$ shows the presence of Pb^{++} ion.

To confirm that the precipitate is $PbCrO_4$, dissolve it by adding a few drops of 6 *M* NaOH solution to the suspension. If necessary, separate by filtration any undissolved residue and to the filtrate add acetic acid to reprecipitate $PbCrO_4$.[4]

The precipitate remaining on the filter may contain AgCl and Hg_2Cl_2, and if Pb^{++} ion has been found present, an additional quantity may be still left on the filter. To remove the greater part of the Pb^{++} ion from the filter, add 2 ml. of hot water and discard the washings. Repeat this operation three times, using 2 ml. of hot water each time.

Note 4. *The NaOH solution containing the plumbite ion is neutralized with HAc rather than with HCl to prevent too high a H⁺ ion concentration which in turn would prevent the precipitation of lead chromate. Explain.*

B–2. Test for Hg₂⁺⁺ Ion. Now treat the residue of the filter paper with 10 drops of 6 *M* NH_4OH solution and collect the liquid which passes through the filter in a small test tube. Pour this solution over the filter a second time and collect it again. Label this solution **B–3** and reserve for the Ag⁺ ion test. If the residue on the filter becomes decidedly black, the presence of Hg_2^{++} ion is strongly indicated. The black residue is the result of the formation of the white ammono-basic salt, $Hg(NH_2)Cl$, and black metallic mercury.[5] (The black metallic mercury masks the white ($Hg(NH_2)Cl$.)

Note 5. *If there is any doubt about the presence of Hg₂⁺⁺ ion, it may be confirmed in the following manner:*

Transfer the precipitate to a small evaporating dish or casserole. Treat with 10 drops of aqua regia and heat the mixture carefully over a free flame until the excess aqua regia is completely removed and the residue for the most part appears to be dissolved. (*Make certain that the excess aqua regia is removed; otherwise it will oxidize the Sn^{++} ion in the next step of the test and render it valueless.*) *Then add about 5 drops of water and finally 2 drops of 0.1 M $SnCl_2$ solution. A white or gray precipitate confirms the presence of Hg_2^{++} ion in the original solution.*

B–3. Test for Ag^+ Ion. The filtrate **B–3** reserved for the detection of Ag^+ ion is treated with 6 M HNO_3 added drop by drop until the solution is acidic. A white precipitate of AgCl shows Ag^+ ion to be present.[6]

NOTE 6. *If the amount of Ag^+ ion present in the solution is very small, as compared with that of the Hg_2^{++} ion, and if the filtration is slow, the $Ag(NH_3)_2^+$ ion may be reduced to free silver according to the following equation and thereby be retained on the filter.*

$$2Hg_{(s)} + 2Ag(NH_3)_2^+ + 2Cl^- = Hg_2Cl_2 + 2Ag_{(s)} + 4NH_3$$

It is not very probable that all the silver would be retained in this way. If the final test for silver is very doubtful, then add 6 M HNO_3 and heat in order to dissolve the black precipitate. Add a few drops of 1 M HCl to the solution. The silver will precipitate from the nitric acid solution as AgCl. To confirm that the resulting white precipitate is AgCl, dissolve it in ammonia. The mercury will be in the form of $HgCl_2$ which is soluble and which, in the presence of ammonia, produces $Hg(NH_2)Cl$.

Equations for Pertinent Reactions

$$Ag^+ + Cl^- = AgCl_{(s)}$$
$$Hg_2^{++} + 2Cl^- = Hg_2Cl_{2(s)}$$
$$Pb^{++} + 2Cl^- = PbCl_{2(s)}$$
$$Pb^{++} + CrO_4^{--} = PbCrO_{4(s)}$$
$$PbCrO_{4(s)} + 3OH^- = HPbO_2^- + CrO_4^{--} + H_2O$$
$$HPbO_2^- + CrO_4^{--} + 3H^+ = PbCrO_{4(s)} + 2H_2O$$
$$Hg_2Cl_{2(s)} + 2NH_3 = Hg_{(s)}(\text{black}) + Hg(NH_2)Cl + NH_4^+ + Cl^-$$
$$AgCl_{(s)} + 2NH_3 = Ag(NH_3)_2^+ + Cl^-$$
$$Ag(NH_3)_2^+ + Cl^- + 2H^+ = AgCl_{(s)} + 2NH_4^+$$

CHAPTER 13

The Copper-Arsenic Group

Hg^{++}, Pb^{++}, Bi^{+++}, Cu^{++}, and Cd^{++}; H_3AsO_4, H_3AsO_3, H_3SbO_4, Sb^{+++}, Sn^{++}, and Sn^{++++}

The copper-arsenic group of ions is precipitated by hydrogen sulfide in dilute (0.2–0.3 M) HCl solution. This procedure serves to separate these ions from those of subsequent groups. If the concentration of the hydrogen ion is too great, the sulfides of cadmium and lead will fail to precipitate, and some of the other more soluble sulfides may likewise fall into this category. On the other hand, if the concentration of the hydrogen ion is too small, considerably lower than 0.2 M, zinc, nickel, and cobalt sulfides will precipitate if the corresponding ions are present.

The H^+ ion regulates the concentration of the S^{--} ion when H_2S is passed into the solution. The higher the concentration of the H^+ ion, the lower the concentration of the S^{--} ion, as may be readily seen by an examination of the following equilibrium for a saturated solution of H_2S.

$$(H^+)^2(S^{--}) = 1.3 \times 10^{-21} \qquad (2)$$

If the concentration of the H^+ ion is maintained at 0.3 M, it follows from the above expression that the concentration of the S^{--} ion in such a solution is approximately 1.4×10^{-20} mole per liter. This condition is favorable for the precipitation of the sulfides of the copper-arsenic group.

After the sulfides have been precipitated they may be

separated according to the differences in solubility they show with various reagents. These differences in solubility may be explained by a consideration of the equilibria between the sulfides and their respective ions. (MS represents any metal sulfide of the group.)

$$MS_{(s)} = M^{++} \qquad + \qquad S^{--} \qquad (3)$$

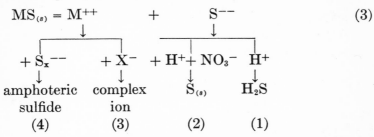

The above general equilibrium may be shifted to the right (MS dissolved) either by the removal of the M^{++} ion or the S^{--} ion. This may be accomplished in four different ways as indicated in equation (3).

(1) If MS is not too insoluble, H^+ ion alone suffices.

(2) If MS is very insoluble, H^+ and NO_3^- (or aqua regia) are necessary. Free sulfur is formed in this case.

(3) M^{++} may form a very stable complex ion with X^- (CN^- ion is an example). This method is not generally applicable.

(4) If M^{++} forms an amphoteric sulfide, $(NH_4)_2S$ or $(NH_4)_2S_x$ will dissolve the MS. The sulfides of arsenic, antimony, and tin behave in this way.

Preliminary Experiments

1. Mix 1 ml. of 0.1 M solutions of each of the following salts: $Hg(NO_3)_2$, $Cu(NO_3)_2$, and $Cd(NO_3)_2$. To the mixture, in a saturating flask, add H_2S (or 15 drops of thioacetamide solution and heat until the solution is saturated. Centrifuge, discard the centrifugate, and wash the precipitate thoroughly to eliminate NO_3^- ion. Pour 2 ml. of 6 M HCl over the precipitate, stir thoroughly, and centrifuge. Decant the HCl solution into a saturating flask. Now add sufficient NH_4OH to the HCl solution to neutralize it. Make the solution 0.2 M in H^+ ion by adding the

correct amount of HCl. Pass H_2S gas into the latter solution and note the result. Explain.

2. Prepare 10 ml. of each of the following HCl solutions: 6 M, 2 M, 0.2 M, .02 M, and .002 M. In making the dilutions use the medicine dropper to measure 1 ml. portions and a graduate for larger volumes. (For example, to make 10 ml. of .002 M HCl, add 1 ml. of .02 M solution to the graduate and dilute with water to 10 ml.) Add 2 ml. of each of the above HCl solutions to 2 ml. of each of the following salt solutions: 0.1 M $CuSO_4$, 0.1 M $CdSO_4$ and 0.1 M $ZnSO_4$. (Nitrates of these ions may be used instead of the sulfates.) Thus, the resulting solutions (15 in all) contain H^+ ion at a concentration of one-half that of the original solution, and the positive metal ion at a concentration of .05 M. Pass H_2S gas into each of these solutions and note the appearance and the color of any precipitate which may form. Record your observations in a chart similar to that given below. Explain the results on the basis of the ionization of H_2S in acid solution and the solubilities of the different sulfides.

(H^+)	0.05 M $CuSO_4$	0.05 M $CdSO_4$	0.05 M $ZnSO_4$
0.001 M			
0.01 M			
0.1 M			
1.0 M			
3.0 M			

3. Prepare the following $Pb(NO_3)_2$ solutions: (a) .01 M, by adding 9 ml. of water to 1 ml. of 0.1 M $Pb(NO_3)_2$; (b) .001 M, by adding 9 ml. of water to 1 ml. of solution (a); (c) .0001 M, by adding 9 ml. of water to 1 ml. of solution (b); (d) .00001 M, by adding 9 ml. of water to 1 ml. of solution (c); and (e) .000001 M, by adding 9 ml. of water to 1 ml. of solution (d). Saturate 3 ml. of each of these solutions with H_2S and note the limiting concentration which gives a distinctly visible precipitate. (Note: Very finely divided suspensions appear as colored solutions.) The concentration of the S^{--} ion in these solutions is approximately 1.3×10^{-13} M. From the $K_{S.P.}$ for PbS (4×10^{-26}) calculate the minimum concentration of Pb^{++} that should give a precipitate provided a supersaturated solution of PbS is not

formed. Compare this calculated value of (Pb^{++}) with that corresponding to the limit of visibility determined above.

4. In the following chart the ions of the copper-arsenic group are listed horizontally and a number of reagents vertically. In the blank spaces provided in a similar chart made in your notebook give the products of the reactions when the given reagent is added drop by drop to a solution of the ion in question. If the product is a precipitate, indicate this fact by denoting the solid phase as, for example, $CuS_{(s)}$. Indicate the color of all precipitates and solutions containing new products. If the reaction does not give a precipitate but produces new ions, indicate these in the appropriate places. If no reaction takes place as far as you can ascertain, write *no reaction*. From your knowledge of the chemical properties of these ions, *fill in as many blank spaces as possible without carrying out the experiments.. If you are not familiar with the reaction in question perform an experiment to obtain the desired information.*

Reagent added	Hg^{++}	Pb^{++}	Bi^{+++}	Cu^{++}	Cd^{++}	As^{+++}	Sb^{+++}	Sn^{++}	Sn^{++++}
6 M NaOH									
6 M NaOH in excess									
3 M NH₄OH									
3 M NH₄OH in excess									
0.1 M NaCl									
H₂S in 0.3 M HCl									

5. The sulfides of the copper-arsenic group are listed horizontally and reagents vertically, in the following chart. Indicate in the appropriate space in a similar chart in your notebook whether the given reagent will dissolve the sulfide. Also give the formula of any new substances formed in the reaction. *Perform experiments only if necessary.* (In the event the precipitates dissolve slowly in the cold, particularly in the presence of nitric acid and aqua regia, heat the mixtures.)

	HgS	PbS	Bi$_2$S$_3$	CuS	CdS	As$_2$S$_3$	Sb$_2$S$_3$	SnS	SnS$_2$
0.3 *M* HCl									
Dilute HNO$_3$									
Aqua regia									
(NH$_4$)$_2$S									
(NH$_4$)$_2$S$_x$									

6. BiCl$_3$ is hydrolyzed in water solution to the basic salt, BiOCl. Devise and perform an experiment to show that the reaction is reversible.

7. Devise and carry out experiments to verify the order of solubility of CuC$_2$O$_4$, Cu(OH)$_2$, Cu(NH$_3$)$_4$$^{++}$, and CuS.

8. To 2 drops of 0.1 *M* Pb(NO$_3$)$_2$ solution add 3 drops of 0.1 *M* (NH$_4$)$_2$SO$_4$ solution to precipitate PbSO$_4$. To the solution containing the precipitate add 3 *M* NH$_4$Ac solution, drop by drop, until the PbSO$_4$ dissolves. Lead acetate is very soluble. What conclusions can you draw regarding the extent of ionization of Pb(Ac)$_2$ in solution? Now add to the solution about 10 drops of 1 *M* (NH$_4$)$_2$SO$_4$ solution to reprecipitate PbSO$_4$. Explain.

9. To 5 drops of 0.1 *M* SnCl$_2$ solution add 1 ml. of water and saturate with H$_2$S. Brown SnS is precipitated. Add to the suspension an equal volume, about 1 ml., of 15 *M* NH$_4$OH and again saturate with H$_2$S. Note that the brown SnS does not dissolve.

   To 5 drops of 0.1 *M* SnCl$_2$ solution add 1 ml. of water and then add 2 drops of 3 percent H$_2$O$_2$ solution. Warm gently. Saturate the solution with H$_2$S; a yellow precipitate appears. Now add to the suspension an equal volume of 15 *M* NH$_4$OH and saturate with H$_2$S. The precipitate is found to dissolve. Explain the results of these two experiments.

10. To a small test tube containing 12 drops of 0.1 *M* Cu(NO$_3$)$_2$ solution and 12 drops of 0.1 *M* Cd(NO$_3$)$_2$ solution add enough water to make the total volume 3 ml. Add 6 drops of 6 *M* HCl solution and then saturate the solution with solid NH$_4$Cl. Pass H$_2$S into the solution, centrifuge, and divide the centrifugate into two equal portions. To one portion add 1 ml. of 2 *M* NaAc solution. To the other portion add 10 volumes of water. In each

case a precipitate is obtained. Explain what happens in each step of this experiment. (NOTE: *Cd++ ion in the presence of large amounts of Cl⁻ ion forms a complex ion, presumably having the composition; CdCl₄⁻⁻. For every CdCl₄⁻⁻ ion which dissociates, one Cd++ ion and four Cl⁻ ions are produced.*)

11. To 12 drops of 0.1 M arsenic acid test solution add 2 ml. of water, 3 drops of 6 M HCl, 1 drop of 1 M NH₄I, and heat the solution to boiling. Saturate the solution for several minutes with H₂S. Centrifuge. Add 1 ml. of water to the precipitate in the test tube. Now add 2 ml. of 6 M NaOH solution. Place a few drops of 0.1 M AgNO₃ solution on a piece of filter paper large enough to cover the mouth of the test tube. Have ready a very small piece of absorbent cotton. Now add a few granules of metallic aluminum to the test tube containing the solution, place the absorbent cotton well down into the mouth of the test tube, and cap the test tube with the piece of filter paper wet with the silver nitrate solution. Heat the solution very gently to start the reaction between the aluminum and the NaOH solution. In the course of a minute or two the filter paper will turn black. Aluminum reacts with the sodium hydroxide solution with the liberation of hydrogen. In the presence of trivalent arsenic, arsine gas is also produced. When the arsine gas comes in contact with the AgNO₃ on the filter paper, the Ag⁺ ion is reduced to metallic silver. Compare this test with a blank test using water in place of the arsenic acid solution. Equations for the reactions are:

$$2Al_{(s)} + 2OH^- + 2H_2O = 2AlO_2^- + 3H_2$$
$$As_2S_{3(s)} + 4OH^- = AsS_3^{---} + AsO_2^- + 2H_2O$$
$$AsO_2^- + 2Al_{(s)} + OH^- + H_2O = 2AlO_2^- + AsH_{3(g)}$$
$$6Ag^+ + AsH_{3(g)} + 3H_2O = 6Ag_{(s)} + H_3AsO_3 + 6H^+$$

(Note that the arsine test is applicable only to trivalent arsenic. Therefore, in this experiment NH₄I was added to reduce the pentavalent arsenic to the trivalent state. For a direct arsine test, 0.1 M NaAsO₂ should be used instead of the arsenic acid solution.)

12. To each of three test tubes add two drops of 0.1 M SnCl₂ solution. To one of these test tubes add 2 ml. of water, to the second add 1 ml. of water and 1 ml. of 12 M HCl, and to the third add 2 ml. of 12 M HCl. Now add 2 drops of 0.1 M HgCl₂ solution

to each of these three solutions, and allow them to stand for a minute or two. Write equations for the reactions involved in the formation of Hg_2Cl_2 and metallic mercury. Postulate an explanation for the inhibiting effect of the high Cl^- ion concentration present in the second and third tubes. (Ammonium chloride produces the same effect as HCl.)

13. Place 2 drops of 0.1 M $SbCl_3$ solution in a small test tube and add 10 drops of water. Make the solution alkaline with 6 M NH_4OH solution and then add 6 M HAc until just acidic. (Do not be concerned about the fact that the precipitate does not dissolve in the HAc.) Add 1 drop of 6 M HAc in excess. Heat the solution almost to boiling and drop into it a few small crystals of $Na_2S_2O_3$, sodium thiosulfate. Allow the test tube to stand for about five minutes; do not shake. Note the formation of the orange-red antimony oxysulfide at the interface.

Obtain a sample of an unknown from the laboratory instructor. In this sample each unknown ion is present at a minimum concentration of about .02 mole per liter. Reserve a part of this solution to make any tests you see fit (other than adding H_2S), to obtain preliminary information as to which ions may be present (Preliminary Experiment #4 will be of assistance here). If the original solution is alkaline and clear, it cannot contain Hg^{++} and Bi^{+++} ions. If the solution is alkaline and clear and NH_4OH is absent, then Hg^{++}, Bi^{+++}, Cd^{++}, and Cu^{++} ions are not present. Why?

C–D. Precipitation of the Copper-Arsenic Group. Test the solution with litmus paper *[1] to determine whether it is neutral, acidic, or alkaline. If acidic, add 5 drops of 3 percent H_2O_2[2] to 3 ml. of the solution in a 25 ml. Erlenmeyer flask, heat to boiling and then add 15 M NH_4OH drop by drop until the solution gives an alkaline reaction with litmus paper. Test the solution for alkalinity after the addition of each drop. Add 6 M HCl drop by drop until the solution is acidic to litmus (this will not require more than two or three drops). Now add one drop of 6 M HCl for each ml. of solution. The solution should be 0.3 M with respect to hydrogen ion.[3,4]

If the original solution is alkaline, add 6 M HCl drop by drop until just acidic and then add one drop of 6 M HCl for each ml. of solution. Now add the 5 drops of H_2O_2 and heat to boiling.

---

* All notes indicated by superior numbers are to be found at the end of their respective sections.

Procedure for the Analysis of the Copper-Arsenic Group

SCHEMATIC OUTLINE

Solution: Cu^{++}, Hg^{++}, Bi^{+++}, Cd^{++}, Pb^{++}, H_3AsO_4, H_3AsO_3, H_3SbO_4, Sb^{+++}, Sn^{++}, and Sn^{++++}.

Make 0.3 M in H^+ ion — Add 3% H_2O_2 — Heat — Add 1 M NH_4I — Add H_2S — Cool — Add H_2S.

(C–D)

Precipitate: CuS, HgS, Bi_2S_3, CdS, PbS, As_2S_3, Sb_2S_3, SnS_2.
Treat with 15 M NH_4OH, 6 M NH_4OH and H_2S.

(C–D–1)

| Residue: CuS, HgS, Bi_2S_3, CdS, PbS. Treat with 6 M HNO_3. **(C)** | | | Solution: $AsS_3{}^{---}$, $SbS_3{}^{---}$, $SnS_3{}^{--}$. Add 6 M HCl. **(D)** | | |

Residue: HgS. Dissolve in aqua regia. Add 0.1 M $SnCl_2$. **(C–1)**	Solution: Bi^{+++}, Cd^{++}, Pb^{++}, Cu^{++}. Add concentrated H_2SO_4. Evaporate.		Residue: As_2S_3. Add 6 M $NaOH$ and Al. **(D–1)**	Solution: Sb^{+++}, Sn^{++++}.	
Precipitate: Hg_2Cl_2 and Hg.	Ppt.: $PbSO_4$. Add 3 M NH_4Ac. Add 1 M K_2CrO_4. **(C–2)**	Solution: Bi^{+++}, Cd^{++}, Cu^{++}. Add 15 M NH_4OH. Blue color of $Cu(NH_3)_4{}^{++}$ indicates Cu^{++}. **(C–3)**	Black ppt. with $AgNO_3$. Test for arsenic.	Evaporate. Introduce iron wire. Add 0.1 M $HgCl_2$. **(D–2)**	Add 6 M NH_4OH. Add 6 M HAc. Add solid $Na_2S_2O_3$. **(D–3)**
	Ppt.: $PbCrO_4$.	Ppt.: $Bi(OH)_3$. Add Na_2SnO_2 Solution. **(C–4)**	Solution: $Cd(NH_3)_4{}^{++}$, $Cu(NH_3)_4{}^{++}$. Add 6 M HCl. Add NH_4Cl. Add H_2S. **(C–5)**	Ppt.: Hg_2Cl_2 and Hg. Test for tin.	Red color. Test for Sb.
		Ppt.: Bi. (black)			
			Ppt.: CuS	Solution: $CdCl_4{}^{--}$ Add 2 M $NaAc$. Add H_2S.	
				Ppt.: CdS. (yellow)	

Add one drop of 1 M NH_4I solution.[5] (Do not be disturbed if a precipitate appears either at this point or when NH_4OH is added.) Heat the solution to boiling and saturate for one minute with H_2S according to the procedure described on page 236. Heat to boiling again, and again saturate with H_2S for another minute (or add 15–20 drops of thioacetamide solution and continue heating). Even with iodide ion present the precipitation of arsenous sulfide may be slow. Cool the solution under the tap and saturate with H_2S once more.[6]

Pour the solution into a 10 ml. test tube; wash out the Erlenmeyer flask with 1 ml. of water, and add to the original solution in the test tube. Centrifuge for one minute. Decant the solution into the 25 ml. Erlenmeyer flask (which has in the meantime been cleaned). If the solution which is decanted contains a small amount of sulfide which, because of surface tension, has not settled during the centrifugation, it should be passed through a filter before pouring into the Erlenmeyer flask. Test this solution with methyl violet paper.[3] Adjust the H^+ ion concentration *if necessary* to 0.3 M by adding a drop or two of 3 M NH_4OH.[7] Again pass H_2S into the cold solution to test for completeness of sulfide precipitation [8] (or add 15–20 drops of 1 M thioacetamide solution and heat for 10 minutes). If precipitation is not complete saturate again with H_2S (or use thioacetamide solution in the usual manner) and add this solution to the test tube containing the previously precipitated sulfides and centrifuge again. When precipitation is complete discard the supernatant liquid after centrifugation. To the sulfides left in the bottom of the 10 ml. test tube after centrifugation add 2 ml. of water. Wash down the side of the test tube with an additional ml. of water. Stopper the test tube and shake to bring the sulfides into suspension. Centrifuge again and discard the supernatant.[9,10] Wash again. Add 1 ml. of 15 M NH_4OH to the precipitate in the 10 ml. test tube.

NOTE 1. *In making tests with litmus, dip a thin glass rod into the solution to be tested and press the end of the rod against the paper.*

NOTE 2. *The H_2O_2 is added to bring about the oxidation of Sn^{++} ion to Sn^{++++} ion. SnS forms a gelatinous precipitate which is dissolved only in $(NH_4)_2S_x$, while SnS_2 is readily soluble in this reagent. By converting Sn^{++} ion to Sn^{++++} ion it is possible to use $(NH_4)_2S$ instead of $(NH_4)_2S_x$ in separating the arsenic from the copper group. This procedure has two distinct advantages: (1) CuS is retained practically completely in the copper group, and (2) the objectionable later precipitation of free sulfur together with the sulfides is eliminated.*

NOTE 3. *If the ions of weak acids (such as acetate) are present it is advisable to determine and adjust the H^+ ion concentration to 0.3 M by means of methyl violet paper. To determine the color of methyl violet which corresponds to 0.3 M make a solution of 3 drops of 6 M HCl in 3 ml. of water and use this solution as a standard for comparison. If no methyl violet paper is available it may be made by "chalking" a piece of filter paper with an indelible pencil, wetting* *it with water and then drying it high over the Bunsen burner. In testing the acidity with methyl violet paper, make certain the paper is dry before judging its color.*

NOTE 4. *Ignore any precipitate which may be present in the original unknown solution, or in the solution after the H^+ ion concentration has been adjusted. Owing to the extremely low solubility of the sulfides of this group, any other slightly soluble salts will be converted to the corresponding sulfides by H_2S.*

NOTE 5. *The precipitation of As_2S_5 is a slow one while the precipitation of As_2S_3 is rapid. The iodide ion reduces the arsenic acid to arsenous acid and allows the precipitation to take place relatively rapidly. The iodine formed in this reaction is reduced to the iodide ion by the H_2S and can then react again with more arsenic acid. The iodide ion is therefore a catalyst for the precipitation of As_2S_3 from arsenic acid.*

NOTE 6. *The precipitation of CdS is much faster in a cold solution.*

NOTE 7. *H^+ ion is produced when the sulfides are precipitated.*

$$M^{++} + H_2S = MS_{(s)} + 2H^+$$

NOTE 8. *Free sulfur is usually formed when H_2S is passed into the acid solution. The original unknown or test solution may contain NO_3^- ion which in acid solution reacts with H_2S to form sulfur.*

$$3H_2S + 2NO_3^- + 2H^+ = 3S_{(s)} + 2NO + 4H_2O$$

NOTE 9. *If Cl^- ion is carried over with the precipitate when washing is insufficient, it will interfere in the separation of HgS from the other sulfides later. HgS is not soluble in HNO_3 but it will dissolve in HNO_3 if Cl^- is present (aqua regia).*

NOTE 10. *If a colloidal suspension is formed add 1 ml. of 4 M NH_4NO_3 to it or to 3 ml. of distilled water and use this solution for washing.*

C–D–1. *Separation of the Arsenic Group from the Copper Group.* To the suspension obtained from **C–D** add 6 M NH_4OH to make a total volume of about 3 ml. Now saturate this solution with H_2S (or add 15–20 drops of 1 M thioacetamide solution and heat for 10 minutes). In carrying out this operation use a glass tube drawn to a fine tip, connect this tube to the hydrogen sulfide generator and insert the tip into the test tube (see page 239). After saturating with H_2S, heat the solution gently but do not boil. Centrifuge and reserve the supernatant liquid which contains the dissolved sulfides of arsenic, antimony, and tin.

Repeat the NH_4OH–H_2S treatment of the precipitate and combine supernatant liquid with the one previously obtained. Label this solution D.

Add 3 ml. of water and 5 drops of 4 M NH$_4$NO$_3$ solution to the precipitate C in the test tube. Shake to obtain a suspension and centrifuge discarding the supernatant wash water. Repeat the washing (see note 10). Add 1 ml. of water to the precipitate.

C. Separation of HgS. To the suspended copper group sulfides C add an equal volume of 6 M HNO$_3$. Heat the mixture to boiling and continue to boil until no more precipitate appears to dissolve. If any residue remains, it should be either black or almost white (not brown) in color. Continue further treatment immediately. (It will be recalled that HgS does not dissolve in dilute HNO$_3$ while all other sulfides of the copper group dissolve readily. However, if chloride ion remains with the precipitate, dilute aqua regia will be formed upon the addition of nitric acid and mercury may dissolve. It was for this reason that the precipitate had to be washed thoroughly.) Cool the solution and centrifuge. The residue may contain HgS and free sulfur, and may also contain undissolved sulfides.[11] Pour the supernatant liquid into another 10 ml. test tube and label it C–2.

If the liquid in the test tube labeled C–2 contains floating particles on its surface, then, with the aid of a pointed glass rod, transfer the globule of free sulfur back to the test tube which may contain the HgS. Add 1 ml. of 15 M NH$_4$OH. Saturate the solution with H$_2$S (or add 15–20 drops of 1 M thioacetamide solution and heat for 10 minutes). If necessary agitate the globule of sulfur to bring it into solution. Any imbedded sulfides will not dissolve. Centrifuge if necessary and discard the supernatant liquid. Wash twice with 3 ml. of water, centrifuge, and discard the wash water.

On the other hand, if the test tube C–2 does not contain any floating particles on the surface of the solution, add 10 drops of water and 10 drops of 6 M HNO$_3$. Heat to dissolve residual copper group sulfides other than HgS. Centrifuge. Decant the solution, combining it with C–2. Any residue may now contain HgS, free sulfur, or both .[12]

Note 11. *The free sulfur formed in this reaction may imbed into it an appreciable amount of the sulfides which will then be protected against the action of the HNO$_3$. The sulfur must therefore be separated from the sulfides and the residual sulfides again treated with this reagent.*

Note 12. *A black residue is not in itself sufficient evidence for the presence of mercury. The specific test for Hg^{++} ion should be made. Nor does a white residue indicate the absence of mercury. With more concentrated HNO$_3$ a white insoluble double salt of mercuric nitrate and mercuric sulfide is formed.*

C–1. Test for Hg^{++} Ion. The residue from C which may contain HgS is to be dissolved in aqua regia and this solution is to be tested for the presence of Hg^{++} ion.

To the precipitate in the 10 ml. test tube add 2 drops of 15 M HNO_3 and 10 drops of 12 M HCl. Heat to boiling and agitate with a stirring rod until the greater part of the residue is dissolved. Add 1 ml. of water, centrifuge, if necessary, and then transfer the supernatant liquid to a small casserole. Evaporate the solution over an open flame (*use hood*) until only 2 or 3 drops of liquid remain.[13] (Do not evaporate to dryness; $HgCl_2$ is volatile.) Add 1 ml. of water and transfer the solution to a small test tube. Centrifuge, if necessary. Add 2 or 3 drops of 0.1 M $SnCl_2$ solution. If Hg^{++} ion is present a white precipitate of Hg_2Cl_2 will appear which will turn gray or black due to the further reduction of the Hg_2Cl_2 to metallic mercury.

Note 13. *A high Cl^- ion concentration inhibits the reaction between Sn^{++} and $HgCl_2$. Therefore it is necessary to remove the greater part of the HCl before this test is made. (See Preliminary Experiment 12.)*

C–2. Test for Pb^{++} Ion. Transfer the solution C–2 to a small casserole, and add 8 drops of 6 M H_2SO_4. Evaporate the solution until white, *dense* fumes of SO_3 appear.[14] These fumes are not to be confused with steam. They will appear only when there is practically no liquid left in the casserole. *Cool well*, and *very cautiously* add 1 ml. of water.[15] After cooling, pour the solution into a 10 ml. test tube; rinse the casserole with 0.5 ml. of water, and add the wash water to the solution. If a finely divided white precipitate of $PbSO_4$ appears, centrifuge. Pour the supernatant liquid into another test tube and label it C–3. Wash the precipitate with 0.5 ml. of water, centrifuge, and add the wash water to C–3. Do not allow any $PbSO_4$ to be carried over into solution C–3.

To the precipitate in the test tube add 1 ml. of 3 M NH_4Ac solution and heat. If a precipitate still appears in the solution, centrifuge and discard the residue. Add 2 drops of 1 M K_2CrO_4 solution to the clear solution. A yellow precipitate of $PbCrO_4$ confirms the presence of Pb^{++} ion. This precipitate should be centrifuged to be sure that it is yellow in color. Any white precipitate in the yellow test solution, which might have appeared inadvertently because of a previous error, might be mistaken for a yellow precipitate if the solution is not centrifuged.

NOTE 14. *The purpose of heating until dense SO_3 fumes appear is to make certain that all HNO_3 has been removed. $PbSO_4$ does not precipitate in the presence of HNO_3. The nitric acid is distilled from the solution just before the white fumes appear. Both the $NO_3{}^-$ ion and excess H^+ ion interfere with the precipitation of $PbSO_4$. With large H^+ ion concentration $HSO_4{}^-$ is formed and the concentration of $SO_4{}^{--}$ is consequently diminished. Furthermore, lead nitrate is a relatively weak salt. Therefore in HNO_3 solution both the Pb^{++} ion and $SO_4{}^{--}$ ion are present in relatively low concentrations.*

NOTE 15. *Except when dealing with very small quantities, water should never be added to concentrated H_2SO_4; rather H_2SO_4 is added to water. When adding water to H_2SO_4 the water may run down the side of the vessel below the surface of the H_2SO_4. Then the large amount of heat evolved may cause the rapid evaporation of the unmixed water and give rise to an explosion.*

C–3. Test for Cu^{++} Ion. To solution *C*–3 add 15 M NH_4OH solution drop by drop until alkaline. If copper is present, a deep blue color is obtained. If this is the case, add a few drops of NH_4OH in excess to be sure that the copper hydroxide first formed is dissolved with the formation of $Cu(NH_3)_4{}^{++}$ ion. Shake well while adding NH_4OH. The deep blue color is sufficient evidence for the presence of Cu^{++} ion. This solution, which may contain a precipitate, is to to be labeled *C*–4. Heat the solution gently.

C–4. Test for the Bi^{+++} Ion. If a precipitate appears [16] when NH_4OH is added in the test for Cu^{++} ion or after heating gently (a deep blue color may obscure the precipitate), centrifuge the solution. Label the clear supernatant solution *C*–5 and save for the Cd^{++} ion test. Add 3 ml. of water to the test tube; shake and centrifuge again. Discard the washings. Repeat the washing [17] and again discard the wash water.

Now pour on the precipitate in the test tube a freshly prepared cold solution of sodium stannite, Na_2SnO_2,[18] and heat. If bismuth is present, a black precipitate of metallic bismuth will appear. Allow to stand for 5 minutes if the black precipitate does not appear immediately.

NOTE 16. *Even though copper is absent and the solution is "water-white" the $Bi(OH)_3$ precipitate may be so slight that it is not easily recognized. Therefore, the confirmatory test for bismuth with sodium stannite should be made in all cases.*

NOTE 17. *$NH_4{}^+$ ion interferes with the reaction between Na_2SnO_2 and $Bi(OH)_3$. Therefore, a thorough washing of the precipitate is necessary.*

NOTE 18. *For the preparation of Na_2SnO_2 solution add 6 M NaOH drop* *by drop to 2 ml. of 0.1 M SnCl$_2$ solution until the precipitate of Sn(OH)$_2$, which first forms, just dissolves. The final solution probably will not be clear but will be opalescent.*

C–5. Test for Cd^{++} Ion. *If Cu^{++} ion is found to be present* in the solution proceed as follows. To the solution **C–5** contained in a 10 ml. test tube add 6 M HCl dropwise until the solution is just acidic. Then add 6 drops of 6 M HCl in excess. Saturate the solution with solid NH$_4$Cl. Decant and saturate the solution with H$_2$S (or add 15–20 drops of 1 M thioacetamide solution and heat for 10 minutes). Centrifuge, and discard the precipitate which is CuS. To the solution add 1 ml. of 2 M NaAc solution. When the H$^+$ ion concentration is sufficiently low a yellow precipitate of CdS will form if Cd^{++} ion is present.[19] If no precipitate appears saturate again with H$_2$S. No yellow precipitate indicates the absence of Cd^{++} ion in the original solution.

If Cu^{++} ion is not present, merely add 6 M HCl dropwise to solution **C–5** until it is just acidic. Saturate the solution with solid NH$_4$Cl. Add 1 ml. of 2 M NaAc solution and saturate with H$_2$S (or add 15–20 drops of 1 M thioacetamide solution and heat for 10 minutes). A yellow precipitate of CdS indicates the presence of Cd^{++} ion in the original solution.[19]

Note 19. *The high Cl$^-$ ion concentration in this solution forms the CdCl$_4^{--}$ ion, thereby lowering the Cd^{++} ion concentration to such an extent that the CdS is not precipitated provided the H$^+$ ion concentration is maintained at 0.3 M or greater. As the H$^+$ ion concentration is lowered by the addition of NaAc solution, the S^{--} ion concentration increases sufficiently to precipitate CdS. If Pb^{++} ion is not completely removed by the H$_2$SO$_4$ treatment (C–2), one might expect some PbS to precipitate with the CdS. However, Pb^{++} ion also forms complex ions with both Cl$^-$ and Ac$^-$ ions and does not precipitate as PbS in this solution even when the H$^+$ ion concentration is lowered to less than 10^{-3} M.*

D. Reprecipitation of the Arsenic Group Sulfides and the Separation of As$_2$S$_3$. Pour the solution **D** into a 25 ml. Erlenmeyer flask. Carefully add 6 M HCl drop by drop with constant stirring until just acidic. Be particularly careful when nearing the neutral point. At this point one drop of the HCl may cause a violent evolution of H$_2$S. Do not add more than one drop of HCl in excess (SnS$_2$ is soluble in relatively dilute HCl solution). Near the end-point test the solution for acidity as each drop of 6 M HCl is added.

When the solution is acidic, i.e., after one drop of 6 M HCl in excess has been added, transfer the solution and precipitate to a 10 ml. test tube. Use 10 drops of water to wash out the Erlenmeyer flask and add this to the transferred solution. Centrifuge and discard the supernatant liquid. Wash the precipitate with 3 ml. of water and discard the wash water. Drain the test tube well from excess water. Add 2 ml. of 12 M HCl and heat gently for 3 minutes or longer. Do not boil. Centrifuge the solution; pour the supernatant liquid into a test tube and label it **D–2.** Repeat the HCl treatment of the residue and combine the supernatant with **D–2.** The test **D–1** is to be made with the residue, which should be yellow it if consists only of As_2S_3.

D–1. Test for Arsenic. In this test any As_2S_3 is converted into AsH_3 which in turn reacts with $AgNO_3$ solution to produce black metallic silver.

To the residue from **D** add 1 ml. of water. Add 2 ml. 6 M NaOH solution. Any As_2S_3 will dissolve. Wet a piece of filter paper, large enough to cover the mouth of the test tube, with 0.1 M $AgNO_3$ solution. Have ready a small piece of absorbent cotton. Now add a few small pieces of metallic aluminum (pellets, not powder) to the solution; place the cotton well into the mouth of the test tube, and then cap the test tube with the filter paper, wet with the $AgNO_3$ solution. Heat the solution gently to initiate the reaction between the aluminum and the NaOH solution. If arsenic is present the underside of the filter paper will turn a gray or black color [20] due to the free silver formed by the reaction between the AsH_3 gas and the $AgNO_3$ solution,[21] (see Preliminary Experiment 11).

NOTE 20. *Do not carry out this experiment near the H_2S generator. Any appreciable amount of H_2S in the air will also discolor the $AgNO_3$ paper.*

NOTE 21. *This test is only applicable to arsenic in the trivalent state. Antimony in any form will not interfere. However, if the arsenic originally present is in the pentavalent state, and the test is carried out as indicated in the preceding directions, it is essential that the pentavalent arsenic be reduced to the trivalent state by means of Na_2SO_3. On the other hand, if the test is carried out in an acid medium not only will the pentavalent arsenic as well as the trivalent arsenic be reduced to arsine (AsH_3), but any antimony present will also be reduced to stibine (SbH_3), which resembles arsine very closely. In basic solution the test is specific for trivalent arsenic.*

D–2. Test for Tin. Transfer 1 ml. of the solution **D–2** to a casserole. Label the rest of the solution **D–3,** and reserve it for the antimony test. To **D–2** in the casserole add a few very small pieces of fine iron wire [22] and carefully heat the casserole over the open flame *in the hood* until all but a drop or two of the solution has evaporated (see Note 13).   Do not evaporate the solution completely to dryness. $SnCl_2$ is somewhat volatile and may be lost by heating too strongly.   Add 1 ml. of water, centrifuge, and pour the solution into a small test tube.   If a few pieces of carbon (from the wire) or metallic antimony carry over into the test tube, do not be concerned; they will not interfere with the test.   Add 2 drops of 0.1 M $HgCl_2$

NOTE 22.   *The iron reduces the stannic to stannous chloride.   The Fe^{++} ion, which is also formed, does not interfere with the test.*

---

solution.   A white or gray precipitate of Hg_2Cl_2 and Hg indicates the presence of tin in the original solution.

D–3.   Test for Antimony.   Transfer about 1 ml. of solution **D–3** to a casserole and evaporate about one-half of it (*use the hood*). Transfer the solution to a small test tube and add 6 M NH_4OH dropwise until the solution is just alkaline.   Make acidic with 6 M HAc.   Add 1 drop of 6 M HAc in excess and heat to boiling.   (Do not be disturbed if a precipitate which appeared in this procedure does not dissolve.)   Drop into the hot solution a small pinch of sodium thiosulfate, $Na_2S_2O_3$, crystals.   Do not agitate or disturb the surface. A two-phase system will form with the $Na_2S_2O_3$ in the bottom of the test tube and an orange-red colored antimony oxysulfide is produced at the interface if Sb^{+++} is present.   If no orange-red color appears, heat very gently and allow to stand.   No red coloration at the end of a few minutes indicates that Sb^{+++} ion was not present in the original solution.   A white precipitate at the interface of the two phases is only free sulfur.

Equations for Pertinent Reactions

$H_2O_2 + Sn^{++} + 2H^+ = Sn^{++++} + 2H_2O$

$Sn^{++++} + 2H_2S = SnS_{2(s)} + 4H^+$

$2H_3AsO_3 + 3H_2S = As_2S_{3(s)} + 6H_2O$

$2Sb^{+++} + 3H_2S = Sb_2S_{3(s)} + 6H^+$

$M^{++} + H_2S = MS_{(s)} + 2H^+$

$$(M^{++} \text{ is bivalent metal ion})$$

$2Bi^{+++} + 3H_2S = Bi_2S_{3(s)} + 6H^+$

$H_3AsO_4 + 2I^- + 2H^+ = I_2 + H_3AsO_3 + H_2O$

$I_2 + H_2S = 2H^+ + 2I^- + S_{(s)}$

$NH_4OH + H_2S = NH_4^+ + HS^- + H_2O$

$SnS_{2(s)} + HS^- + OH^- = SnS_3^{--} + H_2O$

$As_2S_{3(s)} + 3HS^- + 3OH^- = 2AsS_3^{---} + 3H_2O$

$Sb_2S_{3(s)} + 3HS^- + 3OH^- = 2SbS_3^{---} + 3H_2O$

$3MS_{(s)} + 2NO_3^- + 8H^+ = 3M^{++} + 2NO + 3S_{(s)} + 4H_2O$

$3HgS_{(s)} + 2NO_3^- + 6Cl^- + 8H^+ = 3HgCl_2 + 2NO + 3S_{(s)} + 4H_2O$

$2HgCl_2 + Sn^{++} = Sn^{++++} + Hg_2Cl_{2(s)} + 2Cl^-$

$Pb^{++} + SO_4^{--} = PbSO_{4(s)}$

$PbSO_{4(s)} + 2Ac^- = Pb(Ac)_2 + SO_4^{--}$

$Pb(Ac)_2 + CrO_4^{--} = PbCrO_{4(s)} + 2Ac^-$

$Cu^{++} + 4NH_3 = Cu(NH_3)_4^{++}$

$Bi^{+++} + 3NH_4OH = Bi(OH)_{3(s)} + 3NH_4^+$

$Sn^{++} + 4OH^- = SnO_2^{--} + 2H_2O$

$3SnO_2^{--} + 2Bi(OH)_{3(s)} = 2Bi_{(s)} + 3SnO_3^{--} + 3H_2O$

$Cd^{++} + 4Cl^- = CdCl_4^{--}$

$CdCl_4^{--} + H_2S = CdS_{(s)} + 2H^+ + 4Cl^-$

$SnS_3^{--} + 2H^+ = SnS_{2(s)} + H_2S$

$2AsS_3^{---} + 6H^+ = As_2S_{3(s)} + 3H_2S$

$2SbS_3^{---} + 6H^+ = Sb_2S_{3(s)} + 3H_2S$

$SnS_{2(s)} + 4H^+ = Sn^{++++} + 2H_2S$

$Sb_2S_{3(s)} + 6H^+ = 2Sb^{+++} + 3H_2S$

$As_2S_{3(s)} + 4OH^- = AsS_3^{---} + AsO_2^- + 2H_2O$

$AsO_2^- + 2Al + OH^- + H_2O = 2AlO_2^- + AsH_{3(g)}$

$6Ag^+ + AsH_{3(g)} + 3H_2O = 6Ag_{(s)} + H_3AsO_3 + 6H^+$

$Sn^{++++} + Fe = Fe^{++} + Sn^{++}$

$Sn^{++} + 2HgCl_2 = Sn^{++++} + Hg_2Cl_{2(s)} + 2Cl^-$

$Hg_2Cl_{2(s)} + Sn^{++} = Sn^{++++} + 2Hg_{(s)} + 2Cl^-$

$2Sb^{+++} + 2Na_2S_2O_3 + 3H_2O = Sb_2OS_{2(s)} + 4Na^+ + 2SO_4^{--} + 6H^+$

CHAPTER 14

The Aluminum-Zinc Group

Al^{+++}, Cr^{+++}, Fe^{+++}, Co^{++}, Ni^{++}, Fe^{++}, Mn^{++}, and Zn^{++} Ions

The aluminum-zinc group is precipitated in a solution which contains ammonium hydroxide, ammonium chloride, and ammonium sulfide ($NH_4OH + H_2S$). In this procedure the hydroxides of Al^{+++} and Cr^{+++} ions and the sulfides of Fe^{+++}, Fe^{++}, Ni^{++}, Co^{++}, Mn^{++}, and Zn^{++} ions are precipitated. With the silver and copper-arsenic groups eliminated, no other ions precipitate.

The Al^{+++}, Cr^{+++}, and Fe^{+++} ions constitute what is commonly called the aluminum group. The ions of the aluminum group are trivalent while those of the zinc group are bivalent in general. The ions of both groups show other valences besides two and three; however, when these same ions are trivalent it is convenient to place them in the aluminum group; and when they show a valence of two, they are designated as belonging to the zinc group. The ions of the zinc group form stronger and more soluble bases than those of the aluminum group and, accordingly, their salts are hydrolyzed to a smaller extent in water solution. Of the members of the zinc group, only zinc hydroxide is amphoteric. The ions of the aluminum group form very insoluble hydroxides. These ions are appreciably hydrolyzed by water, and when treated with solutions of $(NH_4)_2CO_3$ or Na_2CO_3, their hydroxides are precipitated. When $(NH_4)_2S$ is used as the precipitating reagent, aluminum and chromium are precipitated as hydroxides, while iron is precipitated as *ferric sulfide*, Fe_2S_3. Both aluminum and chromium hydroxides are amphoteric while ferric hydroxide does not display this property.

Of the alkaline earth group hydroxides, magnesium hydroxide is quite insoluble but it is by no means as insoluble as the hydroxides of aluminum and chromium. One might predict magnesium hydroxide to be precipitated with aluminum and chromium hydroxides according to the procedure indicated above. The precipitation of magnesium hydroxide is prevented by the addition of ammonium chloride to the precipitating reagent. The effect of the ammonium chloride is apparent; the high concentration of NH_4^+ ion, by the common ion effect, reduces the concentration of the OH^- ion sufficiently so that the product, $(Mg^{++})(OH^-)^2$, is less than the solubility product constant. Consequently, a mixture of ammonium hydroxide, ammonium chloride, and ammonium sulfide serves to precipitate the aluminum-zinc group, thereby separating the ions of this group from those of the alkaline earth and alkali metal groups.

Preliminary Experiments

1. In the following chart the ions of the zinc-aluminum group are listed horizontally and a number of reagents vertically. In the blank spaces provided in a similar chart made in your notebook give the products of the reactions when the specified reagent is added drop by drop to a solution of the ion in question. If the product is a precipitate, indicate this fact by denoting the solid phase as, for example, $Al(OH)_{3(s)}$. Indicate the color of all precipitates and solutions containing new products. If the reaction does not give a precipitate but produces new ions, indicate these in the appropriate places. If no reaction takes place as far as you can ascertain, write *no reaction*. From your knowledge of the chemical properties of these ions *fill in as many blank spaces as possible without carrying out the experiments. If you are not familiar with the reaction in question perform an experiment to obtain the desired information.*

2. Devise an experiment for the detection of Fe^{++} ion in the presence of Fe^{+++} ion. Carry out the experiment to verify your

conclusion. Use solutions containing these ions at a concentration of .02 molar.

Reagent Added	Al^{+++}	Cr^{+++}	Fe^{+++}	Fe^{++}	Co^{++}	Ni^{++}	Mn^{++}	Zn^{++}
6 M NaOH								
6 M NaOH in excess								
6 M NH₄OH								
6 M NH₄OH in excess								
NH₄OH + NH₄Cl (soln. 1 M in NH₄Cl)								
0.5 M Na₂CO₃								
H₂S in 0.3 M HCl								
(NH₄)₂S								

3. Devise and perform an experiment to identify Co^{++} ion in the presence of Ni^{++} ion. (.02 M solutions.)
4. Devise and carry out procedures to separate and identify the individual ions in each of the following groups. In each case use 3 ml. of solution containing each of the three ions in question at a concentration of .02 M.
   (a) Al^{+++}, Cr^{+++}, and Fe^{+++}
   (b) Al^{+++}, Mn^{++}, and Zn^{++}
   (c) Fe^{+++}, Zn^{++}, and Co^{++}
   (d) Cr^{+++}, Ni^{++}, and Mn^{++}
5. To 2 ml. of a solution containing Fe^{++} and Zn^{++} each at .02 M concentration, add 1 ml. of 1 M HAc and saturate with H₂S. Write the equation for the reaction which takes place. To the above solution now add NH₄OH until alkaline. What happens? Explain your results on the basis of the difference in solubility between ZnS and FeS.
6. To 3 ml. of 0.5 M Na₂HPO₄ solution add 4.8 ml. of 0.5 M NaH₂PO₄ solution. The concentration of the HPO_4^{--} ion in the mixture is approximately 0.192 M, while that of the $H_2PO_4^-$ ion is 0.31 M. Since the equilibrium constant for the following expression has a value of 6.2×10^{-8},

$$\frac{(H^+)(HPO_4^{--})}{(H_2PO_4^-)} = 6.2 \times 10^{-8}$$

it is evident that the concentration of the H^+ ion in this mixture is about 1×10^{-7} mole per liter, the same as that of pure water. Such a solution is one of the more common "buffer" solutions. In order to understand the manner in which a buffer solution functions, carry out the following experiments:

(a) To one-half (3.9 ml.) of the above mixture in a 25 ml. graduated cylinder add a few drops of phenolphthalein indicator and then slowly pour into this solution 0.1 M NaOH until the indicator changes color. Note the amount of NaOH solution used. What is the concentration of the H^+ ion at this point? (See indicator chart, page 83.)

(b) To the other portion of the buffer mixture add a few drops of methyl orange indicator in a 25 ml. graduated cylinder and then add 0.1 M HCl until the indicator changes color. Note the amount of HCl solution used. Now what is the concentration of the H^+ ion at this point? (See indicator chart, page 83.)

(c) Using 3.9 ml. of pure water instead of the buffer solution repeat experiments (a) and (b). (Note: The H^+ ion concentration is the same in pure water as in the buffer solution.)

(d) If the same amount of base and of acid used in (a) and (b), respectively, were added separately to pure water, what would be the concentration of the H^+ ion in each case? Compare with the results of (a) and (b). Explain the difference in behavior of these solutions.

(e) Write equations for the reactions taking place in (a) and (b). Disregard any reaction involving either H_3PO_4 or PO_4^{---} ion.

(f) Explain how a solution containing both NH_4OH and NH_4Cl can act as a buffer.

7. To 1 ml. of 6 M HNO$_3$ contained in a small casserole add 1 drop of 0.1 M Mn(NO$_3$)$_2$ solution. Add a small spatula-full of solid sodium bismuthate and heat to boiling. Add 1 ml. of water and pour into a test tube. Allow the solid to settle and note the purple color of the MnO_4^- ion.

8. To 1 ml. of water contained in a test tube add 3 drops of 0.1 M Mn(NO$_3$)$_2$ solution. Add 6 M NaOH until alkaline and then add 5 drops of the reagent in excess. Now add 5 drops of 3 per cent H_2O_2 solution. Note the formation of black MnO_2. The equation for the reaction is

$$Mn(OH)_{2(s)} + HO_2^- = MnO_{2(s)} + H_2O + OH^-$$

Centrifuge or filter and transfer the MnO_2 to a casserole. Add 1 ml. of 6 M HNO_3 and then add a small spatula-full of solid sodium bismuthate. Heat to boiling. Dilute with 1 ml. of water and pour the mixture into a 10 ml. test tube. After the residue has settled, note the purple color of the MnO_4^- ion in the solution.

9. Add 12 drops of 0.1 M $FeSO_4$ solution and 12 drops of 0.1 M $Zn(NO_3)_2$ solution to 2 ml. of water in a 10 ml. test tube. Make alkaline with 6 M NH_4OH and saturate with H_2S. Centrifuge or filter and wash the precipitate with 3 ml. of water. To the precipitate in a 10 ml. test tube add 3 ml. of a solution made by combining 2 parts of a saturated Na_2SO_4 solution with 1 part of a 2 M $NaHSO_4$ solution. Heat to boiling. Stir well or shake. Note that the FeS is dissolved by this reagent while the ZnS is not. Explain on the basis of the difference in the solubility product constants of ZnS and FeS.

10. To a small casserole add 12 drops of 0.1 M $Co(NO_3)_2$ solution, 12 drops of 0.1 M $Ni(NO_3)_2$ solution, 2 drops of 0.1 M $Zn(NO_3)_2$ solution, and then add 2 drops of 6 M HCl. Evaporate to dryness. Now add 2 ml. of a saturated solution of Na_2SO_4, 1 ml. of 2 M $NaHSO_4$ solution, and 10 drops of 3 M NH_4Ac solution. Saturate the solution with H_2S for at least one minute. No precipitate should appear at this point. Warm in the flame and gradually raise the temperature almost to boiling. A white precipitate of ZnS appears. Centifuge or filter the solution and to the supernatant liquid or the filtrate, as the case may be, add 6 M NH_4OH solution until alkaline. If no precipitate appears, saturate again with H_2S. A black precipitate is a mixture of CoS and NiS. Explain this experiment.

11. Add 1 drop of 0.1 M $Fe(NO_3)_3$ solution to 10 ml. of water Shake thoroughly. What is the concentration of the Fe^{+++} ion in this solution? Now add 6 drops of this solution to 3 ml. of water. What is the concentration of the Fe^{+++} ion in the latter solution? To the latter solution add 1 drop of 3 M HCl and 2 drops of 1 M KCNS solution. Note the sensitivity of this test.

12. Place 3 drops of 0.1 M $Al(NO_3)_3$ solution in a 10 ml. test tube, add 3 ml. of water, 3 drops of 3 M NH_4Ac solution, and 4 drops of aluminon reagent. Make the solution alkaline with 6 M NH_4OH, and heat. Note the formation of the red lake.

13. Prepare 3 ml. of a solution 0.02 M with respect to Fe^{++} and Zn^{++}

ions and 0.1 M in HAc. Saturate with H_2S; ZnS should precipitate. Now make the solution 0.1 M with respect to NaAc. FeS should now precipitate.

(a) What were the H^+ and S^{--} ion concentrations when the ZnS began to precipitate?

(b) What were their concentrations when NaAc was added?

(c) Show by calculation that the FeS could not have precipitated before the NaAc was added.

Obtain from the laboratory instructor a sample of a solution containing ions of the aluminum-zinc group only. If the solution is strongly alkaline and contains no NH_4OH, it is evident from the properties of the ions of this group that only Al^{+++}, Cr^{+++}, and Zn^{++} ions can be present. If the solution is acidic, all ions of the group may be present.

E–F. Precipitation of the Aluminum-Zinc Group.

Place 3 ml. of this solution in an Erlenmeyer flask. Reserve the remainder to make any tests you may see fit (other than adding $NH_4OH + H_2S$), to obtain preliminary information as to which ions may be present.

To 3 ml. of the unknown solution add 1 ml. 5 M NH_4Cl solution; make alkaline with 15 M NH_4OH and add 10 drops of the latter solution in excess. If no precipitate appears at this point, Al^{+++}, Cr^{+++}, and Fe^{+++} ions are absent. (Precipitated aluminum hydroxide is usually very finely divided and often is not visible. If it is doubtful that a precipitate is present, centrifuge the solution and examine carefully.) Saturate the solution, which may contain a precipitate, with H_2S.[1] Centrifuge and test the supernatant solution for complete precipitation by adding 2 drops of 15 M NH_4OH,[2] then heat, and again saturate with H_2S.[3] Combine any precipitate with that obtained originally. Wash the precipitate with 3 ml. of water and discard the washings. The collected precipitate may contain $Al(OH)_3$, $Cr(OH)_3$, FeS, NiS, CoS, MnS, and ZnS.

NOTE 1. *In a hot solution any $Cr(OH)_3$ present may be transformed into an insoluble form. This transformation is prevented by keeping the solution cold during the first precipitation.*

NOTE 2. *If the solution is not sufficiently alkaline during the first addition of H_2S, MnS will not precipitate. When more NH_4OH is added and the solution is again saturated with H_2S, the Mn^{++} ion, if present, may then be precipitated as the pink MnS.*

NOTE 3. *All the Zn^{++} ion may not be removed from the solution as ZnS during the first saturation with H_2S since under some circumstances the rate of the precipitation of this sulfide is low when the solution is cold. The ZnS will then precipitate from the hot solution.*

Procedure for the Analysis of the Aluminum-Zinc Group

SCHEMATIC OUTLINE

Solution: Al^{+++}, Cr^{+++}, Fe^{+++}, Fe^{++}, Mn^{++}, Zn^{++}, Co^{++}, and Ni^{++}.
   Add 5 M NH₄Cl and 15 M NH₄OH.
   Add H₂S.

(E–F)

Precipitate: $Al(OH)_3$, $Cr(OH)_3$, FeS, MnS, ZnS, CoS, NiS.
   Add saturated Na₂SO₄ and 2 M NaHSO₄.

(E–F–1)

Residue: ZnS, CoS, NiS.
Dissolve in 6 M HCl and 6 M HNO₃.
Evaporate to dryness.
Add saturated Na₂SO₄, and 2 M NaHSO₄.

(E)

Solution: Zn^{++}, Co^{++}, Ni^{++}.
Add H₂S.

(E–1)

Ppt.: ZnS. (white).

Solution: Co^{++}, Ni^{++}. Boil — Add Br₂ water.

Add 6 M KNO₂. (E–2)

Precipitate: K₃Co(NO₂)₆. (yellow).

Add 3 M NH₄OH and dimethylglyoxime. (E–3)

Precipitate: Nickel dimethylglyoxime. (red).

Solution: Al^{+++}, Cr^{+++}, Fe^{++}, Mn^{++}.
Add 6 M H₂SO₄ — boil.
Add Br₂ water. Boil — Add 6 M NH₄OH.

(F)

Precipitate: $Al(OH)_3$, $Cr(OH)_3$, $Fe(OH)_3$, $[Mn(OH)_3]$.
Dissolve in 3 M HCl.
Treat with 6 M NaOH.
Add 3% H₂O₂.

(F–2)

Residue: $Fe(OH)_3$. (MnO_2). (F–2)

Add 3 M HCl. Add 1 M KCNS. (red).

Solution: AlO_2^-, CrO_4^{--}.
Add 12 M HCl.
Add 6 M NH₄OH.

(F–3)

Ppt.: $Al(OH)_3$. Add 3 M HCl. Add aluminon reagent. Add 6 M NH₄OH.

Ppt.: $Al(OH)_3$ + dye (red).

Solution: CrO_4^{--}. Add 6 M HAc and 0.2 M Pb(Ac)₂.

(F–4)

Ppt.: PbCrO₄. (yellow).

Solution: Mn^{++}.
Add 6 M HNO₃.
Add sodium bismuthate.

(F–1)

Solution: MnO_4^-. (purple).

E–F–1. Separation of ZnS, CoS, and NiS. To the combined precipitates from **E–F**, contained in a 10 ml. test tube, add 3 ml. of a solution made by combining one part, by volume, of a saturated solution of Na₂SO₄ and one part of 2 M NaHSO₄.[4]

Agitate and stir the mixture vigorously for about two minutes. If any reaction occurs during this time, as may be observed by the evolution of gas, continue to stir until the reaction ceases. Do not heat. Centrifuge. Test residue, if any, with a small portion of the buffer solution (freshly prepared) to insure complete reaction and solution of $Al(OH)_3$, $Cr(OH)_3$, Fe_2S_3, FeS, and MnS, which may be present. Label the supernatant liquid **F.** This solution contains any or all of the ions: Cr^{+++}, Al^{+++}, Fe^{+++}, Fe^{++}, and Mn^{++}. The precipitate **E** may contain the undissolved sulfides of zinc, cobalt, and nickel. Wash the precipitate with 3 ml. of water and discard the washings. Add 1 ml. of 6 M HCl and 1 ml. of 6 M HNO_3 to the precipitate in the test tube. Heat to boiling and then transfer to a small casserole. Work the mass of sulfur with a stirring rod for several minutes; then remove and discard the sulfur.

Evaporate the solution to dryness. Remove the flame under the casserole just as the last drop is evaporating; that is, do not overheat the dry salt. With the aid of the capillary syringe add 1 ml. of 2 M $NaHSO_4$ solution to the salt in the casserole, after it has cooled, and pour into a 10 ml. test tube. Label this **E–1.** Rinse the casserole with 2 ml. of saturated Na_2SO_4 solution and add to **E–1.**

NOTE 4. *The Na_2SO_4 and $NaHSO_4$ produce a buffer solution with a hydrogen ion concentration of about 10^{-2} mole per liter. HSO_4^- ion is a relatively weak acid with a dissociation constant of 10^{-2}.*

$$\frac{(H^+)(SO_4^{--})}{(HSO_4^-)} = 10^{-2}$$

Since the ratio $\frac{(SO_4^{--})}{(HSO_4^-)}$ is approximately equal to one, the H^+ ion concentration is therefore approximately equal to 10^{-2} mole per liter. ZnS, CoS, and NiS do not dissolve rapidly in a solution of this H^+ ion concentration.

E–1. Test for Zn^{++} Ion. Add 10 drops of 3 M NH_4Ac solution to solution **E–1** which may contain the ions Zn^{++}, Ni^{++}, and Co^{++}. Saturate the cold solution with H_2S for at least one minute. Warm in a flame and gradually raise the temperature almost to boiling. If zinc is present, a white or very light gray [5] precipitate of ZnS will appear.[6]

Centrifuge and retain supernatant, which may contain Co^{++} and Ni^{++} ions.

In case the precipitate is too dark to identify it as ZnS, treat it with 1 ml. of cold 1 M HCl, centrifuge, decant the solution to another test tube, and make alkaline with 3 M NH_4OH. Any residual H_2S in the solution may precipitate ZnS at this point. If no precipitate of ZnS appears, saturate the solution with H_2S. This procedure should give a white or light gray precipitate if zinc is present, and eliminate any NiS or CoS which may have precipitated with ZnS in the buffer solution. If the precipitate is still too dark this operation may be repeated.

Heat the supernatant, which may contain Co^{++} and Ni^{++} ions, to boiling for several minutes to expel the H_2S. Add a few drops of bromine water [7] and continue heating. Add 1 ml. of water. Divide this solution into two equal portions to use for tests for Ni^{++} and Co^{++} ions. Label one of these portions *E–2* and the other *E–3*.

NOTE 5. *If this precipitate is allowed to stand, it may become darker in color due to the precipitation of some CoS or NiS or both. An initial white or gray precipitate is sufficient evidence for the presence of Zn^{++} ion. If equilibrium were attained CoS and NiS would be precipitated, but the rate of precipitation of these two sulfides is much lower than that for ZnS.*

NOTE 6. *A slight turbidity may be due to free sulfur. To distinguish sulfur from ZnS, make the solution distinctly acidic with HCl. The sulfur will not dissolve while the ZnS will.*

NOTE 7. *The purpose of adding the bromine water is to complete the removal of H_2S by oxidation to free sulfur.*

$$H_2S + Br_2^- = S_{(s)} + 2Br^- + 2H^+$$

E–2. Test for Co^{++} Ion. To the solution *E–2* add an equal volume of $6M$ KNO_2 solution. Warm and allow to stand for a few minutes. (If a white precipitate appears, it is probably $KHSO_4$ due to its high concentration in the medium.) A yellow- or olive-colored precipitate of $K_3[Co(NO_2)_6]$ indicates the presence of Co^{++} ion. If no yellow precipitate appears, add 3–5 drops of 6 M HAc and warm again before reaching a final conclusion.

E–3. Test for Ni^{++} Ion. To solution *E–3* add 6 M NH_4OH drop by drop [8,9] until the solution is alkaline. Add 4 drops of dimethylglyoxime reagent. A red precipitate of nickel dimethylglyoxime indicates the presence of Ni^{++} ion.

If Co^{++} ion is present a brown soluble cobalt dimethylglyoxime is first formed. In such a case it may be necessary to add more of the dimethylglyoxime reagent to bring about the precipitation of the nickel salt. If there is any doubt about the color of the precipitate, centrifuge or filter the solution.

NOTE 8. *If Fe^{+++} ion has not been completely removed, some $Fe(OH)_3$ may be precipitated at this point. Centrifuge or filter the solution to remove it.*

NOTE 9. *If the solution turns black at this point, it is because the H_2S has not been previously completely removed and NiS precipitates. If this is the case, make acidic with 6 M HCl, add 10 drops in excess, add 10 drops of 6 M HNO_3, place in a casserole and evaporate to dryness again. After dissolving the residue in water, add 6 M NH_4OH drop by drop until just alkaline and proceed as before.*

___

F. Separation of Mn^{++} from Al^{+++}, Cr^{+++}, and Fe^{++} Ions. If solution **F** is not clear, centrifuge and discard the precipitate. To the clear solution **F** add 10 drops of 6 M H_2SO_4, place it in a casserole and boil until the volume is reduced to about 1 ml. Add 3 drops of bromine water and continue heating to remove any excess Br_2.[10] Add water to restore the volume to 2 ml. Transfer to a 10 ml. test tube. Carefully make alkaline with 6 M NH_4OH and add 10 drops in excess.[11] (The solution should now be decidedly alkaline to litmus paper.) If Al^{+++}, Cr^{+++}, or Fe^{+++} ions are present a precipitate of the corresponding hydroxides will appear.[12] $Mn(OH)_2$ does not precipitate with this low OH^- ion concentration. Centrifuge and retain the solution for the Mn^{++} ion test. Label it **F–1.** Wash the precipitate with 2 ml. of water and add wash water to **F–1.** Repeat the washing and discard the wash water.

Dissolve the precipitate in 1 ml. of 3 M HCl and label it **F–2.**

___

NOTE 10. *The H_2S must be completely removed from the solution, otherwise MnS will form when the NH_4OH is added. This will vitiate the separation of Mn^{++} ion from the other ions. Besides oxidizing the H_2S to free sulfur, the bromine oxidizes Fe^{++} ion to Fe^{+++} ion. This procedure is carried out in order to obtain $Fe(OH)_3$ rather than $Fe(OH)_2$. $Fe(OH)_3$ is less soluble and not as gelatinous as $Fe(OH)_2$.*

NOTE 11. *Excess NH_4OH is added here to retain in solution, as $Zn(NH_3)_4^{++}$ ion, any Zn^{++} ion which may be present because of the partial solution of ZnS by the buffer solution in E–F–1.*

NOTE 12. *In alkaline solution oxygen of the air oxidizes Mn^{++} ion with the consequent formation of insoluble $Mn(OH)_3$. A small amount of $Mn(OH)_3$ appearing at this point will be later converted to MnO_2. This will not interfere with other tests unless present in relatively large amounts. It is therefore desirable that the student make this separation as rapidly as possible.*

___

F–1. Test for Mn^{++} Ion. Transfer 5 drops of the solution **F–1,** which may contain Mn^{++} ion, to a casserole and add 1 ml. of 6 M HNO_3. Now add a very small amount of solid sodium bismuthate (from the tip of the spatula). If Mn^{++} ion is present, a purple color will form due to the MnO_4^- ion. This test for Mn^{++} ion is a very sensitive one. In order to make certain that Mn^{++} ion was in the original unknown and not present as an impurity, compare the test with that of a known solution. If this color does not appear, heat to boiling. If the brown color of the sodium bismuthate obscures the color of the solution, allow it to stand for a time until the effervescence has stopped, and then centrifuge. If the color is very intense, dilute the solution with water.[13,14]

If Zn^{++} ion was not found in test **E–1** and if it was present in the original solution in small amount, an appreciable amount of the ZnS may have been dissolved by the buffer solution in **E–F–1**. In such a case, reserve the remainder of solution **F–1** for the auxiliary Zn^{++} ion test **E–X**. If Zn^{++} ion was found in **E–1**, the remainder of the solution **F–1** may be discarded.

NOTE 13. *The MnO_4^- ion first formed may be destroyed by reaction with the Br^- ion.*

$$10Br^- + 2MnO_4^- + 16H^+ = 2Mn^{++} + 5Br_2 + 8H_2O$$

If no purple color is obtained, heat the solution to drive off the Br_2 and then add another pinch of sodium bismuthate. This reaction also takes place with Cl^- ion. It is for this reason that reagents contributing this ion to the solution have been avoided.

NOTE 14. *If no positive test for Mn^{++} ion is obtained, it is possible that the manganese was retained with the hydroxides, $Fe(OH)_3$, $Cr(OH)_3$, and $Al(OH)_3$, as $Mn(OH)_2$. In such an event the Mn^{++} ion may be detected in F–2.*

E–X. Auxiliary Zn^{++} Ion Test. To the remainder of the solution **F–1** add 6 *M* HCl until acidic and then add 2 drops of the reagent in excess. Transfer the solution to a casserole and evaporate to dryness. Now add 10 drops of 2 *M* $NaHSO_4$ solution, 1 ml. of saturated Na_2SO_4 solution, and 5 drops 3 *M* NH_4Ac solution. Pour the solution into a small test tube, cool if necessary, and saturate with H_2S for at least one minute (or add 15–20 drops of 1 *M* thioacetamide solution and heat for ten minutes). Warm in a flame and gradually raise the temperature almost to boiling. If Zn^{++} ion is present at this point, a white or very light gray precipitate of ZnS will appear. If no precipitate of ZnS appears either here or in **E–1**, Zn^{++} ion is absent in the original solution.

F–2. Test for Fe^{+++} Ion. Add 2 ml. of 6 *M* NaOH to the acid solution **F–2** which may contain Fe^{+++}, Cr^{+++}, and Al^{+++} ions. At this point a reddish brown precipitate indicates the presence of Fe^{+++} ion although this color may be somewhat obscured if Cr^{+++} ion is also present. Add 1 ml. of 3 percent H_2O_2.[15] Heat to boiling and keep hot for several minutes. Neutralize the solution with 12 M HCl, then make alkaline with 6 M NaOH, adding 5 drops in excess. Heat to boiling. Centrifuge the solution and pour the supernatant liquid through a filter, retaining the filtrate for tests for aluminum and chromium and label it **F-3**. Wash the precipitate with 3 ml. of water and centrifuge again, discarding the wash water. Repeat the washing.[16]

To the precipitate add 1 ml. of 3 M HCl. Centrifuge the solution, if necessary, and pour the supernatant solution into another test tube. (Save the residue.)[17] Dilute with 1 ml. of water. Add 2 drops of 1 M KCNS solution. A deep red color indicates or confirms the presence of Fe^{+++} ion. A very light pink color which might appear at this point may be due to a small amount of iron which has crept into the solution as an impurity in the reagents. This test for the Fe^{+++} ion is a very sensitive one. Compare the test with that of a solution known to contain 0.01 M Fe^{+++} ion.

NOTE 15. *If Mn^{++} ion was originally present and was not washed out of the hydroxides or was withheld as $Mn(OH)_3$, a black precipitate of MnO_2 will appear at this point. It will not interfere with the test for Fe^{+++} ion.*

If a black precipitate does appear here, separate it either by decantation or centrifugation, wash, and then carry out test for manganese by the addition of HNO_3 and $NaBiO_3$ as described in F-1, page 292.

Care should be taken to make certain that the CrO_2^- ion is completely oxidized by the H_2O_2 to CrO_4^{--} ion; otherwise it may interfere with the test for the Al^{+++} ion later in the procedure, in the event Al^{+++} ion is also present.

NOTE 16. *If the precipitate is not thoroughly washed, the $NaOH$ retained with the precipitate will neutralize the HCl added later and the $Fe(OH)_3$ may not be completely dissolved.*

NOTE 17. *If Mn^{++} ion was not detected in F-1 and if a black residue remains at this point, carry out the following test for the Mn^{++} ion. Transfer the residue to a small casserole with 2 ml. of 6 M HNO_3. Add one small spatula-full of solid sodium bismuthate and heat to boiling. Dilute with 2 ml. of water and centrifuge if necessary. If the black residue contained MnO_2 the resulting solution will appear purple in color due to the MnO_4^- ion. (See F-1.)*

F-3. Test for Al^{+++} Ion. The solution **F-3** may contain AlO_2^- ion and CrO_4^{--} ion. Carefully neutralize the solution with 12 M HCl. Make alkaline with 6 M NH_4OH and add 10 drops of the NH_4OH in excess. Heat. A white gelatinous precipitate indicates the presence of Al^{+++} ion in the original solution. If the solution is not yellow an appreciable amount of CrO_4^{--} ion is not present.

Filter [18] (do not centrifuge) this solution, even though it may appear to contain no precipitate. Retain the filtrate for the test for chromium and label it *F–4*. Wash the precipitate with 1 ml. of water. Discard the wash water. Wash again. Pour 1 ml. of 3 *M* HCl over the filter and collect the solution in a 10 ml. test tube. Wash the filter with 1 ml. of water and add this to the acid solution. Add 3 drops of 3 *M* NH₄Ac solution and 3 drops of aluminon reagent.[19] Heat gently and allow to stand for 5 minutes. Add ammonium carbonate reagent until the solution is slightly alkaline, then add 5 drops in excess. A red flocculent precipitate of Al(OH)₃ with the red dye adsorbed to it indicates presence of Al⁺⁺⁺ in the original solution.

It is imperative that the color of the final aluminon precipitate be compared with that obtained by the identical treatment of an 0.02 *M* Al(NO₃)₃ solution before deciding whether Al⁺⁺⁺ ion is present.

If the color obtained in the aluminon test is not identical with that of the blank, the difference may be due to the presence of Fe(OH)₃ or Cr(OH)₃, small amounts of which may have inadvertently been carried through. If such is the case, add 2 drops of concentrated HNO₃ to the aluminon precipitate, heat, and repeat procedures *F–2* and *F–3*.

Note 18. *The Al(OH)₃ precipitate is often very difficult to observe at this point. Any H₂O₂ which may be present may decompose and the oxygen liberated will adhere to the Al(OH)₃ causing it to rise to the surface of the solution. This effect makes centrifugation inadvisable.*

Note 19. *These reagents must be added to the solution in the order given in the test. The conditions for the formation of the red lake have been determined empirically.*

F–4. Test for CrO₄⁻⁻ Ion. To the solution which contains the CrO₄⁻⁻ ion (it should be yellow if present) add 6 *M* acetic acid [20] drop by drop until the solution is just acidic. Add a few drops of 0.2 *M* Pb(Ac)₂ solution. A deep yellow precipitate of PbCrO₄ indicates the presence of chromium in the original solution.

Note 20. *If the yellow color of the CrO₄⁻⁻ ion disappears when the HAc is added, the CrO₄⁻⁻ has probably been reduced to the green Cr⁺⁺⁺ ion by H₂O₂ which was previously not removed by boiling. If this should happen, Cr(OH)₃ may again be precipitated upon the addition of NH₄OH. The Cr(OH)₃ may then be converted to the CrO₄⁻⁻ ion and the test repeated.*

Equations for Pertinent Reactions

$Al^{+++} + 3NH_4OH = Al(OH)_{3(s)} + 3NH_4^+$

$Cr^{+++} + 3NH_4OH = Cr(OH)_{3(s)} + 3NH_4^+$

$2Fe^{+++} + 3S^{--} = Fe_2S_{3(s)}$

$M^{++} + S^{--} = MS_{(s)}$ $\qquad (M^{++} = Co^{++}, Ni^{++}, Mn^{++}$ and $Zn^{++})$

$Al(OH)_{3(s)} + 3H^+ = Al^{+++} + 3H_2O$

$MnS_{(s)} + 2H^+ = Mn^{++} + H_2S$

$CoS_{(s)} + 2NO_3^- + 4H^+ = Co^{++} + 2NO_2 + S_{(s)} + 2H_2O$

$H_2S + Br_2 = S_{(s)} + 2H^+ + 2Br^-$

$Co^{++} + 2HAc + 7NO_2^- + 3K^+$
$$= NO + H_2O + 2Ac^- + K_3Co(NO_2)_{6(s)}$$

$Ni^{++} + 2NH_4OH + 2C_4H_6N_2O_2H_2 = NiC_8H_{14}N_4O_{4(s)} + 2NH_4^+ + 2H_2O$

$Fe^{+++} + 3NH_4OH = Fe(OH)_{3(s)} + 3NH_4^+$

$4Mn^{++} + O_2 + 8NH_4OH + 2H_2O = 4Mn(OH)_{3(s)} + 8NH_4^+$

$2Mn^{++} + 5NaBiO_{3(s)} + 14H^+ = 2MnO_4^- + 5Bi^{+++} + 5Na^+ + 7H_2O$

$10Br^- + 2MnO_4^- + 16H^+ = 2Mn^{++} + 5Br_2 + 8H_2O$

$Fe^{+++} + 3OH^- = Fe(OH)_{3(s)}$

$Al(OH)_{3(s)} + OH^- = AlO_2^- + 2H_2O$

$Cr(OH)_{3(s)} + OH^- = CrO_2^- + 2H_2O$

$2CrO_2^- + 3HO_2^- = 2CrO_4^{--} + OH^- + H_2O$

$Fe(OH)_{3(s)} + 3H^+ = Fe^{+++} + 3H_2O$

$Fe^{+++} + 6CNS^- = Fe(CNS)_6^{---}$

$2Mn(OH)_{3(s)} + HO_2^- = 2MnO_{2(s)} + OH^- + 3H_2O$

$2MnO_{2(s)} + 3NaBiO_{3(s)} + 10H+$
$$= 2MnO_4^- + 3Bi^{+++} + 3Na^+ + 5H_2O$$

$CrO_4^{--} + PbAc_2 = PbCrO_{4(s)} + 2Ac^-$

CHAPTER 15

The Alkaline
Earth Group
of Ions

Ba^{++}, Sr^{++}, Ca^{++}, and Mg^{++} Ions

The alkaline earth metals and magnesium are all included in the second main group of the periodic table. All exhibit single valence, plus two; accordingly, they form only one series of compounds. These elements are highly electropositive and therefore they are excellent reducing agents. The hydroxides of these elements are strong and may be regarded as completely ionized in aqueous solutions; they show no amphoteric properties. The ions of these elements are not hydrolyzed, and they show little tendency to form complex ions. However, they are characterized by the formation of a relatively large number of slightly soluble salts.

Calcium, strontium, and barium resemble each other very closely in their physical and chemical properties. Magnesium, on the other hand, is less electropositive than the alkaline earth elements and differs chemically from them in many respects. In the analytical procedures magnesium is separated from the alkaline earth ions and treated separately.

Barium Ion, Ba^{++} — Strontium Ion, Sr^{++} — Calcium Ion, Ca^{++}. Tables 14, 15, and 16 list some of the slightly soluble compounds of these ions in equilibrium with their saturated solutions. These compounds are arranged according to decreasing concentration of the metal ion at equilibrium. Although there are many other slightly soluble compounds of these ions, the tables give those most frequently encountered by the student in the separation and identification of the ions according to the analytical procedures. In addition, where accurate quantitative data are lacking regarding the solubility of the compounds, no attempt has been made to place them in the tables. An examination of the three tables demonstrates the similarity of the alkaline earth ions.

TABLE 14

EQUILIBRIA INVOLVING BARIUM ION

Decreasing Concentration of Ba^{++} Ion		
$Ba^{++} + 2OH^-$	$= Ba(OH)_{2(s)}$
$Ba^{++} + 2F^-$	$= BaF_{2(s)}$
$Ba^{++} + S_2O_3^{--}$	$= BaS_2O_{3(s)}$
$Ba^{++} + SiF_6^{--}$	$= BaSiF_{6(s)}$
$Ba^{++} + SO_3^{--}$	$= BaSO_{3(s)}$
$Ba^{++} + C_2O_4^{--}$	$= BaC_2O_{4(s)}$
$Ba^{++} + 2IO_3^-$	$= Ba(IO_3)_{2(s)}$
$Ba^{++} + CO_3^{--}$	$= BaCO_{3(s)}$
$Ba^{++} + CrO_4^{--}$	$= BaCrO_{4(s)}$
$Ba^{++} + SO_4^{--}$	$= BaSO_{4(s)}$
$3Ba^{++} + 2PO_4^{---}$	$= Ba_3(PO_4)_{2(s)}$

TABLE 15

EQUILIBRIA INVOLVING STRONTIUM ION

Decreasing Concentration of Sr^{++} Ion		
$Sr^{++} + 2OH^-$	$= Sr(OH)_{2(s)}$
$Sr^{++} + CrO_4^{--}$	$= SrCrO_{4(s)}$
$Sr^{++} + 2F^-$	$= SrF_{2(s)}$
$Sr^{++} + SO_4^{--}$	$= SrSO_{4(s)}$
$Sr^{++} + C_2O_4^{--}$	$= SrC_2O_{4(s)}$
$Sr^{++} + CO_3^{--}$	$= SrCO_{3(s)}$
$3Sr^{++} + 2PO_4^{---}$	$= Sr_3(PO_4)_{2(s)}$

The molar solubility of some of the members of these tables is very nearly the same. Accordingly, the order may be reversed by making the concentration of the anion of the more soluble salt relatively high. For example, $BaCO_3$ is only slightly less soluble than $Ba(IO_3)_2$. On the basis of the order

TABLE 16

EQUILIBRIA INVOLVING CALCIUM ION

Decreasing Concentration of Ca^{++} Ion		
$Ca^{++} + CrO_4^{--}$	$= CaCrO_{4(s)}$
$Ca^{++} + 2OH^-$	$= Ca(OH)_{2(s)}$
$Ca^{++} + 2IO_3^-$	$= Ca(IO_3)_{2(s)}$
$Ca^{++} + SO_4^{--}$	$= CaSO_{4(s)}$
$3Ca^{++} + 2PO_4^{---}$	$= Ca_3(PO_4)_{2(s)}$
$Ca^{++} + 2F^-$	$= CaF_{2(s)}$
$Ca^{++} + SO_3^{--}$	$= CaSO_{3(s)}$
$Ca^{++} + CO_3^{--}$	$= CaCO_{3(s)}$
$Ca^{++} + C_2O_4^{--}$	$= CaC_2O_{4(s)}$

given in Table 14; CO_3^{--} ion reacts with a saturated solution of $Ba(IO_3)_2$ to produce solid $BaCO_3$. It must be remembered that the order in these tables is based entirely upon the concentration of the positive ion at equilibrium with the slightly soluble salt.

Ammonium hydroxide does not give a precipitate with solutions containing the ions, Ba^{++}, Ca^{++}, and Sr^{++}. The most insoluble hydroxide of the three ions is $Ca(OH)_2$, but even in this case NH_4OH does not furnish a high enough concentration of OH^- to precipitate $Ca(OH)_2$. A small amount of precipitate of $CaCO_3$ might be formed with this reagent due to the presence of CO_3^{--} ions produced by absorption of CO_2 from the atmosphere. In dealing with this group it is, therefore, essential that all precipitating reagents be as free as possible from CO_3^{--} ions.

Ammonium carbonate or sodium carbonate precipitates from neutral or alkaline solutions of these ions the corresponding relatively insoluble *carbonates.* These carbonates are somewhat soluble in solutions containing ammonium salts of strong acids. This effect is due to the hydrolysis of the NH_4^+ with the eventual production of HCO_3^- ions as the following equilibrium system demonstrates.

$$MCO_{3(s)} \qquad = M^{++} \qquad + CO_3^{--}$$
$$+$$
$$NH_4^+ + H_2O \quad = NH_4OH + H^+ \qquad\qquad (4)$$
$$\Updownarrow$$
$$HCO_3^-$$

$$(M = Ca, \; Sr, \; or \; Ba)$$

This process uses up CO_3^{--} which can be regenerated only by more MCO_3 going into solution.

The alkaline earth carbonates are readily soluble in solutions of acids.

$$MCO_{3(s)} = M^{++} + CO_3^{--}$$
$$+$$
$$H^+ \qquad\qquad (5)$$
$$\Updownarrow$$
$$HCO_3^- + H^+ = H_2CO_3 = H_2O + CO_{2(g)}$$

The H^+ ion combines with CO_3^{--} to first produce HCO_3^- ion. With relatively high H^+ ion concentration the H_2CO_3 produced exceeds the solubility of CO_2 in water at one atmosphere pressure. This effect demands a supply of HCO_3^- ions which in turn requires the production of more CO_3^{--} ions, and the latter process involves solution of MCO_3. Acetic acid produces sufficient H^+ ions to dissolve the carbonates of this group with the liberation of CO_2. The alkaline earth metal carbonates are also somewhat soluble in H_2CO_3 solutions. Obviously, in this case CO_2 is not liberated, but the increased solubility is due to formation of HCO_3^- ion.

$$MCO_{3(s)} = M^{++} \qquad + CO_3^{--}$$
$$+$$
$$H_2CO_3 \quad = HCO_3^- + H^+ \qquad\qquad (6)$$
$$\Updownarrow$$
$$HCO_3^-$$

Water of "temporary hardness" contains Ca^{++} and HCO_3^- ions in appreciable quantities, which have been produced by the above process (6) from limestone and water containing H_2CO_3.

The addition of SO_4^{--} ion to solutions containing the alkaline earth metal ions causes the precipitation of the *sulfate* in each case. Of these, $BaSO_4$ is the least and $CaSO_4$ the most soluble. The molar solubility of $CaSO_4$ is about 800 times as great as that of $BaSO_4$. The solubility of all insoluble sulfates is increased only slightly by the addition of very strong acids. This small solubility effect of H^+ ion is due to the fact that H^+ and SO_4^{--} ions have some tendency to combine to form HSO_4^- ion. In contrast to the HCO_3^- ion, the HSO_4^- ion is a moderately strong acid. In .01 M solutions the extent of ionization of the HSO_4^- ion is about 65 percent. Since a saturated solution of $BaSO_4$ produces such a small concentration of SO_4^{--} ion its solubility is increased only to an inappreciable extent in the presence of strong acids. $SrSO_4$ and $CaSO_4$, however, are considerably more soluble in such solutions.

A solution containing an appreciable concentration of CrO_4^{--} ion will precipitate *barium chromate, strontium chromate,* and *calcium chromate.* $BaCrO_4$ is the least soluble and $CaCrO_4$ the most soluble of the group. The molar solubility of $CaCrO_4$ is almost 10,000 times as great as that of $BaCrO_4$, while the molar solubility of $SrCrO_4$ is about 400 times that of $BaCrO_4$. Since the $HCrO_4^-$ ion is a very weak acid, strong acids will dissolve $BaCrO_4$. The equilibrium involved is

$$BaCrO_{4(s)} = Ba^{++} + CrO_4^{--}$$
$$+$$
$$H^+ \qquad\qquad (7)$$
$$\updownarrow$$
$$2HCrO_4^- = Cr_2O_7^{--} + H_2O$$

It is obvious that $BaCrO_4$ cannot be precipitated from solutions of high H^+ ion concentration.

Acetic acid does not furnish sufficient H^+ ions to shift the equilibrium (7) to the right appreciably. The situation is somewhat different with $SrCrO_4$ and $CaCrO_4$. Since these chromates are so much more soluble than $BaCrO_4$ they furnish considerable quantities of CrO_4^{--} ions in their saturated solutions. In these solutions the concentration of the CrO_4^{--} ion is sufficiently high so that acetic acid will dissolve the solid chromate. In other words, solutions containing acetic acid and Sr^{++} or Ca^{++} ions will not give a precipitate of $SrCrO_4$ or of $CaCrO_4$ upon the addition of soluble chromate. This serves as a means of separating Ba^{++} ion from Sr^{++} and Ca^{++} ions.

Ammonium oxalate precipitates *barium, strontium,* and *calcium oxalates.* The solubility of all three salts is of the same order of magnitude; BaC_2O_4 is only about 8 times as soluble as CaC_2O_4 and twice as soluble as SrC_2O_4 in terms of moles per liter of solution. Strong acids and even hot acetic acid will dissolve BaC_2O_4 readily. The same is true for SrC_2O_4 but CaC_2O_4 is somewhat less soluble and, although it is soluble in solutions containing a high concentration of H^+ ion, it fails to dissolve to a large extent in acetic acid solutions. This result gives a method for separating Ca^{++} ion from Sr^{++} and Ba^{++} ions. Since both $H_2C_2O_4$ and $HC_2O_4^-$ ion are moderately weak acids the solubility of relatively insoluble oxalates in solutions of strong acids can be explained by equilibrium considerations similar to those of equations (5) and (7). In the precipitation of CaC_2O_4 by ammonium oxalate solution it is desirable to add NH_4OH. The latter tends to prevent the hydrolysis of the NH_4^+ ion, thereby decreasing the concentration of H^+ ion in the solution, a condition necessary for more complete precipitation.

In neutral solutions containing Ba^{++}, Sr^{++}, and Ca^{++} ions, Na_2HPO_4 solution precipitates the corresponding salts of these ions.

$$M^{++} + HPO_4^{--} = MHPO_{4(s)} \qquad (8)$$

In the presence of NH_4OH the normal salts are precipitated since

$$HPO_4^{--} + OH^- = PO_4^{---} + H_2O \qquad (9)$$

and $\qquad 3M^{++} + 2PO_4^{--} = M_3(PO_4)_{2(s)} \qquad (10)$

The dihydrogen phosphate salts, $M(H_2PO_4)_2$, are relatively soluble. Both $M_3(PO_4)_2$, and $MHPO_4$ are readily soluble in dilute solutions of strong acids and even in acetic acid, due to the formation of the HPO$_4^{--}$ and H$_2$PO$_4^-$ ions, respectively.

Flame Tests. When heated in the Bunsen flame, barium salts impart to it a yellowish green color; strontium salts, a bright red color; and calcium salts, a brick red color. When present in a mixture of salts the color due to either barium or calcium does not persist long.

Magnesium Ion, Mg^{++}. Magnesium differs markedly from the alkaline earth metals in that its sulfate and chromate are highly soluble and its oxalate and carbonate are moderately soluble. It is apparent that the same reagents cannot be used for the precipitation and separation of magnesium as for the alkaline earth metal ions. The following table gives a list of slightly soluble magnesium compounds in equilibrium with their ions and arranged in the order of decreasing Mg^{++} ion concentration.

TABLE 17

EQUILIBRIA INVOLVING MAGNESIUM ION

Decreasing Concentration of Mg^{++} Ion		
	Mg^{++} + C$_2$O$_4^{--}$	= MgC$_2$O$_{4(s)}$
	Mg^{++} + CO$_3^{--}$	= MgCO$_{3(s)}$
	Mg^{++} + 2F$^-$	= MgF$_{2(s)}$
	3Mg^{++} + 2PO$_4^{---}$	= Mg$_3$(PO$_4$)$_{2(s)}$
	Mg^{++} + 2OH$^-$	= Mg(OH)$_{2(s)}$
	Mg^{++} + NH$_4^+$ + PO$_4^{---}$	= MgNH$_4$PO$_{4(s)}$

Alkali hydroxides and ammonium hydroxide precipitate **magnesium hydroxide** from solutions containing Mg^{++} ion. The Mg(OH)$_2$ is not soluble in an excess of any of these reagents. On the other hand, it is soluble in the presence of appreciable amounts of NH$_4^+$ ion. The precipitation of the hydroxide by NH$_4$OH may be expressed by

$$Mg^{++} + 2NH_4OH = Mg(OH)_{2(s)} + 2NH_4^+ \qquad (11)$$

It is evident that the presence of NH$_4^+$ ions in excess decreases the concentration of the OH$^-$ ion; this effect is sufficient to cause the Mg(OH)$_2$ to dissolve. In other words, the equilibrium above is shifted to the left. Advantage is taken of this property in the separation of Ba^{++}, Sr^{++}, and Ca^{++} ions from Mg^{++} ion. To the solution containing all these ions is added a solution containing NH_4OH and $(NH_4)_2CO_3$. $CaCO_3$, $SrCO_3$, and $BaCO_3$ precipitate since the CO_3^{--} ion concentration is sufficiently high to exceed the respective solubility product constants. $MgCO_3$ does not precipitate since it is moderately soluble, nor does $Mg(OH)_2$ precipitate since the concentration of the NH_4^+ ion in the solution is high and the concentration of the OH^- ion too low to exceed the solubility product constant for $Mg(OH)_2$.

In dilute solutions, ammonium oxalate does not give a precipitate with Mg^{++} ion. However, in the more concentrated solutions of the reagent a precipitate appears having the composition, $MgC_2O_4 \cdot 2H_2O$.

A solution of Na_2HPO_4 when added to one containing Mg^{++} ions gives a white precipitate of $MgHPO_4 \cdot 7H_2O$. On the other hand, if NH_4OH and NH_4Cl are present, PO_4^{---} ion gives a characteristic white, crystalline precipitate of $MgNH_4PO_4$ since,

$$HPO_4^{--} + NH_4OH = PO_4^{---} + NH_4^+ + H_2O \qquad (12)$$

and

$$PO_4^{---} + Mg^{++} + NH_4^+ = MgNH_4PO_{4(s)} \qquad (13)$$

It is evident that $MgNH_4PO_4$ is soluble in relatively weak acids.

Several organic reagents have been found applicable as characteristic tests for Mg^{++} ion. Of these one of the most sensitive and successful makes use of *p-nitrobenzeneazoresorcinol* as the reagent (*S.* and *O. reagent*). It is claimed that as little as 1/500 milligram of Mg^{++} ion can be detected by this reagent. A convenient concentration for its use is a 0.5 percent solution of the dye in 1 percent sodium hydroxide solution.

Preliminary Experiments

1. In the following chart the ions of the alkaline earth group are listed horizontally and a number of reagents vertically. In the blank spaces provided in a similar chart made in your notebook

give the products of the reactions when the specified reagent is added drop by drop to a solution of the ion in question. If the product is a precipitate, indicate this fact by denoting the solid phase as, for example, $BaCO_{3(s)}$. Indicate the color of all precipitates and solutions containing new products. If no reaction takes place as far as you can ascertain, write *no reaction*. *From your knowledge of the chemical properties of these ions fill in as many blank spaces as possible without carrying out the experiments. If you are not familiar with the reaction in question, perform an experiment to obtain the desired information.*

Reagent added	Ba^{++}	Sr^{++}	Ca^{++}	Mg^{++}
6 M NH_4OH				
6 M NaOH				
6 M NH_4OH + H_2S				
$(NH_4)CO_3$				
1 M K_2CrO_4 in 1 M HAc solution				
6 M H_2SO_4				
0.1 M $(NH_4)_2C_2O_4$				

2. On the basis of the relative positions of $BaCO_3$ and $BaSO_4$ in Table 14, predict what would take place if solid $BaCO_3$ were treated with Na_2SO_4 solution. Prepare some solid $BaCO_3$ by adding Na_2CO_3 solution to one of $BaCl_2$. Centrifuge and wash the precipitate to remove any excess CO_3^{--} ion. Test your prediction by adding some of the solid $BaCO_3$ to hot 1 M Na_2SO_4 solution. After centrifuging, test the filtrate for CO_3^{--} ion by adding HCl, noting evolution of CO_2. Write the equation for the reaction taking place.

3. How may the reaction of (2) be reversed? Devise an experiment to determine whether it is possible to carry out this reversal to an appreciable extent. Make certain the $BaSO_{4(s)}$ is free from excess SO_4^{--} ion. Use a saturated solution of K_2CO_3. In making a test for SO_4^{--} ion in the presence of CO_3^{--} ion, the CO_3^{--} ion must first be removed by the addition of excess HCl or HNO_3.

4. Prepare the two following solutions: (a) 2 drops of 0.1 M $Mg(NO_3)_2$

solution and 2 ml. of water, (b) 2 drops of 0.1 M $Mg(NO_3)_2$ solution, 1 ml. of 5 M NH_4Cl solution, and 1 ml. of water. To each of these solutions add 2 drops of 15 M NH_4OH. Explain why a precipitate of $Mg(OH)_2$ is obtained in solution (a) but not in solution (b).

5. Add 6 drops of 0.1 M $Mg(NO_3)_2$ solution to 2 ml. of water and with this solution perform test H on page 310 for the Mg^{++} ion. Note particularly the appearance of the precipitate $MgNH_4PO_4$ and of the lake formed between the *S. and O. reagent* and the $Mg(OH)_2$.

6. The purpose of this experiment is to acquaint the student with the principles of equilibrium as applied to the precipitation of $CaSO_4$ and $SrSO_4$.

HSO_4^- ion is a weak acid with a dissociation constant equal to 1.26×10^{-2}.

$$\frac{(H^+)(SO_4^{--})}{(HSO_4^-)} = 1.26 \times 10^{-2}$$

Under the conditions existing in the following problem the H^+ ion concentration is about 1.3 M and the HSO_4^- ion concentration about 1 M. The SO_4^{--} ion concentration is, therefore, approximately equal to $1 \times 10^{-2} M$. Since the solubility product constant for $SrSO_4$ has a value of 7.6×10^{-7} the concentration of the Sr^{++} ion, after the $SrSO_4$ has been precipitated, is only approximately $7.6 \times 10^{-5} M$.

The solubility product constant for $CaSO_4$ is equal to 2.4×10^{-5}, and with the SO_4^{--} ion concentration equal to about 1×10^{-2} (as it is in this solution), the Ca^{++} ion concentration can be as high as about $2 \times 10^{-3} M$ without the precipitation of $CaSO_4$. The concentration of the SO_4^{--} ion in the solution remains practically constant even though a small amount is removed by the precipitation of $SrSO_4$. As SO_4^{--} ion is consumed, it is regenerated from the HSO_4^- ion. The SO_4^{--} ion concentration is therefore "buffered."

One of the difficulties sometimes encountered in the precipitation of these sulfates is that they tend to form supersaturated solutions when incipient crystals are not present. Because of this difficulty the analytical procedure adopted for the alkaline earth group is not based upon the principle stated above. The following experiments will illustrate these points.

Prepare each of the following test solutions: (a) 3 drops of 0.1 M $Ca(NO_3)_2$ and 3 drops of 0.1 M $Sr(NO_3)_2$, (b) 6 drops of 0.1 M $Sr(NO_3)_2$, (c) 6 drops of 0.1 M $Ca(NO_3)_2$, and (d) 10 drops of 0.1 M $Sr(NO_3)_2$ and 1 drop of 0.1 M $Ca(NO_3)_2$. With each of these solutions perform the following operations (work with one solution at a time).

Add 10 drops of 6 M HNO_3 and 1.5 ml. of 2 M $NaHSO_4$ solution. Heat to boiling. Any precipitate formed is $SrSO_4$. If $SrSO_4$ does not precipitate in (a), (b), and (d), seed the solution with $SrSO_4$. This can be done by making a suspension of $SrSO_4$ from solutions of Na_2SO_4 and $Sr(NO_3)_2$ and then by dipping the stirring rod into this suspension and transferring the adhering crystals to the solution in question. A small drop of the suspension may be added instead.

Cool the solution under the tap and centrifuge. Reserve the precipitate for a later flame test. Label it (1). To the supernatant liquid add 15 M NH_4OH dropwise until alkaline, cooling the solution under the tap as the NH_4OH is added. Now heat the solution. If Ca^{++} ion is present, a precipitate of $CaSO_4$ should form when the solution is heated. Centrifuge. Reserve any precipitate for a later test. Label it (2).

Make calculations involving the solubility products of $CaSO_4$ and $SrSO_4$ to determine whether the precipitation of these salts is behaving according to expectation.

To the supernatant liquid add 1 ml. of 0.1 M $(NH_4)_2C_2O_4$ solution. Shake the solution and allow it to stand for a few minutes. If Ca^{++} ion is present, a faint precipitate of CaC_2O_4 may appear (CaC_2O_4 does not precipitate readily when the SO_4^{--} ion concentration is high).

Wash the precipitate (2) with water. Discard the wash water and to the precipitate add 1 ml. of $(NH_4)_2CO_3$ reagent. Stir and heat the solution. Any solid sulfate will be converted to carbonate. Centrifuge. Wash and discard the wash water. Now dissolve the precipitate in 1 ml. of 1 M HCl. Add 6 M NH_4OH until alkaline and then add only one drop of 0.1 M $(NH_4)_2C_2O_4$ solution. If Ca^{++} ion is present, a white precipitate of CaC_2O_4 will appear.

Wash the precipitate (1), if any was formed, and treat it with 1 ml. of $(NH_4)_2CO_3$ reagent. Heat and stir. The $SrSO_4$ is converted to $SrCO_3$. Centrifuge. To the solid $SrCO_3$ add 3 drops of 6 M HCl and with this solution make a flame test for strontium.

7. Carry out flame tests on different solutions containing the ions of the alkaline earth group. Add a few drops of 6 M HCl to each solution. It is essential to become familiar with these tests. Check these tests using the spectroscope, if it is available.

8. For each of the following cases devise a method for separating and identifying the two ions in question.

(a) Ba^{++} and Ca^{++}

(b) Mg^{++} and Ca^{++}

(c) Ba^{++} and Mg^{++}

(d) Sr^{++} and Mg^{++}

(e) Ba^{++} and Sr^{++}

Procedure for the Analysis of the Alkaline Earth Group

SCHEMATIC OUTLINE

<table>
<tr><td colspan="2">Solution: Ba^{++}, Sr^{++}, Ca^{++}, and Mg^{++}.
Add 5 M NH_4Cl, 15 M NH_4OH and $(NH_4)_2CO_3$.
(G–H)</td><td colspan="2"></td></tr>
<tr><td colspan="2">Precipitate: $BaCO_3$, $SrCO_3$, $CaCO_3$.
Dissolve in 6 M HAc.
Add 3 M NH_4Ac. Add 1 M K_2CrO_4.
(G)</td><td colspan="2">Solution: Mg^{++}
(H)</td></tr>
<tr><td>Precipitate:
$BaCrO_4$.
Dissolve in
6 M HCl.
Add 6 M H_2SO_4.
(G–1)

Precipitate:
$BaSO_4$.</td><td>Solution: Sr^{++}, Ca^{++}.
Add $N(C_2H_4OH)_3$ and
$(NH_4)_2SO_4$.

<table><tr><td>Precipitate:
$SrSO_4$.
Add
$(NH_4)_2CO_3$.
(G–2)

Precipitate:
$SrCO_3$.
Dissolve in
6 M HCl.
Apply flame
test.</td><td>Solution: Ca^{++}
Add $(NH_4)_2C_2O_4$
(G–3)

Precipitate:
CaC_2O_4.</td></tr></table></td><td>Add 5 M
NH_4Cl.
Add 15 M
NH_4OH.
Add 0.5 M
Na_2HPO_4.

Precipi-
tate:
$MgNH_4PO_4$</td><td>Add 6 M
NaOH.
Heat to dry-
ness.
Add 6 M HCl
and water.
Add S. and
O. reagent.
Add 6 M
NaOH.

Precipitate:
$Mg(OH)_2$
+ dye
(blue).</td></tr>
</table>

G–H. Precipitation of the Alkaline Earth Group. Obtain from the laboratory instructor a sample of the unknown to be analyzed. Saturate 3 ml. of this sample with solid NH_4Cl, decant the supernatant liquid into a 10 ml. test tube, make alkaline with 15 M NH_4OH solution and add 5 drops of 15 M NH_4OH in excess. Heat the solution almost to boiling [1] (*do not boil*) and with constant stirring add 2 ml. of the prepared $(NH_4)_2CO_3$ reagent. Allow the solution to stand for a few minutes and centrifuge. To the supernatant liquid add a few drops of the $(NH_4)_2CO_3$ reagent to test for completeness of precipitation, and combine any precipitate formed with that originally obtained. Continue testing for completeness of precipitation until no more precipitate is formed. The white carbonates of Ba^{++}, Ca^{++}, and Sr^{++} ions may be present in the precipitate (*G*). The centrifugate (*H*) may contain the Mg^{++} ion.[2]

NOTE 1. *The purpose of heating at this point is to prevent the formation of too gelatinous a precipitate which is not easily washed.*

NOTE 2. $Mg(OH)_2$ *has a sufficiently large solubility product constant that it will not precipitate when the OH^- ion concentration is as low as in this buffered solution.*

G-1. Test for Ba^{++} Ion. Wash the white carbonate precipitate (*G*) with 3 ml. of warm water, centrifuge and discard the washings. Repeat the washing and again discard the washings.

To the precipitate in the test tube add dropwise 6 M HAc, about 6–8 drops, until the precipitate is just dissolved. Use the stirring rod to agitate the precipitate and solution after the addition of each drop of 6 M HAc.

Add 10 drops of 3 M NH$_4$Ac solution and dilute with 3 ml. of water. Now add 10 drops of 1 M K$_2$CrO$_4$ solution. A yellow precipitate of BaCrO$_4$ indicates the presence of Ba^{++} ion in the original solution. Heat the solution and centrifuge. Retain the supernatant and label it **G-2.** This will contain any Ca^{++} and Sr^{++} ions present in the original solution. Wash the collected BaCrO$_4$ precipitate twice, using 3 ml. of water each time. Discard the washings.

To confirm the presence of Ba^{++} ion, dissolve the yellow BaCrO$_4$ with 1 ml. of 6 M HCl. Apply the flame test. Add to the solution 2 drops of 6 M H$_2$SO$_4$ to precipitate the white BaSO$_4$. The color of the solution will make the precipitate appear yellow. Centrifuge to ascertain whether the precipitate is white.

G-2. Test for Sr^{++} Ion. Adjust the volume of the orange-yellow solution which is to be tested for both Sr^{++} and Ca^{++} ions to 3 ml. either by evaporation or dilution as the case may be. Place one-half (1.5 ml.) of this solution in a small test tube and add 30 drops of triethanolamine [3] and 3 ml. of 1 M (NH$_4$)$_2$SO$_4$ solution. Heat to boiling. A white precipitate or clouding of the solution indicates the presence of Sr^{++} ion. If a precipitate appears, centrifuge the solution and retain the supernatant (*G-3*) to test for the Ca^{++} ion.

To confirm the presence of Sr^{++} ion, first wash the precipitate of SrSO$_4$ several times with water.

To the precipitate now add 2 ml. of the $(NH_4)_2CO_3$ reagent, heat and stir. The $SrSO_4$ will be converted to $SrCO_3$. Centrifuge and to the precipitate add 3 drops of 6 M HCl, and with a piece of Chromel wire looped at the end make the flame test for Sr^{++} ion. The strontium salts impart a deep red color to the flame.

NOTE 3. *Triethanolamine, $N(C_2H_4OH)_3$, is an organic derivative of ammonia and forms a more stable complex with the Ca^{++} ion than with Sr^{++} ion, thereby preventing the precipitation of $CaSO_4$.*

G–3. Test for Ca^{++} Ion. Add to the centrifugate *G–3* 10 drops of 0.25 M $(NH_4)_2C_2O_4$ solution. Heat to boiling. A white precipitate or clouding of the solution indicates the presence of Ca^{++} ion.[4] Centrifuge, decant the supernatant liquid and discard. Wash the precipitate twice with 3 ml. of water. Heat the precipitate vigorously with full heat of the burner and cool. Add a few drops of 12 M HCl to the residue and carry out a flame test.

NOTE 4. *The calcium triethanolamine complex is not so stable that it prevents the precipitation of the relatively insoluble CaC_2O_4.*

H. Test for the Mg^{++} Ion. To one-half of the centrifugate **H** add 10 drops of 5 M NH_4Cl, 5 drops of 15 M NH_4OH, and 10 drops of 0.5 M Na_2HPO_4 solution in the order named. Stir the mixture and allow it to stand for a few minutes. The appearance of a white crystalline precipitate of $MgNH_4PO_4$ is a test for the Mg^{++} ion.

Place the other portion of the solution **H** in a casserole and add 15 M HNO_3 until vigorous evolution of gas ceases, then add 10 drops of 15 M HNO_3 in excess and heat to dryness under a hood.[5] Continue heating strongly (under a hood) until dense white fumes are no longer evolved and no significant amount of residue remains. Even with magnesium present this residue will be difficult to observe. Wash down the sides of the cool casserole with 20 drops of 3 M HCl, add 2 ml. of water, heat gently, make just alkaline with 6 M NaOH, and then just acidic with 3 M HCl. Transfer the solution to a test tube. Add 1–3 drops of *S. and O. reagent*[6] and then add 6 M NaOH dropwise until alkaline. Add 3 drops of 6 M NaOH in excess. If Mg^{++} ion is present, $Mg(OH)_2$ will precipitate with the dye adsorbed to it to give a characteristic blue colored lake. If there is any doubt about the test, the blue lake may be centrifuged and washed with water to remove the effect of the colored supernatant liquid. The lake should be a bright blue.

NOTE 5. *The purpose of heating at this point is to eliminate the NH_4^+ ion which is present in the basic solution mostly as NH_3. The NH_4^+ ion interferes with the formation of the lake.*

NOTE 6. *S. and O. refers to Suitsu and Okuma who first proposed the use of this reagent, p-nitrobenzeneazoresorcinol, in the test for Mg^{++} ion. It is essential that all of the ammonia be removed from the solution before the S. and O. reagent is added.*

The S. and O. reagent becomes purple to blue in color in alkaline solution. This color should not be confused with the test for magnesium, which consists of a precipitate of $Mg(OH)_2$ colored light blue. To make certain that the color is due to magnesium, centrifuge the mixture, decant the dark supernatant liquid, and examine the precipitate, if present. Also, compare the test for the unknown with that of a solution known to contain 0.02 M Mg^{++} ion.

Equations for Pertinent Reactions

$$M^{++} + CO_3^{--} = MCO_{3(s)} \qquad (M^{++} = Ba^{++}, Ca^{++} \text{ or } Sr^{++})$$

$$MCO_{3(s)} + 2HAc = M^{++} + CO_2 + 2Ac^- + H_2O$$

$$Ba^{++} + CrO_4^{--} = BaCrO_{4(s)}$$

$$2BaCrO_{4(s)} + 2SO_4^{--} + 2H^+ = 2BaSO_{4(s)} + Cr_2O_7^{--} + H_2O$$

$$Sr^{++} + SO_4^{--} = SrSO_{4(s)}$$

$$SrSO_{4(s)} + CO_3^{--} = SrCO_{3(s)} + SO_4^{--}$$

$$SrCO_{3(s)} + 2H^+ = Sr^{++} + CO_2 + H_2O$$

$$Ca^{++} + C_2O_4^{--} = CaC_2O_{4(s)}$$

$$Mg^{++} + NH_4^+ + PO_4^{---} = MgNH_4PO_{4(s)}$$

$$Mg^{++} + 2OH^- = Mg(OH)_{2(s)}$$

CHAPTER 16

Analysis of
the Positive
Ions

In the analysis of all of the common metal ions the procedure employed is that of first separating them into several groups, each of which contains ions exhibiting a common chemical property which is the basis for the separation. For example, only Ag^+, Hg_2^{++}, and Pb^{++} ions react with Cl^- ion to form relatively insoluble chlorides. These three ions then constitute one group in the analytical classification. A second group is made up of those ions which form insoluble sulfides with H_2S in acid solution. A third group consists of ions which form either insoluble hydroxides or sulfides when treated with NH_4OH, NH_4Cl, and H_2S. A fourth group consists of Ca^{++}, Sr^{++}, Ba^{++}, and Mg^{++} ions. These groups, together with the alkali metal group, have already been considered in the five previous chapters.

We shall now devote our attention to the analysis of unknown samples which may contain ions belonging to any of the five groups. In this chapter we shall consider these group separations and a number of complications which may arise due to the presence of certain anions. Specific directions for the separations will be given up to a point where the student can conveniently be referred back to the group procedure with which he is familiar.

At this point we cannot emphasize too strongly the need for making certain that any given group is completely separated from the solution and that the group precipitate is thoroughly washed. The presence of any ion foreign to·a group may well give rise to unnecessary complications and lead to error in the analysis.

The following procedure applies to ions already in solution.

Schematic Outline for Separation of Groups

Solution: Ions of groups **A, B, C–D, E–F,** and **G–H.** Test for ions of group **A.** Add HCl.				
Precipitate: AgCl Hg₂Cl₂ PbCl₂ **(B)**	**Solution:** Ions of groups **C–D, E–F,** and **G–H.** Make (H⁺) 0.3 *M*, add H₂O₂, and saturate with H₂S.			
	Precipitate: (C–D). CuS As₂S₃ HgS Sb₂S₃ Bi₂S₃ SnS₂ CdS PbS Treat with NH₄OH + H₂S.	**Solution:** Ions of groups **E–F** and **G–H.** Add NH₄OH, NH₄Cl, and H₂S.		
		Precipitate: (E–F). ZnS Al(OH)₃ CoS Cr(OH)₃ NiS FeS MnS Treat with Na₂SO₄ and NaHSO₄.	**Solution:** Ions of group **G–H.** Add NH₄OH and (NH₄)₂CO₃.	
	Residue: CuS HgS Bi₂S₃ CdS PbS **(C)**	**Solution:** AsS₃⁻⁻⁻ SbS₃⁻⁻⁻ SnS₃⁻⁻ **(D)**	**Precipitate:** CaCO₃ SrCO₃ BaCO₃ **(G)**	**Solution:** Mg⁺⁺ **(H)**
		Residue: ZnS CoS NiS **(E)**	**Solution:** Al⁺⁺⁺ Cr⁺⁺⁺ Fe⁺⁺ Mn⁺⁺ **(F)**	

The solution containing the unknown should first be tested with litmus. If it is strongly alkaline, several positive ions are evidently absent. If it is acidic, all positive ions may be present provided Cl⁻ ion is absent. Reserve 1 ml. of the solution for making any tests you may see fit to determine the presence or absence of some ions, and thereby simplify or confirm the analysis.

A. The Alkali Metal Group. Carry out tests for NH₄⁺, Na⁺, and K⁺ ions, using the original solution, according to the procedures *A–1, A–2,* and *A–3* described on page 260.

B. Precipitation of the Silver Group.[1] If the clear original solution is alkaline, add 6 *M* HCl until neutral. To 3 ml. of the neutral solution, or to 3 ml. of the clear original solution if acidic, add 1 drop of 6 *M* HCl. If no precipitate appears, the ions of the silver group are absent; proceed directly to the copper-arsenic group. In the event of the formation of a precipitate, add 4 more drops of 6 M HCl,[2] stir, and pour the contents of the test tube into a filter supported by a 40 mm. funnel.[3] Test the filtrate for completeness of precipitation by adding one drop of 6 M HCl. Make certain that precipitation is complete.[4] Wash the precipitate B with 1 ml. of 1.5 M HCl and add the wash solution [5] to the filtrate. Label the filtrate C-H; it may contain ions of all groups excepting the silver group. Again wash the precipitate with 1 ml. of 1.5 M HCl and *discard* the wash solution. The precipitate B may consist of AgCl, Hg_2Cl_2, and $PbCl_2$. It should be examined for the presence of these ions according to procedures B-1, B-2, and B-3 outlined on pages 264–265.

NOTE 1. *In the original unknown solution a white solid may be present due to the hydrolysis of bismuth, antimony, arsenic, or tin ions. This solid must be removed by centrifugation or filtration before the test is made for the presence of the silver group (white precipitate upon the addition of HCl). After the removal of the silver group chlorides, the original white solid should be added to the filtrate containing the ions of the remaining groups. In the precipitation of the ions of the copper-arsenic group, the white hydrolysis products will be converted to the less soluble sulfides.*

NOTE 2. *If Sb^{+++} and Bi^{+++} ions are present in the original solution (acidic), the addition of HCl may initially cause the oxychlorides, SbOCl and BiOCl, to precipitate. However, further addition of HCl will dissolve these oxychlorides. Care should be taken not to confuse the oxychloride precipitate with the silver group chloride precipitate.*

NOTE 3. *In the analysis of the silver group it is much more convenient to use filtration rather than centrifugation operations.*

NOTE 4. *The solubility of $PbCl_2$ in the acid solution is much greater than that of AgCl and Hg_2Cl_2. Therefore Pb^{++} ion is only partially removed at this point. However, it will appear again in the copper group as PbS. If the original solution contains Pb^{++} ion in small amount, no $PbCl_2$ may be precipitated in the silver group.*

NOTE 5. *The silver group precipitate is washed to remove occluded liquid which may contain ions of other groups. An HCl solution is used instead of water to reduce the amount of $PbCl_2$ in the wash solution and to prevent the precipitation of SbOCl and BiOCl on the filter.*

C–D. Precipitation of the Copper-Arsenic Group.[6] To the filtrate C-H obtained from the separation of the silver group, and contained in a 25 ml. Erlenmeyer flask, add 5 drops of 3 percent

H_2O_2 and heat the solution to boiling. Before precipitation is carried out with H_2S the H^+ ion concentration must be made approximately equal to 0.3 M. Since the solution may contain an excess of H^+ ion, it must first be neutralized before the proper amount of acid is added. Add 6 M NH_4OH dropwise until the solution is just alkaline. Disregard any precipitate which may appear. Add a drop or two of 6 M HCl to make the solution just acidic and then add 1 drop of 6 M HCl for each ml. of the solution (see footnote 3, page 274). Add 1 drop of 1 M NH_4I solution. (Do not be disturbed if a precipitate appears here.)

Heat the solution to boiling and saturate for one minute with H_2S. Heat to boiling again, and again saturate with H_2S. Cool the solution under the tap and saturate with H_2S once more.[7,8] (In the precipitation of the copper-arsenic group, thioacetamide may be used in place of H_2S gas as a source of H_2S. For instructions see pages 239 and 240.)

Pour the solution into a 10 ml. test tube; wash out the Erlenmeyer flask with 1 ml. of water, and add to the solution in the test tube. Centrifuge for one minute. Dip the end of a small stirring rod into the supernatant liquid to obtain enough solution to be tested with methyl violet paper for the H^+ ion concentration (see footnote 3, page 274). If necessary, pour the supernatant liquid into another 10 ml. test tube, adjust the H^+ ion concentration by adding a drop or two of 3 M NH_4OH with vigorous stirring, and again pass H_2S into the cold solution to test for completeness of precipitation. Centrifuge, decant the supernatant liquid, and combine any precipitate with that previously formed. Label the supernatant liquid *E–H;* it may contain ions of the aluminum-zinc and alkaline earth groups. The precipitate *C–D* contains the sulfides of any of the copper-arsenic group ions which may be present.

If it was not found necessary to adjust the H^+ ion concentration after the methyl violet test, decant the supernatant liquid *E–H* from the precipitate *C–D.*

To the sulfide precipitate *C–D* add 2 ml. of water and then wash down the side of the test tube with an additional ml. of water. Use a stirring rod to bring the sulfides into suspension. Centrifuge and add the supernatant wash water to solution *E–H.* Wash twice with 3 ml. of water and discard the wash water each time. Now add 1 ml. of 15 M NH_4OH to precipitate *C–D.*

Carry out the procedure for separating the copper group from the arsenic group as described under **C–D–1,** page 275, and continue the analysis of these two groups from that point on.

NOTE 6. *Notes 1–10 on pages 274 and 275 apply to this separation and should be consulted at this point.*

NOTE 7. *If the Cl⁻ ion concentration should be inordinately high, as would be the case if the original solution were clear and contained SbCl₃, BiCl₃, or SnCl₄ in HCl solution, then it might prevent the precipitation of CdS because of the formation of the CdCl₄⁻⁻ complex ion. If the CdS is not completely precipitated in the copper-arsenic group, it will appear with the final ZnS precipitate in group E–F and can be detected there.*

NOTE 8. *If chromium is present in the original solution as Cr₂O₇⁻⁻ ion or the manganese as MnO₄⁻ ion, these ions will be reduced by the H₂S in the acid solution to Cr⁺⁺⁺ and Mn⁺⁺ ions respectively.*

E–F. Precipitation of the Aluminum-Zinc Group. Place the solution **E–H** in a casserole or small beaker and evaporate until the solution has a volume of about 2 ml. Add 3 drops of Br_2 water and heat for one minute to remove the last traces of H_2S. Then transfer the solution to a 25 ml. Erlenmeyer flask, wash the casserole or beaker with 1 ml. of water (use the capillary syringe), and add the wash water to the evaporated solution. Cool the solution.

To the solution add 10 drops of 5 M NH_4Cl[9,10]; make alkaline with 15 M NH_4OH and add 10 drops of the reagent in excess. If no precipitate is obtained here, Al^{+++}, Cr^{+++}, and Fe^{+++} ions are absent. Saturate the solution, which may already contain a precipitate, with H_2S. Centrifuge and test the supernatant liquid for completeness of precipitation by adding 2 drops of 15 M NH_4OH, heating, and again saturating with H_2S. Combine any precipitate with that obtained previously. Save the supernatant liquid for later tests and label it **G–H.** It may contain the ions of the alkaline earth group. Wash the precipitate, **E–F–1,** with 3 ml. of water and add the wash water to **G–H.** Wash the precipitate again and discard the wash water. Using this precipitate continue the analysis of the aluminum-zinc group by beginning with the procedure described in **E–F–1** on page 289.[11]

NOTE 9. *If the original solution was strongly acidic and a relatively large amount of NH_4OH was needed to neutralize it in operation C–D, then the NH_4Cl may be omitted here.*

NOTE 10. *The solution must contain a relatively large amount of NH_4^+*

ion so that the OH^- *ion concentration will be decreased to such a low level that* $Mg(OH)_2$ *will not be precipitated with this group.*

NOTE 11. *If the* Cl^- *ion concentration was high in the precipitation of the copper-arsenic group, cadmium would not be completely removed there (see footnote 7). It would appear as CdS in the precipitation of the aluminum-zinc group and it would not be dissolved by the* Na_2SO_4–$NaHSO_4$ *buffer. In the test for* Zn^{++} *ion, in which ZnS is precipitated in HAc solution, CdS would also precipitate if present. If the ZnS precipitate has a decided yellow color, it should be tested for the presence of* Cd^{++} *ion as follows. Centrifuge the solution and reserve the filtrate for* Ni^{++} *and* Co^{++} *ion tests. Wash the precipitate twice with 2 ml. of water containing 2 drops of 6 M HAc, and discard the wash water in each case. Dissolve the precipitate in 3 M HCl added dropwise with constant stirring. Add 2 ml. of water, then neutralize the solution with 6 M NH_4OH. Add 3 M HCl until the solution is just acidic and then add 1 drop of 6 M HCl in excess for each ml. of solution (about 3 drops will be required). Saturate the solution with* H_2S, *keeping the solution cold. If* Cd^{++} *ion is present in appreciable amounts, CdS will precipitate. Centrifuge and to the supernatant add 10 drops of 2 M NaAc solution. If* Zn^{++} *ion is present, ZnS will precipitate at this point due to the increase in the* S^{--} *ion concentration brought about by the lowering of the* H^+ *ion concentration by* Ac^- *ion.*

G–H. Precipitation of the Alkaline Earth Group. Evaporate solution **G–H** in a casserole until the volume is reduced to about 3 ml. If the solution contains an appreciable amount of NH_4Cl (see footnotes 9 and 10), it will not be necessary to add the salt at this point. Test with litmus to make certain that the solution is alkaline. If it is alkaline, add 3 drops of 15 M NH_4OH; if it is not alkaline, make alkaline with 15 M NH_4OH and then add 3 drops of the reagent in excess. Heat the solution almost to boiling (*do not boil*) and with constant stirring add 2 ml. of $(NH_4)_2CO_3$ reagent. Allow the solution to stand for a few minutes and then centrifuge. To the supernatant liquid add a few drops of the $(NH_4)_2CO_3$ reagent to test for completeness of precipitation, and combine any precipitate formed with that originally obtained. Continue testing for completeness of precipitation until no more precipitate is formed. The centrifugate may contain Mg^{++} ion and should be examined according to procedure **H**, page 310. The precipitate should be washed twice with 3 ml. of warm water and then examined for the presence of Ba^{++}, Ca^{++}, and Sr^{++} ions according to procedures **G–1**, **G–2**, and **G–3**, pages 309–310.

CHAPTER *17*

Identification
of Some of the
Negative Ions

In this section we shall consider the methods for identifying the more common negative ions (anions). Consideration will be given only to the following ions and their acid or complex derivatives.

TABLE 18

Bromide	Br^-	Nitrite	NO_2^-
Carbonate	CO_3^{--}	Sulfate	SO_4^{--}
Chloride	Cl^-	Sulfide	S^{--}
Chromate	CrO_4^{--}	Sulfite	SO_3^{--}
Iodide	I^-	Thiocyanate	CNS^-
Nitrate	NO_3^-		

It is obvious that in any given unknown sample, containing positive and negative ions, the larger the number of positive ions present the smaller must be the number of negative ions, and *vice versa*. As the number of positive and negative ions increases, the greater is the probability that pairs of ions of relatively insoluble or very slightly soluble salts will be present. A knowledge of the positive ions present in a solution immediately eliminates certain negative ions; likewise, a knowledge of the negative ions eliminates certain positive ions. Thus, if Ag^+ ion is found to be present and if the solution is not ammoniacal, S^{--}, Cl^-, Br^-, I^-, and CNS^- ions cannot be present. Likewise, if Pb^{++} or Ba^{++} ions are found in the unknown and the unknown sample is soluble in water or dilute acid solution, it is evident that SO_4^{--} ion must be absent. Strong oxidizing ions will not exist in solutions containing ions which function as reducing agents and *vice versa*. When the positive ions of a given unknown have been identified, it is possible, from a consideration of the insolubility of the compounds of these particular ions, to eliminate as many of the negative ions as possible. Such a procedure often leads to a simplification of the detection of negative ions.

Arsenite and arsenate ions may be present in an unknown. However, in this text we shall not attempt to identify them as such; they will appear in the tests for arsenic in the cation analysis.

The detection of most negative ions derived from weak acids should be carried out in basic, neutral, or only slightly acidic solution. In a solution which is strongly acidic the concentration of such ions will be much lower than in basic solution, and probably too low for precipitation by a positive ion. Designating the negative ion as A^- and the positive metal ion as M^+, these conditions can be readily explained by the following equilibrium:

$$HA = H^+ + A^-$$
$$+$$
$$M^+ \qquad\qquad (14)$$
$$\updownarrow$$
$$MA_{(s)}$$

If the unknown solution is strongly acidic, the equilibrium will be shifted to the left, which effect increases the concentration of the HA molecules and in turn decreases the concentration of A^- ions. The concentration of the latter may be decreased in this manner to such an extent as to escape detection. On the other hand, the introduction of a strong base to such a solution serves to remove H^+ ions, thereby shifting the equilibrium to the right and increasing the concentration of A^- ions sufficiently to precipitate the salt MA. Negative ions considered here which show a pronounced tendency to combine with H^+ ion are: CO_3^{--}, CrO_4^{--}, S^{--}, SO_3^{--}, and CNS^-.

If, however, the weak acid derived from the negative ion produces a gas, then the presence of H^+ ion is a favorable condition for the detection of the negative ion. The ions, S^{--}, SO_3^{--}, and CO_3^{--} fall into this category and the equilibria involved in these cases are as follows:

$$S^{--} + 2H^+ = H_2S_{(aq.)} = H_2S_{(g)} \uparrow \qquad (15)$$

$$SO_3^{--} + 2H^+ = H_2SO_3 = H_2O + SO_{2(g)} \uparrow \qquad (16)$$

$$CO_3^{--} + 2H^+ = H_2CO_3 = H_2O + CO_{2(g)} \uparrow \qquad (17)$$

The addition of a strong acid to solutions containing S^{--}, SO_3^{--}, and CO_3^{--} ions shifts the equilibrium in each case to the right. When the solubility of the substances produced is exceeded, H_2S, SO_2, or CO_2 will escape from solution as gases. These gases may then be detected by suitable methods. These equilibria can also be shifted to the right by the application of heat since gases are less soluble at high than at low temperatures.

Many of the positive metal ions interfere with the tests for the negative ions and therefore it is necessary at the outset to remove these positive ions from the solution. Inasmuch as the carbonates of most positive ions are relatively insoluble in alkaline solution, these ions may be precipitated as such in this medium. It is obvious that the test for CO_3^{--} ion must be made before this same ion is added as a reagent.

No such systematic scheme of analysis as that applied to the positive ions is applicable to the negative ions. Instead of using the same solution throughout the analysis it has been found necessary or expedient to make a number of isolated tests on different portions of the unknown solution. The procedure adopted here is that of making preliminary elimination tests in order that individual characteristic tests applied later may be reduced to as small a number as possible. The elimination tests are given schematically in Table 19 and, in detail, on the following pages. Some of the elimination tests are subsidiary to others and in some cases it will not be necessary to make all of these tests. These tests as outlined in Table 19 apply only to those anions in solution. After the elimination tests have been made, it will be possible to determine which ions cannot be present and conclusive characteristic tests for these particular ions may therefore be omitted.

Some confusion may arise in the use of elimination tests if the student does not thoroughly understand their purpose. The elimination tests are to be carried out with the definite view toward determining which ions are *not present* rather than to make positive tests for those ions which are present. The positive tests are to be made *after* the elimination tests have been made. If, for example, no precipitate is obtained when a solution containing HNO_3 and $AgNO_3$ is added to a solution prepared for the anion analysis, then Cl^-, Br^-, I^-, and CNS^- ions are absent. On the other hand, if a precipitate were obtained upon the addition of HNO_3 and $AgNO_3$, then no definite information would be forthcoming since such a precipitate might contain any or all of the silver salts of these ions. If all the anions listed in the table were present, the elimination tests would be practically worthless. The fewer the number of anions present the greater is the amount of information obtainable from the elimination tests.

In the analysis of most commercial and natural substances the student will encounter relatively few cases in which more than two or three anions are present in a single sample. For such cases the elimination tests are very valuable.

The detailed procedure given here for the analysis of the anions is only one of many possible schemes. The student is encouraged to use his ingenuity, together with his knowledge of the chemical properties of both anions and cations, to make variations in the scheme. He should also devise additional confirmatory tests when his knowledge of facts and originality of thought permit.

TABLE 19

PRELIMINARY ELIMINATION TESTS

Test	1	2	3-A	3-B	3-C	4	5	Positive tests to be made for
Anions, or derivatives of, considered in analysis	No gas evolved upon addition of acid to alkaline solution indicates absence of	No precipitate by $BaCl_2$ in acidic solution of low H^+ ion concentration indicates absence of	No precipitate upon addition of HNO_3 and $AgNO_3$ indicates absence of	If precipitate obtained in 3-A is completely soluble in $0.25\ M$ NH_4OH, it indicates absence of	If no precipitate is obtained when HNO_3 is added to filtrate from 3-B, it indicates absence of	No blue precipitate when original solution is treated with HCl, $FeCl_3$, and $K_3Fe(CN)_6$ indicates absence of	No dark brown or black color upon addition of $MnCl_2$ in $12\ M$ HCl indicates absence of	
CO_3^{--}	CO_3^{--}							
S^{--}	S^{--}					S^{--}		
SO_3^{--}	SO_3^{--}					SO_3^{--}		
CrO_4^{--}		CrO_4^{--}					CrO_4^{--}	
SO_4^{--}		SO_4^{--}						
Cl^-			Cl^-		Cl^-			
Br^-			Br^-	Br^-				
I^-			I^-	I^-		I^-		
CNS^-			CNS^-	CNS^-				
NO_3^-							NO_3^-	
NO_2^-						NO_2^-	NO_2^-	

Procedure for the Detection of Anions

The following procedures are designed only for anions present in a soluble state. The preparation of the solution which involves the removal of those cations which will interfere with the anion analysis is as follows. This solution is known as the Na_2CO_3 *prepared solution.*

Dissolve about 0.15 grams (150 mg.) in 10 ml. of water. Test this solution (or the sample already in the dissolved form) with litmus. If acidic, add 6 M NaOH drop by drop until just alkaline or until a precipitate first forms. To this solution, or to the original solution which was found to be alkaline, add 1 drop of 1.5 M Na_2CO_3 solution. If no precipitate forms either with NaOH or Na_2CO_3, this alkaline solution is ready for anion analysis.

If a precipitate forms, add 2 ml. of 1.5 M Na_2CO_3 solution to the 10 ml. sample in a casserole and boil for ten minutes. Continue to add water as it is lost by evaporation. Note whether any NH_3 is evolved (note odor or test with wet litmus paper). The mixture should then be centrifuged. If necessary add enough water to make the final volume 10 ml. This solution is then ready for the anion analysis. The Na_2CO_3 treatment should convert all insoluble salts into soluble sodium salts and insoluble carbonates.

Preliminary Elimination Tests

Prepare a chart such as Table 19 leaving out the characterization of the test at the top of each column and leaving blank all spaces except those in the first column; i.e., the formulae for the ions on which tests are to be made. After each preliminary test, check off in the appropriate spaces those ions which are known to be absent. After all preliminary tests have been made, it will be obvious which ions can possibly be present (the horizontal rows which are unmarked).

Test 1. This test is to be performed only if the original unknown is completely soluble in water to give an alkaline solution. It must be applied before any Na_2CO_3 has been added.

Place 5 drops of the unknown solution in a small test tube and heat gently (*do not boil*). Holding the tube to the light observe carefully whether a gas is evolved when 2 drops of 6 M HCl are added.

If no gas is evolved, CO_3^{--}, S^{--}, and SO_3^{--} ions cannot be present. (Check these ions in column **1** of the chart if they are shown to be absent; leave spaces blank if a gas is observed.)

Test 2. To 1 ml. of the Na_2CO_3 prepared solution add 3 M HAc drop by drop, counting the number of drops added, until the litmus paper just turns pink. Now continue to add the same number of drops of 3 M HAc as have already been added. Then add 2 drops of 0.1 M $BaCl_2$ solution. If a precipitate is not formed, CrO_4^{--} and SO_4^{--} ions are absent. In such a case make a record of it in the chart. If a yellow precipitate is formed, CrO_4^{--} ion is known to be present. (SO_4^{--} ion may also be present.) If the precipitate is white, SO_4^{--} ion is present and CrO_4^{--} ion is absent. Test for completeness of precipitation and add 2 drops of 0.1 M $BaCl_2$ solution in excess. Centrifuge the solution and reserve the centrifugate for the next test.

If SO_3^{--} ion is present in the original solution in relatively large amounts, $BaSO_3$ may precipitate here. Unless SO_3^{--} ion has been found to be absent in test *1,* wash the precipitate thoroughly with water, and add a few drops of 6 M HCl to the precipitate. Determine whether SO_3^{--} ion is present by noting any evolution of gas. Note that $BaSO_3$ and $BaCrO_4$ will dissolve in HCl while $BaSO_4$ will not.

Test 3–A. To 1 ml. of the Na_2CO_3 prepared solution acidify with 6 M HNO_3 and add 10 drops in excess. Boil to destroy H_2S and then centrifuge if necessary. To the cooled solution add 5 drops of 0.1 M $AgNO_3$. If no precipitate forms, Cl^-, Br^-, I^-, and CNS^- ions are absent. Make a record of absence. If no precipitate forms, do not carry out tests *3–B* and *3–C.* If a precipitate forms [1] test for completeness of precipitation by adding more $AgNO_3$ solution. Centrifuge and save the precipitate for test *3–B* and *3–C.*

NOTE 1. *If the S^{--} ion has not been completely removed, a black precipitate of Ag_2S may be formed.*

Test 3–B. To the *thoroughly* washed precipitate from *3–A* add 4 ml. of water, 4 drops of 6 M NH_4OH, and 10 drops of 0.1 M $AgNO_3$ solution. (The relative amounts of water, NH_4OH, and $AgNO_3$ are important in this test. Follow directions closely.) Agitate the precipitate with a glass rod. If the precipitate dissolves completely, Br^-, I^-, and CNS^- ions are not present. Save this mixture for *3–C.*

The complete solution of the precipitate by NH_4OH at this concentration is sufficient evidence that Cl^- ion is present.

Test 3–C. If the precipitate in **3–B** is completely dissolved by NH_4OH, carry out this test only to confirm the presence of Cl^- ion. If the precipitate did not dissolve completely in the NH_4OH, it may have dissolved partially.

Centrifuge the ammoniacal solution from **3–B** if necessary. Acidify the solution with HNO_3. If no precipitate forms, Cl^- ion is absent. A heavy [2] white precipitate confirms the presence of the Cl^- ion.

NOTE 2. *A very faint precipitate at this point may be due to Br^- or CNS^- ion.*

Test 4. To 3 drops of the Na_2CO_3 prepared solution add 1 ml. of water, 2 drops of 6 M HCl, 2 drops of 0.1 M $FeCl_3$, and 1 drop of *freshly prepared* saturated $K_3Fe(CN)_6$ (ferricyanide) solution. Allow the mixture to stand several minutes. If a deep blue precipitate does not form, S^{--}, I^-, SO_3^{--}, and NO_2^- ions are absent.[3,4,5]

NOTE 3. *This test depends upon the fact that the above ions in acidic solution reduce Fe^{+++} ion to Fe^{++} ion. The Fe^{++} ion then combines with the $Fe(CN)_6^{---}$ ion to give Prussian Blue.*

NOTE 4. *To be sure that none of the reagents contains either Fe^{++} ion or a reducing agent, make a blank test using all reagents, omitting only the prepared solution. Compare the intensities of the blue color obtained here with that obtained with the unknown solution.*

NOTE 5. *To prepare a saturated solution of $K_3Fe(CN)_6$, place a few crystals of the salt in a small test tube, add 10 drops of water and agitate with a stirring rod.*

Test 5. To 3 drops of the Na_2CO_3 prepared solution add dropwise 12 drops of a saturated solution of $MnCl_2$ in 12 M HCl and heat the mixture to boiling. If no dark brown or black color appears, the following ions are absent: CrO_4^{--}, NO_3^-, and NO_2^-[6]. A slight darkening, which indicates the presence of traces of oxidizing ions, may be overlooked.

NOTE 6. *Any one of the above mentioned ions in strong acid solution oxidizes $MnCl_2$ solution to the dark colored $MnCl_3$ solution.*

After all preliminary tests have been made and checks for absent ions have been placed in the appropriate spaces in the prepared chart, note which ions have not been checked. *Confirmatory tests need to be made for these ions only.*

POSITIVE TESTS FOR ANIONS

The following tests are based on the assumption that all negative ions included in this scheme are present in the solution. However, only the tests for those ions which have not been previously eliminated should be carried out. If the instructor does not include all ions given here as possibilities, the student can merely strike out those ions not considered.

Sulfate, Sulfite, and Chromate Ions

Test for SO$_4^{--}$ Ion. Place 5 drops of the Na$_2$CO$_3$ prepared solution in a small test tube and dilute with 1 ml. of water. Acidify by adding 6 M HCl dropwise. Add 2 drops of 6 M HCl in excess. Now add 1 ml. of 0.1 M BaCl$_2$ solution. A white precipitate of BaSO$_4$ indicates the presence of SO$_4^{--}$ ion in the original solution. Centrifuge the solution and discard the precipitate. Save the supernatant for the CrO$_4^{--}$ and SO$_3$ ion tests. Add 1 drop of 0.1 M BaCl$_2$ solution to insure completeness of precipitation.

Test for SO$_3^{--}$ Ion. To the filtrate obtained in the test for the SO$_4^{--}$ ion add 5 drops of bromine water. A white precipitate indicates the presence of SO$_3^{--}$ ion in the original solution. If no precipitate is obtained, add 1 drop of 0.1 M BaCl$_2$ to be certain that Ba^{++} ion is present in excess. Centrifuge the solution.

Test for CrO$_4^{--}$ Ion. If CrO$_4^{--}$ ion is present in the solution, a yellow precipitate would have been obtained in preliminary test **2**. The solution would also have a yellow color.

To confirm, or again test for CrO$_4^{--}$ ion, add to the supernatant from the test for SO$_3^{--}$ ion 10 drops of 2 M NaAc solution.[7] If CrO$_4^{--}$ (or Cr$_2$O$_7^{--}$) ion is present, a yellow precipitate of BaCrO$_4$ will form.

NOTE 7. *The addition of Ac$^-$ ion lowers the H$^+$ ion concentration by the formation of the weak acid, HAc. When the H$^+$ ion concentration is lowered, the CrO$_4^{--}$ ion concentration is increased sufficiently to combine with Ba^{++} ion to form solid BaCrO$_4$.*

$$H_2O + Cr_2O_7^{--} \text{ (acid solution)} = 2H^+ + 2CrO_4^{--}$$

Thiocyanate Ion

To 1 ml. of water in a small test tube add 5 drops of the Na_2CO_3 prepared solution. Add 6 M HNO_3 dropwise until the solution is acidic. Now add 3 drops of 0.1 M $Fe(NO_3)_3$ solution. A bright red color indicates the presence of CNS^- ion.

Chloride, Bromide, and Iodide Ions

If the previous elimination test *3–B* has shown that Br^-, I^-, and CNS^- ions are absent, do not carry out the following tests. The positive Cl^- ion test was made in the elimination test *3–C* and no further test for this ion need be considered.

If the elimination tests showed that Br^- or I^- ions may possibly be present, proceed as follows.

Test for I^- Ion. Place 5 drops of the Na_2CO_3 prepared solution in a small test tube and dilute with 10 drops of water. Neutralize with 6 M HNO_3, add 2 drops of the HNO_3 in excess. Now cover the surface of the liquid with about 10 drops of CCl_4. Add a quantity of 0.1 M $Fe(NO_3)_3$ solution [8] equal in volume to the aqueous solution already in the test tube, and shake. A violet color in the CCl_4 layer indicates the presence of I^- ion.[9]

If the CCl_4 layer turns purple, remove it from the surface with a capillary syringe and add more CCl_4 and shake again. Again discard the CCl_4 layer. Repeat this operation until the CCl_4 layer remains colorless.

NOTE 8. *The Fe^{+++} ion oxidizes the I^- ion to free iodine.*

NOTE 9. *Other ions may react with the Fe^{+++} ion added here, but these reactions will not interfere with the iodine formation if an excess of the Fe^{+++} ion is present.*

Test for Br^- Ion. Now transfer the solution to a casserole and heat to boiling to drive off any residual iodine. After cooling, pour the solution back into the test tube. Add 10 drops of 6 M HNO_3, again add 1 ml. of CCl_4 and then add 0.1 M $KMnO_4$ solution [10] dropwise until the aqueous solution is distinctly purple. Shake the mixture. A yellow or orange color in the CCl_4 layer indicates the presence of Br^- ion. If the concentration of the bromine in the CCl_4 layer is small and it is found difficult to distinguish its color, remove about one-half of the CCl_4 with a medicine dropper and transfer it to a 3 ml. test tube. Compare the color of this solution with that of an equal volume of pure CCl_4.

NOTE 10. *The Fe^{+++} ion is not a strong enough oxidizing agent to oxidize Br^- ion to free bromine.*

Nitrate and Nitrite Ions

Test for NO_2^- Ion. To 5 drops of the Na_2CO_3 prepared solution add 2 drops of 6 M H_2SO_4. The solution should be acidic; if it is not, add another drop of the H_2SO_4. To the acidic solution add 5 drops of 0.1 M $FeSO_4$ solution.[11] If NO_2^- ion is present the entire solution will turn dark brown in color.[12] If NO_2^- ion is not present, this solution may be used for the NO_3^- ion test.

NOTE 11. *The $FeSO_4$ solution should be freshly prepared.*

NOTE 12. *Fe^{++} ion in dilute acid solution reduces HNO_2 to NO which in turn combines with excess Fe^{++} ion to form the $Fe(NO)^{++}$ ion. This ion has a characteristic dark brown color.*

Test for NO_3^- Ion. Place 1 ml. of the Na_2CO_3 prepared solution in a casserole and add 10 drops of 0.1 M KI solution and 2 drops of 18 M H_2SO_4. Expel most of the iodine by heating until the solution is faintly yellow or colorless. Add 6 M NaOH until the solution is alkaline and then add 5 drops of the reagent in excess. Warm the solution gently until a piece of moist red litmus paper inserted into the vapors of the boiling solution remains red. Avoid blue coloration of the litmus paper due to spray containing NaOH. Transfer this alkaline solution to a *dry* test tube with a medicine dropper, the exterior of which is also dry. Avoid getting any of the solution on the upper walls of the test tube. Now insert a few granules of metallic aluminum.

Place a loose cotton wad about halfway down the test tube and then hang a piece of moist red litmus paper from the lip of the test tube until the lower end almost reaches (but does not touch) the cotton wad. Cover the test tube with a 10 ml. beaker and gently warm the solution until vigorous action ensues, but not so vigorous that the solution comes in contact with the cotton wad. The cotton wad prevents spray from reaching the litmus. Allow the tube to stand and cool. In 2 to 5 minutes a general blue color over the litmus paper diffusing from the bottom to the top indicates the presence of NO_3^- ion.[13]

NOTE 13. *The test for NO_3^- ion is based upon the removal of NO_2^- ion by I^- ion in acid solution, and the removal of NH_4^+ ion by OH^- ion. All of the other anions are retained in the form of their sodium salts. Then metallic aluminum is used to reduce NO_3^- ion to NH_3 which is detected by litmus.*

Equations for Pertinent Reactions in Anion Procedure

$$CO_3^{--} + 2H^+ = H_2O + CO_{2(g)}$$
$$CO_2 + Ba(OH)_2 = H_2O + BaCO_{3(s)}$$
$$S^{--} + 2H^+ = H_2S_{(g)}$$
$$SO_3^{--} + 2H^+ = H_2O + SO_{2(g)}$$
$$CrO_4^{--} + Ba^{++} \text{ (in HAc)} = BaCrO_{4(s)}$$
$$SO_4^{--} + Ba^{++} \text{ (in HAc)} = BaSO_{4(s)}$$
$$S^{--} + Pb^{++} = PbS_{(s)}$$
$$X^- + Ag^+ = AgX_{(s)} \qquad \text{(where } X^- = Cl^-, Br^-, I^-, \text{ or } CNS^-\text{)}$$
$$AgCl_{(s)} + 2NH_4OH \text{ } (0.25 \text{ } M) = Ag(NH_3)_2^+ + Cl^- + 2H_2O$$
$$Ag(NH_3)_2^+ + Cl^- + 2H^+ = AgCl_{(s)} + 2NH_4^+$$
$$S^{--} + 2Fe^{+++} \text{ (in HCl)} = S_{(s)} + 2Fe^{++}$$
$$SO_3^{--} + H_2O + 2Fe^{+++} \text{ (in HCl)} = SO_4^{--} + 2H^+ + 2Fe^{++}$$
$$2I^- + 2Fe^{+++} \text{ (in HCl)} = I_2 + 2Fe^{++}$$
$$NO_2^- + H_2O + 2Fe^{+++} \text{ (in HCl)} = NO_3^- + 2H^+ + 2Fe^{++}$$
$$CrO_4^{--} + 3Mn^{++} + 8H^+ \text{ (in conc. HCl)} = Cr^{+++} + 4H_2O + 3Mn^{+++}$$
$$NO_3^- + 3Mn^{++} + 4H^+ \text{ (in conc. HCl)} = NO + 2H_2O + 3Mn^{+++}$$
$$NO_2^- + Mn^{++} + 2H^+ \text{ (in conc. HCl)} = NO + H_2O + Mn^{+++}$$

$$CNS^- + Fe^{+++} = FeCNS^{++}$$
$$2I^- + 2Fe^{+++} = 2Fe^{++} + I_2$$
$$10Br^- + 2MnO_4^- + 16H^+ = 5Br_2 + 2Mn^{++} + 8H_2O$$
$$NO_2^- + Fe^{++} + 2H^+ = Fe^{+++} + NO + H_2O$$
$$NO + Fe^{++} = Fe(NO)^{++}$$
$$2NO_2^- + 2I^- + 4H^+ = 2NO + I_2 + 3H_2O$$
$$NH_4^+ + OH^- = NH_3 + H_2O$$
$$3NO_3^- + 5OH^- + 2H_2O + 8Al_{(s)} = 8AlO_2^- + 3NH_{3(g)}$$

APPENDIX

List of Desk Apparatus

2 beakers, 50 ml.

2 beakers, 100 ml.

14 bottles, dropper reagent, 1 ounce

1 glass-stoppered bottle, 1 ounce (tincture)

1 Bunsen burner

1 casserole, 30 ml.

2 clamps (test tube)

1 clamp holder

1 clay triangle

2 cobalt glass pieces (5 cm. × 5 cm.)

1 crucible, porcelain (small)

1 crucible tongs, iron

1 cylinder, graduated, 10 ml.

1 cylinder, graduated, 25 ml.

1 evaporating dish, #00

1 evaporating dish, #000

1 file, triangular

1 flask, Florence, 250 ml.

2 flasks, Erlenmeyer, 25 ml.

1 box filter paper, 40 mm.

1 box filter paper, 55 mm.

2 funnels, 30–40 mm., short stem

1 funnel stand

1 gauze, wire

1 box labels

1 box matches

6 medicine droppers (standard)

1 mortar (small)

1 pipette, 5 ml.

2 lengths 3 mm. glass rod, 30 cm. each

4 lengths 6 mm. glass tubing, 30 cm. each

1 bar soap

1 stand, iron (small)

1 spatula (micro)

1 sponge

1 two-hole rubber stopper to fit 250 ml. flask

1 one-hole rubber stopper to fit 25 ml. flask

1 one-hole rubber stopper to fit 10 ml. test tube

1 tube litmus paper, blue

1 tube litmus paper, red

1 tube methyl violet paper

2 pieces 8 mm. gum rubber tubing, 30 cm. each

1 piece 1 cm. gas tubing, 60 cm.

1 test tube holder (small)

10 test tubes, 7.5 cm. × 1 cm.

12 test tubes (Pyrex), 10 cm.

2 test tubes, 15 cm.

1 test tube brush (small)

1 test tube rack (small)

2 towels

1 tray for 14 reagent bottles

2 watch glasses, 50 mm.

1 wing top

2 pieces wire, iron or Chromel, 15 cm. in length to be used for flame tests

List of Reagents

ACIDS	CONCENTRATION (MOLAR)
Acetic, dilute..	6
Hydrochloric, conc.	12
Hydrochloric, dilute..................................	6
Hydrochloric..	3
Nitric, conc.	15
Nitric, dilute...	6
Sulfuric, conc.	18
Sulfuric, dilute......................................	6

BASES	
Ammonium hydroxide, conc.	15
Ammonium hydroxide, dilute..........................	6
Ammonium hydroxide.................................	3
Potassium hydroxide.................................	6
Sodium hydroxide....................................	6
Sodium hydroxide....................................	0.1

SALT SOLUTIONS, TEST SOLUTIONS, AND SPECIAL REAGENTS

Aluminon reagent, 1 g. of the ammonium salt of aurin tricarboxylic acid in 1 liter of water	
*Aluminum nitrate...................................	0.1
Ammonium acetate..................................	3
Ammonium carbonate reagent, dissolve 200 g. of ammonium carbonate in 500 ml. of 3 M ammonium hydroxide and dilute to 1 liter.	
Ammonium chloride.................................	5
Ammonium iodide...................................	1
Ammonium molybdate, dissolve 40 g. of MoO_3 in a mixture of 100 ml. of water and 60 ml. of 15 M NH_4OH. Add this solution slowly and with vigorous stirring to one containing 200 ml. of 15 M HNO_3 and 450 ml. of water.	
*Ammonium nitrate...................................	0.1
Ammonium nitrate...................................	4
Ammonium oxalate..................................	0.2

* Reagents indicated by an asterisk are to be used as test solutions both for cations and anions. Some of these reagents are also needed for other purposes.

LIST OF REAGENTS

Ammonium sulfate....................................	1
Ammonium sulfate....................................	0.1
*Antimony trichloride, dissolve in 500 ml. of 6 M HCl and dilute to 1 liter......................................	0.1
Arsenic oxide, dissolve in hot water and add a small amount of HCl to obtain a clear solution......................	0.1
Arsenous oxide, dissolve in 30 ml. of 6 M HCl and dilute to 1 liter..	0.1
Barium chloride......................................	0.1
Barium hydroxide (saturated)	
*Barium nitrate......................................	0.1
*Bismuth nitrate, add to 1 liter of 1.5 M HNO_3...........	0.1
Bromine, liquid (not on shelf)	
Bromine water, saturate water with a few drops of liquid bromine.	
*Cadmium nitrate....................................	0.1
Cadmium sulfate.....................................	0.1
Calcium chloride.....................................	0.1
Calcium nitrate......................................	0.1
Carbon tetrachloride	
*Chromium nitrate....................................	0.1
*Cobalt nitrate......................................	0.1
*Cupric nitrate......................................	0.1
Cupric sulfate.......................................	0.1
Dimethylglyoxime, 1% solution, dissolve 10 g. in 1 liter of alcohol.	
Ferric chloride......................................	1
Ferric chloride......................................	0.1
*Ferric nitrate......................................	0.1
Ferrous sulfate......................................	0.1
Hydrogen peroxide, 3% solution	
Lead acetate..	0.2
*Lead nitrate..	0.1
*Magnesia mixture, dissolve 50 g. of $MgCl_2 \cdot 6H_2O$ and 70 g. of NH_4Cl in 400 ml. of water, add 100 ml. of 15 M NH_4OH and dilute to 1 liter. Should be filtered.	
*Magnesium nitrate..................................	0.1
*Manganous nitrate..................................	0.1
Manganous chloride, saturated in 12 M HCl	
Mercuric chloride....................................	0.1

*Mercuric nitrate...................................... 0.1
*Mercurous nitrate.................................... 0.1
Methyl alcohol
Methyl orange (1 g. in 1 liter)
*Nickel nitrate...................................... 0.1
Phenolphthalein, 1% solution in 50% alcohol
*Potassium bromide................................... 0.1
Potassium carbonate, saturated solution
Potassium chlorate................................... 0.1
Potassium chromate................................... 1
*Potassium chromate.................................. 0.1
Potassium ferricyanide............................... 0.1
Potassium ferrocyanide............................... 0.1
*Potassium iodide.................................... 0.1
*Potassium nitrate................................... 0.1
Potassium nitrite.................................... 6
Potassium permanganate............................... .01
Potassium thiocyanate................................ 1
*Potassium thiocyanate............................... 0.1
S. and O. reagent for magnesium — p-nitrobenzeneazore-
   sorcinol. Dissolve 1.2 g. of the dye in 250 ml. of 0.25 M
   NaOH.
*Silver nitrate...................................... 0.1
Sodium acetate....................................... 2
Sodium arsenate...................................... 0.1
Sodium arsenite...................................... 0.1
Sodium tetraborate (borax)........................... .05
Sodium carbonate..................................... 1.5
*Sodium carbonate.................................... 0.1
*Sodium chloride..................................... 0.1
Sodium fluoride...................................... 0.1
*Sodium nitrite...................................... 0.1
Sodium dihydrogen phosphate.......................... 0.5
Sodium hydrogen phosphate............................ 0.5
Sodium hydrogen phosphate............................ 0.1
Sodium sulfate, saturated
Sodium sulfate....................................... 1
Sodium hydrogen sulfate.............................. 2
*Sodium sulfide...................................... 0.1
*Sodium sulfite...................................... 0.1

SOLID REAGENTS

Sodium thiosulfate	0.1
*Stannic chloride	0.1
*Stannous chloride, dissolve 22 g. of $SnCl_2 \cdot 2H_2O$ in 75 ml. of 12 M HCl, allow to stand for several hours and then dilute to 1 liter	0.1
*Strontium nitrate	0.1
Triethanolamine	
*Zinc nitrate	0.1
Zinc sulfate	0.1

Solid Reagents

In addition to the following list of solid reagents, which are essential for the procedures in this text, it is desirable that the student have available all the solids used in preparing the previously listed solutions. Substances needed for solid unknowns are of such a varied nature, that the selection of them is left to the discretion of the instructor.

Absorbent cotton	Potassium nitrate
Aluminum, granular, pellets	Potassium permanganate
Ammonium chloride	Sodium bicarbonate
Ammonium sulfate	Sodium bismuthate
Calcium fluoride	Sodium carbonate
Ferrous sulfate	Sodium chloride
Iron, very fine wire	Sodium nitrate
Mercury (not on shelf)	Sodium thiosulfate
Potassium carbonate	Zinc, powdered, granular
Potassium ferricyanide	

TABLE 20

DENSITY-MOLARITY

In making solutions of H_2SO_4, HCl, HNO_3, and NH_3 the concentration of the solution which is to be diluted should always be determined. This can easily be done with the aid of a hydrometer and the following table. If no hydrometer is available a pycnometer may be used or a relatively large amount of the solution (500 ml.) can be weighed on a rather rough balance and the density determined by comparing the weight with an equal volume of water.

For the purposes of this course this table will apply to densities determined between 15° and 25° C.

H₂SO₄		HCl		HNO₃		NH₄OH(NH₃)	
M	d (20° C.)	M	d (20° C.)	M	d (20° C.)	M	d (20° C.)
1	1.060	1	1.016	1	1.032	1	.992
2	1.118	2	1.033	2	1.065	2	.984
3	1.177	3	1.050	3	1.097	3	.976
4	1.234	4	1.066	4	1.130	4	.969
5	1.287	5	1.082	5	1.161	5	.962
6	1.338	6	1.098	6	1.192	6	.955
7	1.388	7	1.113	7	1.221	7	.948
8	1.440	8	1.128	8	1.248	8	.942
9	1.490	9	1.143	9	1.275	9	.935
10	1.539	10	1.158	10	1.300	10	.928
11	1.586	11	1.171	11	1.324	11	.922
12	1.633	12	1.184	12	1.346	12	.916
13	1.678	13	1.196	13	1.367	13	.909
14	1.722			14	1.386	14	.903
15	1.761			15	1.403	15	.897
16	1.795			16	1.417	16	.892
17	1.822						
18	1.834						

Preparation of Unknown Solutions

It is desirable that the student carry out tests with solutions containing given ions at concentrations comparable to those of the unknown solutions. For this purpose it is recommended that all stock solutions contain the ions in question at a concentration of 0.1 M. In making up an unknown the instructor may then conveniently use 0.6 ml. (12 drops) of a 0.1 M solution of each ion included and then dilute to a total volume of 3 ml. This procedure allows for a maximum of five ions each at a concentration of .02 M. If it is desirable to use a larger number of ions for the unknown solution the total volume may be increased to 4 ml. or more. *All test solutions should be made available to the student for carrying out the preliminary experiments.*

Mathematical Operations

In designing the problems for this course, simplicity of mathematical operations has been one of the chief objectives. Since the primary purpose of these problems is the development of an understanding of chemical equilibrium, difficulties with mathematics would tend to impair the progress of the student. There are, however, a few simple mathematical operations, notations and concepts with which it is impossible to dispense. These are given in the nature of a review since it is assumed that the student is familiar with the simplest algebra and the use of logarithms.

The Use of Exponents. The small size and the large numbers of molecules with which we have to deal make it necessary to use numbers that are often beyond everyday range of thought. For example, there are 606,000,000,000,000,000,000,-000 molecules in 1 mole or 1 gram molecule of any substance. Instead of expressing the number in this manner we use an abbreviated form, 6.06×10^{23} (6.06 times ten to the twenty-third power). The factor 10^{23} is equivalent to moving the decimal point twenty-three places to the right in the number 6.06. The number 2000 may be written 2×10^3, that is, 2×1000, for 10^3 is the product obtained when 10 is multiplied by itself 3 times; i.e., $10 \times 10 \times 10$. One million would be 10^6, and one billion, 10^9. The number 206,000 could be written in any one of the following ways:

0.206×10^6	206×10^3
$2.06\ \ \times 10^5$	2060×10^2
$20.6\ \ \ \times 10^4$	20600×10

The first, second, or third of these are obviously the most convenient.

Numbers very much smaller than 1 are expressed in a similar manner. Two-millionths may be written .000002, but for convenience it is better to write it as 2×10^{-6} (2 times ten to the minus sixth power). In order to convert the second form to the first it is necessary merely to move the decimal point six places to the left. It is the same as $2/10^6$, that is, two divided by one million. Again, this number could be written in any of the following forms:

$$
\begin{array}{ll}
2.0 \ \times 10^{-6} & .002 \quad \times 10^{-3} \\
0.2 \ \times 10^{-5} & .0002 \quad \times 10^{-2} \\
.02 \times 10^{-4} & .00002 \ \times 10^{-1} \\
& .000002
\end{array}
$$

The first two of these forms are the most convenient. The number 10^{-6} is the same as $0.1 \times 0.1 \times 0.1 \times 0.1 \times 0.1 \times 0.1$.

The use of the exponential form greatly facilitates the multiplication and division of either large or small numbers. In multiplying two purely exponential numbers the exponents are added, and this algebraic sum is used as the exponent of the answer. Examples:

$$
\begin{array}{l}
10^3 \times \ \ 10^3 = 10^6 \\
10^3 \times 10^{-2} = 10 \\
10^{23} \times 10^{-6} = 10^{17}
\end{array}
$$

Multiplying 4×10^7 by 6×10^4 becomes 24×10^{11}, that is, $(4 \times 6) \times (10^{7+4})$. Likewise,

$$
\begin{array}{l}
6000 \times 210 = 6 \times 10^3 \times 2.1 \times 10^2 = 12.6 \times 10^5 \\
420 \times 0.000036 = 4.2 \times 10^2 \times 3.6 \times 10^{-5} = 15.12 \times 10^{-3} \\
.00012 \times .00007 = 1.2 \times 10^{-4} \times 7.0 \times 10^{-5} = 8.4 \times 10^{-9}.
\end{array}
$$

The reverse operation is performed by dividing one number by another. For the purely exponential part of the number the exponent of the divisor is subtracted algebraically from that of the dividend and the algebraic difference is used as the exponent of the answer. Thus,

$$10^6 \text{ divided by } 10^2 = 10^4$$

Examples of division are:

(a) $\qquad 4 \times 10^4 \div 2 \times 10^2 = \dfrac{4 \times 10^4}{2 \times 10^2} = \left(\dfrac{4}{2}\right) \times \left(\dfrac{10^4}{10^2}\right)$

$$= 2 \times 10^2$$

(b) $\quad 4 \times 10^4 \div 8 \times 10^{-6} = \left(\dfrac{4}{8}\right) \times \left(\dfrac{10^4}{10^{-6}}\right) = 0.5 \times 10^{4-(-6)}$

$\qquad\qquad\qquad\qquad = 0.5 \times 10^{4+6} = 0.5 \times 10^{10}$

(c) $\quad 3.2 \times 10^{-5} \div 4 \times 10^{-9} = \left(\dfrac{3.2}{4}\right) \times \left(\dfrac{10^{-5}}{10^{-9}}\right) = 0.8 \times 10^{-5-(-9)}$

$\qquad\qquad\qquad\qquad = 0.8 \times 10^{-5+9} = 0.8 \times 10^4 = 8 \times 10^3$

Since the squaring of any number is the operation of multiplying the number by itself, $(2 \times 10^5)^2$ becomes,

$$2 \times 10^5 \cdot 2 \times 10^5 \text{ or } 4 \times 10^{10}$$

In extracting a square root of a purely exponential number, the exponent is merely divided by two and used in the answer:

$$\sqrt{10^4} = 10^2$$

The square root of $4 \times 10^{-4} = \sqrt{4} \times \sqrt{10^{-4}} = 2 \times 10^{-2}$. It is essential that the exponent be an even number in order to simplify the procedure; if it should not be an even number it may be easily changed as shown in the following cases:

(a) $\sqrt{0.4 \times 10^5} = \sqrt{4 \times 10^4}$

(or $(4 \times 10^4)^{\frac{1}{2}}) = \sqrt{4} \times \sqrt{10^4} = 2 \times 10^2$

(b) $\sqrt{2.5 \times 10^{-9}} = \sqrt{25 \times 10^{-10}}$

(or $(25 \times 10^{-10})^{\frac{1}{2}}) = 5 \times 10^{-5}$

(c) $\sqrt{81 \times 10^6} = (81 \times 10^6)^{\frac{1}{2}} = 9 \times 10^3$

The exponent $\frac{1}{2}$ may be substituted for the usual square root sign. Thus $\sqrt{2}$ is the same as $2^{\frac{1}{2}}$, and $\sqrt{3 \times 10^2}$, the same as $(3 \times 10^2)^{\frac{1}{2}}$.

The Use of Logarithms and Exponential Numbers. The common logarithm of any number is the power to which the number 10 must be raised to equal that number. Thus the logarithm of 1000 is 3, that is, the number 10 must be raised to the third power to be equal to 1000. Examples:

Number	Number expressed exponentially	Logarithm
1000	10^3	3
100000	10^5	5
10	10^1	1
1	10^0	0*
.01	10^{-2}	-2
.00001	10^{-5}	-5

To what power must 10 be raised to equal 50? Obviously, the value of this exponent must be between 1 and 2, for 50 lies between 10, the common logarithm of which is 1, and 100, the common logarithm of which is 2. The logarithm of 50 is 1.6990, that is, $50 = 10^{1.6990}$. When the exponent of 10 is not a whole number, we cannot give it the same simple interpretation as was done in the previous section. For example, to move the decimal point 1.6990 places to the right has no meaning. Nevertheless, any number may be expressed entirely in the exponential form. Examples are:

Number	Logarithm of number	Number expressed exponentially
20	1.3010	$10^{1.3010}$
310	2.4914	$10^{2.4914}$
.013	-1.8861	$10^{-1.8861}$

What was stated previously regarding the multiplication of exponential numbers applies here; that is, for multiplication the exponents are added, and for division, the exponents are subtracted. Thus,

$$20 \times 310 = 10^{1.3010} \times 10^{2.4914} = 10^{3.7924} = 6200$$

(The logarithm of 6200 is 3.7924.)

The exponent in question may be found in logarithm tables provided for this purpose. Accordingly, the procedure used to obtain the product of any two or more numbers by the use of logarithms is as follows: The logarithms of the numbers are

* Any finite number raised to the zero power is equal to 1.

taken from the tables and added. This sum of logarithms is the logarithm of the product of the original numbers which again may be obtained from the tables. Thus, to multiply 20 by 310 we add the logarithms of these numbers, 1.3010 and 2.4914, which gives 3.7924. By referring to the logarithm tables we find that the number 6200 corresponds to the logarithm 3.7924.

Similarly, in the process of division, the logarithms are subtracted. In order to divide 6240 by 39 we first find the logarithms for these numbers, 3.7952 and 1.5911, respectively. Subtracting the second from the first we obtain 2.2041 which, by referring to the tables, we find corresponds to 160, the answer. Another example is: Divide 3913 by 13.*

$$\begin{aligned}
\text{Logarithm of 3913} &= 3.5925 \\
\text{Logarithm of} \quad 13 &= \underline{1.1139} \\
\text{Logarithm answer} &= 2.4786
\end{aligned}$$

The answer is 301 since it is the number which corresponds to the logarithm whose value is 2.4786.

Every logarithm is made up of two parts, the characteristic and the mantissa. The characteristic is that part of the logarithm which lies to the left of the decimal point, and the mantissa that part to the right of it. If the logarithm of a number is 4.3060, the characteristic is 4 and the mantissa is .3060. Only the mantissa is found in the logarithm table since the characteristic merely depends upon the position of the decimal point. For example, the logarithm for 316 is found in the tables to be 4996, which is only the mantissa. The characteristic is one less than the number of digits in the number 316, that is, 3 −1 or 2. So the logarithm for the number 316 is 2.4996 (or .4496 + 2). It will be observed that the mantissae for the logarithms of the numbers 316, 31.6 and 3.16 are all the same; only the characteristics are different: 2, 1 and 0 respectively.

The significance of the mantissa and the characteristic can

---

* In actual practice it would not be practical to use logarithms for such a simple case.

perhaps be better understood from the following considerations. The number 316 may be written 3.16×10^2.

logarithm of (3.16×10^2) = logarithm of 3.16 + logarithm of 10^2
logarithm of (3.16×10^2) = .4996 (mantissa)+2 (characteristic)
or   logarithm of 316 = 2.4996

The logarithm of any number less than 1 has a negative value and great care must be used in dealing with such logarithms to avoid mistakes and confusion. The logarithm of such a number may be obtained easily by the same procedure as that given above. For example, the logarithm of .00316 is obtained as follows:

$$.00316 = 3.16 \times 10^{-3}$$
$$\text{logarithm of } .00316 = \text{logarithm of } 3.16 + \text{logarithm of } 10^{-3}$$
$$= .4996 + (-3) = .4996 - 3 = -2.5004$$

The logarithm of any number less than 1 is usually not expressed entirely as a negative number. For example the logarithm of .00316 usually would not be expressed as −2.5004 but rather as .4996 − 3. The abbreviated form for this last expression is $\overline{3}.4996$ or 7.4996 − 10. The reason for adopting this usage is that in this form the mantissae are always added in the process of multiplication; only the characteristics have negative values.

The characteristic of the logarithm of a number less than 1 is equal in magnitude to *one more* than the number of zeros between the first significant figure and the decimal point, and has a negative value. Thus the characteristic of the logarithm of .0013 is − 3, and that of the logarithm of .00006 is − 5. The logarithm of .0013 is then .1139 − 3. (This would be equal to − 2.8861 but for convenience is written as $\overline{3}.1139$ or usually 7.1139 − 10.)

Examples:

	Number	*Logarithm*
(a)	.0167	8.2227 − 10 or $\overline{2}.2227$
	.000003	4.4771 − 10 or $\overline{6}.4771$
	.764	9.8831 − 10 or $\overline{1}.8831$

which are numbered; the divisions between the different numbers and zero are proportional to the logarithms of the numbers. By sliding one piece along the other, the sum of the logarithms of two numbers can be obtained. Since the process of adding the logarithms of two numbers is the same as multiplying the numbers by each other, the slide rule can be used for multiplication. It follows that the reverse operation of division can also be performed on the slide rule.

Students are strongly urged to obtain a slide rule and use it in making the computations necessary in the course. The solutions of problems are enormously expedited by its use. The ordinary 10-inch slide rule has an accuracy of about one part in 500 which is sufficiently accurate for most work in chemistry. Complete directions for its operation accompany every slide rule.

Proportion. The three statements,

(1) A is proportional to B

(2) $A \propto B$

(3) $A = \text{constant} \times B$, or $A = KB$, or $\dfrac{A}{B} = K$,

are identical in meaning. The statements (2) and (3) are abbreviations of statement (1). In statement (3), K is known as the proportionality constant. If we write

$$d = Ks$$

where d is the distance covered in a given time and s is speed, we are saying that the distance covered in a given time is proportional to the speed.

The rate of formation of hydrogen iodide from its elements, hydrogen and iodine, is expressed by the following equation:

$$\text{rate} = k \times (concentration\ of\ H_2) \times (concentration\ of\ I_2)$$

This means that the rate of formation of hydrogen iodide is proportional to the product of the concentrations of the hydrogen and iodine.

Dimensional Formulae. Most physical quantities with which we deal in this text have associated with them dimensional formulae expressed in the fundamental quantities or units of length (l), time (t), mass (m), and temperature (T). Thus, velocity may be expressed in miles per hour, or in centimeters per second, to mention only two of many expressions for velocity. In any event, the dimensional formula for velocity is l/t or lt^{-1}. Acceleration is defined as the change in velocity (v) per unit of time. The dimensional formula for acceleration is lt^{-2} (i.e., $v/t = lt^{-2}$).

The sciences of chemistry and physics use the gram, centimeter, second, degree centigrade system of units. When we adhere to one system we can use more specific fundamental quantities to express dimensional formulae. Thus, instead of time, t, we use the second (sec.); instead of mass (m), the gram (g.); for length we use centimeter (cm.); and for temperature, the degree (deg.).

The following dimensional formulae are those for the centimeter, gram, second (the cgs) system: length (cm.), area (cm.^{2}), volume (cm.^{3}), velocity (cm. sec.$^{-1}$), and acceleration (cm. sec.$^{-2}$). Force is defined as mass $\times$ acceleration; so the dimensions of force are g. cm. sec.$^{-2}$. Work is defined as force $\times$ distance; therefore, the dimensions of work are g. cm.^{2} sec.$^{-2}$. Energy and work have the same dimensions. We know that kinetic energy is equal to $1/2\ mv^2$. The dimensions of this quantity are g. cm.^{2}/sec.^{2}, or g. cm.^{2} sec.$^{-2}$, the same as those for work. Potential energy is equal to mgh, where h is the height above the earth's surface expressed in centimeters and g is the acceleration due to gravity. Potential energy, therefore, has the dimensions g. cm.^{2} sec.$^{-2}$. Concentration may be expressed in grams per milliliter. The dimensions of concentration are g. cm.$^{-3}$.

Very often it is convenient to use derived dimensions instead of the more fundamental ones. For example, we often use gram per liter instead of gram per milliliter for concentration. In this case the dimensions may be written g. liter^{-1} where liter^{-1} is equal to $(1000\ \text{cm.}^3)^{-1}$. Also, we often use the term mole instead of gram. Thus, the concentration can be expressed in terms of mole per liter or mole liter^{-1}.

Pressure is defined as the force per unit area. The dimensions of pressure are, therefore, g. cm. sec.$^{-2}$ cm.$^{-2}$ or g. cm.$^{-1}$ sec.$^{-2}$. If a gas expands under constant pressure and constant temperature, the work done is equal to $p(v_2 - v_1)$ or $p\Delta v$. The dimensions of $p\Delta v$ should be those of work. Multiplying the dimensions of pressure and volume we get g. cm.$^{-1}$ sec.$^{-2}$ $\times$ cm.^{3}, or g. cm.^{2} sec.$^{-2}$, the dimensions of energy or work.

The gas law states that $PV = nRT$, where n is the number of moles of gas and R is a constant. What are the dimensions of R?

$$R = \frac{PV}{nT}$$

The dimensions of both sides of an equation must always be the same. The dimensions of R are therefore,

$$\frac{\text{g. cm.}^{-1} \text{ sec.}^{-2} \times \text{cm.}^3}{\text{mole} \times \text{degree}} = \text{g. cm.}^2 \text{ sec.}^{-1} \text{ mole}^{-1} \text{ degree}^{-1}$$

The fundamental unit of work is the erg. So instead of g. cm.^{2} sec.$^{-2}$ we may write (erg). The dimensions of R are sometimes given as erg mole^{-1} degree^{-1}. In this case the erg is used as a derived unit.

Problems. Mathematical Operations

1. Express the following numbers in the exponential form:

(a)	1,000,000	(m)	.01
(b)	400,000	(n)	.0032
(c)	50,000	(o)	.000007
(d)	9,000	(p)	.00107
(e)	600	(q)	.0000000009
(f)	70	(r)	.00000678
(g)	1,450,000	(s)	0.103
(h)	946,000	(t)	1.0
(i)	59,000	(u)	0.1
(j)	9,627	(v)	.00045
(k)	450	(w)	.000006
(l)	563,200		

2. Express the answers of the following in the exponential form:

    (a) Multiply 4.2×10^4 by 3.0×10^4
    (b) Multiply 2.5×10^{-2} by 2.0×10^5
    (c) Multiply 6.06×10^{23} by 1×10^{-6}
    (d) Multiply 4.0×10^{-4} by 7.0×10^{-3}
    (e) Multiply .00005 by 10
    (f) Multiply .00025 by 400
    (g) Multiply .000007 by 1×10^{10}
    (h) Multiply 60 by 5,000,000
    (i) Multiply 2500 by .0025
    (j) Multiply .00003 by .006
    (k) Multiply 1×10^6 by .0005

3. Express the answers of the following in the exponential form:

    (a) Divide 1×10^6 by 2×10^4
    (b) Divide 3×10^4 by 3×10^{-3}
    (c) Divide 4.2×10^{-3} by 1.3×10^{-4}
    (d) Divide 4.5×10^{-6} by 1.5×10^{-5}
    (e) Divide 9×10^{-20} by 2×10^{-15}
    (f) Divide 4.2×10^6 by 210,000
    (g) Divide 2.5×10^5 by .00005
    (h) Divide 6.6×10^{-7} by 1.1×10^5
    (i) Divide 5.0×10^{-6} by 2,500,000
    (j) Divide 4×10^{-4} by .0008
    (k) Divide 64,000 by 2×10^5
    (l) Divide 2,500,000 by 5×10^{-8}
    (m) Divide .000034 by 1.7×10^3
    (n) Divide .00065 by 1.3×10^{-2}

4. Express the answers of the following operations in terms of the significant figures only: (The quantities represent experimental values.)

    (a) Add the quantities 1834.56, 50 and 0.765
    (b) Subtract 6.0 from 22.45
    (c) Subtract 6.00 from 22.45
    (d) Multiply 0.675 by $(.02)^2$
    (e) Solve for X in the following: $X(6 - X) = .0006$

5. Find the logarithm of the following:

(a) 2156.3   (e) 67.25
(b) 340   (f) 0.387
(c) 1.035   (g) .004
(d) .0000067   (h) 400

6. Give the number (antilogarithm) corresponding to the following logarithms:

(a) 3.6745   (e) $6.4632 - 10$
(b) 2.4362   (f) $\overline{4}.2697$
(c) .2875   (g) $- 2.3628$
(d) $9.3476 - 10$ (h) $- 0.2756$.

7. Solve the following expressions with the use of logarithms:

(a) $V = 350 \times \dfrac{273}{302} \times \dfrac{745}{760}$ Find V

(b) $N = \dfrac{6.06 \times 10^{23}}{1000 \times 22.4 \times 760 \times 10^{-6}}$ Find N

(c) $M = \dfrac{22.4 \times 10^3 \times 2.456}{150}$ Find M

(d) $X = \dfrac{(3.65)^2 \times 24.5 \times 10^{-4} \times 376.2}{3.0 \times 26.5 \times 500}$ Find X

8. Solve the following expressions; use logarithms where desirable:

(a) $(2.54 \times 10^5)^2$
(b) $(3.6 \times 10^{-4})^2$
(c) $(1.2 \times 10^{-3})^3$
(d) $(6.56 \times 10^2)^2 (3.5 \times 10^4)^2$
(e) $(9.2 \times 10^{-2})^2 (2.6 \times 10^8)^2$

9. Extract the square root of the following; use logarithms where desirable:

(a) 4×10^{-6} (e) 25×10^{-5}
(b) $(4 \times 10^{-6})^2$ (f) 6.942×10^3
(c) 3.6×10^9 (g) 24.53×10^{-7}
(d) 0.25×10^{-4} (h) 1.44×10^{-14}

10. Solve the following equations for X:

(a) $X^2 + 4X + 7 = 0$
(b) $X^2 + 0.15X = 2.53$

(c) $X^2 + (1 \times 10^{-4})X - 3.6 \times 10^{-6} = 0$
(d) $X^2 + (1.8 \times 10^{-5})X - 1.8 \times 10^{-6} = 0$

11. Calculate the pH of solutions which contain the following con-centration of the hydrogen ion respectively:

   (a) 1×10^{-4}
   (b) 2×10^{-12}
   (c) 3.5×10^{-6}
   (d) 1×10^{-7}
   (e) 2.56×10^{-5}
   (f) 0.1345

12. From the following pH values calculate the concentration of the hydrogen ion:

   (a) 7.0
   (b) 8.4
   (c) 5.3
   (d) 6.87
   (e) 9.25
   (f) 2.46

13. Express the following statements in the form of an equation:

   (a) At constant temperature, the pressure of a gas varies inversely with the volume.
   (b) At constant pressure, the volume of a gas varies directly with the absolute temperature.
   (c) At constant volume, the pressure of a gas varies directly with the absolute temperature.
   (d) The speed of diffusion of a molecule in the gaseous condition is inversely proportional to the square root of its mass.
   (e) The force of attraction between two bodies is directly proportional to the product of their masses and inversely proportional to the square of the distance between them.

14. What is the dimensional formula for (a) density, (b) frequency, and (c) power (energy per second)?

15. Show by dimensional formulae that the following statement is incorrect: "the work done per second is equal to the potential energy of the body."

TABLE 21

IONIZATION CONSTANTS OF WEAK ACIDS

The equilibrium constants given in this and the following tables appear in two forms. In the column to the right, the value of the constant is given in exponential form for convenience. Some of the data have been taken from the International Critical Tables, but most of the data have been obtained from "Oxidation Potentials" by Wendell M. Latimer, published by Prentice-Hall, Inc., 1952. Other data have been selected after a careful evaluation of the literature references.

Acid	Equilibrium	Ionization Constant (at Room Temperature)	
Acetic	$CH_3COOH = H^+ + CH_3COO^-$	1.85×10^{-5}	$10^{-4.7}$
Arsenic	$H_3AsO_4 = H^+ + H_2AsO_4^-$	2.5×10^{-4}	$10^{-3.6}$
Dihydrogen Arsenate ion	$H_2AsO_4^- = H^+ + HAsO_4^{--}$	5.6×10^{-8}	$10^{-7.3}$
Monohydrogen Arsenate ion	$HAsO_4^{--} = H^+ + AsO_4^{---}$	3.0×10^{-13}	$10^{-12.5}$
Arsenous	$H_3AsO_3 = H^+ + H_2AsO_3^-$	6.0×10^{-10}	$10^{-9.3}$
Benzoic	$C_6H_5COOH = H^+ + C_6H_5COO^-$	6.6×10^{-5}	$10^{-4.2}$
Boric	$H_3BO_3 = H^+ + H_2BO_3^-$	6.0×10^{-10}	$10^{-9.3}$
Carbonic	$H_2CO_3 = H^+ + HCO_3^-$	4.2×10^{-7}	$10^{-6.4}$
Bicarbonate ion	$HCO_3^- = H^+ + CO_3^{--}$	4.8×10^{-11}	$10^{-10.3}$
Bisulfate ion	$HSO_4^- = H^+ + SO_4^{--}$	1.26×10^{-2}	$10^{-1.9}$
Chloracetic	$ClCH_2COOH = H^+ + ClCH_2COO^-$	1.4×10^{-3}	$10^{-2.9}$
Chlorous	$HClO_2 = H^+ + ClO_2^-$	1.1×10^{-2}	$10^{-1.0}$
Bicuprate ion	$HCuO_2^- = H^+ + CuO_2^{--}$	8×10^{-14}	$10^{-13.1}$
Cyanic	$HCNO = H^+ + CNO^-$	2.0×10^{-4}	$10^{-3.7}$
Dichloracetic	$Cl_2CHCOOH = H^+ + Cl_2CHCOO^-$	5.5×10^{-2}	$10^{-1.3}$
Formic	$HCOOH = H^+ + HCOO^-$	2.1×10^{-4}	$10^{-3.7}$
Hydrazoic	$HN_3 = H^+ + N_3^-$	1.9×10^{-5}	$10^{-4.7}$
Hydrocyanic	$HCN = H^+ + CN^-$	4.0×10^{-10}	$10^{-9.4}$
Hydrofluoric	$HF = H^+ + F^-$	6.9×10^{-4}	$10^{-3.2}$
Hydrogen peroxide	$H_2O_2 = H^+ + HO_2^-$	2.4×10^{-12}	$10^{-11.6}$
Hydrogen selenide	$H_2Se = H^+ + HSe^-$	1.9×10^{-4}	$10^{-3.7}$
Hydrogen sulfide	$H_2S = H^+ + HS^-$	1.0×10^{-7}	10^{-7}
Bisulfide ion	$HS^- = H^+ + S^{--}$	1.3×10^{-13}	$10^{-12.9}$

Acid	Equilibrium	Ionization Constant (at Room Temperature)	
Hydrogen telluride	$H_2Te = H^+ + HTe^-$	2.5×10^{-3}	$10^{-2.6}$
Bitelluride ion	$HTe^- = H^+ + Te^{--}$	1.0×10^{-11}	10^{-11}
Hypobromous	$HBrO = H^+ + BrO^-$	2×10^{-9}	$10^{-8.7}$
Hypochlorous	$HClO = H^+ + ClO^-$	3.2×10^{-8}	$10^{-7.5}$
Nitrous	$HNO_2 = H^+ + NO_2^-$	4.5×10^{-4}	$10^{-3.3}$
O-Nitrobenzoic	$C_7H_5NO_4 = H^+ + C_7H_4NO_4^-$	6.1×10^{-3}	$10^{-2.2}$
Oxalic	$H_2C_2O_4 = H^+ + HC_2O_4^-$	3.8×10^{-2}	$10^{-1.4}$
Monohydrogen oxalate ion	$HC_2O_4^- = H^+ + C_2O_4^{--}$	5.0×10^{-5}	$10^{-4.3}$
Phenol	$C_6H_5OH = H^+ + C_6H_5O^-$	1.0×10^{-10}	10^{-10}
Phosphoric	$H_3PO_4 = H^+ + H_2PO_4^-$	7.5×10^{-3}	$10^{-2.1}$
Dihydrogen phosphate ion	$H_2PO_4^- = H^+ + HPO_4^{--}$	6.2×10^{-8}	$10^{-7.2}$
Monohydrogen phosphate ion	$HPO_4^{--} = H^+ + PO_4^{---}$	1×10^{-12}	10^{-12}
Phosphorous	$H_3PO_3 = H^+ + H_2PO_3^-$	1.6×10^{-2}	$10^{-1.8}$
Dihydrogen phosphite ion	$H_2PO_3^- = H^+ + HPO_3^{--}$	7.0×10^{-7}	$10^{-6.2}$
Propionic	$C_2H_5COOH = H^+ + C_2H_5COO^-$	1.4×10^{-5}	$10^{-4.9}$
Salicylic	$C_7H_6O_3 = H^+ + C_7H_5O_3^-$	1.1×10^{-3}	10^{-3}
Selenious	$H_2SeO_3 = H^+ + HSeO_3^-$	2.7×10^{-3}	$10^{-2.6}$
Biselenate ion	$HSeO_3^- = H^+ + SeO_3^{--}$	2.5×10^{-7}	$10^{-6.6}$
Sulfurous	$H_2SO_3 = H^+ + HSO_3^-$	1.25×10^{-2}	$10^{-1.9}$
Bisulfite ion	$HSO_3^- = H^+ + SO_3^{--}$	5.6×10^{-8}	$10^{-7.3}$
Tartaric	$C_4H_4O_6H_2 = H^+ + C_4H_4O_6H^-$	1.1×10^{-3}	10^{-3}
Bitartrate ion	$C_4H_4O_6H^- = H^+ + C_4H_4O_6^{--}$	6.9×10^{-5}	$10^{-4.2}$
Telluric	$H_2TeO_4 = H^+ + HTeO_4^-$	6×10^{-7}	$10^{-6.2}$
Bitellurate ion	$HTeO_4^- = H^+ + TeO_4^{--}$	4×10^{-11}	$10^{-10.4}$
Tellurous	$H_2TeO_3 = H^+ + HTeO_3^-$	2×10^{-3}	$10^{-2.7}$
Bitellurite ion	$HTeO_3^- = H^+ + TeO_3^{--}$	1×10^{-8}	10^{-8}
Aluminum hydroxide	$Al(OH)_3 = H^+ + AlO_2^- + H_2O$	4×10^{-13}	$10^{-12.4}$
Antimony hydroxide	$Sb(OH)_3 = H^+ + SbO_2^- + H_2O$	1×10^{-11}	10^{-11}
Chromium hydroxide	$Cr(OH)_3 = H^+ + CrO_2^- + H_2O$	1×10^{-16}	10^{-16}
Cobaltous hydroxide	$Co(OH)_2 = H^+ + HCoO_2^-$	8×10^{-20}	$10^{-19.1}$
Bicuprate ion	$HCuO_2^- = H^+ + CuO_2^{--}$	8×10^{-14}	$10^{-13.1}$
Cupric hydroxide	$H_2CuO_2 = H^+ + HCuO_2^-$	1.5×10^{-16}	$10^{-15.8}$
Lead hydroxide	$Pb(OH)_2 = H^+ + HPbO_2^-$	2×10^{-16}	$10^{-15.7}$
Manganous hydroxide	$Mn(OH)_2 = H^+ + HMnO_2^-$	1×10^{-19}	10^{-19}
Mercuric hydroxide	$Hg(OH)_2 = H^+ + HHgO_2^-$	1×10^{-15}	10^{-15}
Nickelous hydroxide	$Ni(OH)_2 = H^+ + HNiO_2^-$	6×10^{-19}	$10^{-18.2}$
Silver hydroxide	$AgOH = H^+ + AgO^-$	2×10^{-18}	$10^{-17.7}$
Stannous hydroxide	$Sn(OH)_2 = H^+ + HSnO_2^-$	4×10^{-15}	$10^{-14.4}$
Zinc hydroxide	$Zn(OH)_2 = 2H^+ + ZnO_2^{--}$	1×10^{-29}	10^{-29}
	$Zn(OH)_{2(s)} = Zn(OH)^+ + OH^-$	1.2×10^{-12}	$10^{-11.9}$
	$Zn(OH)^+ = Zn^{++} + OH^-$	4×10^{-5}	$10^{-4.4}$

TABLE 22

IONIZATION CONSTANTS OF WEAK BASES

Base	Equilibrium	Ionization Constant (at Room Temperature)	
Ammonium hydroxide	$NH_4OH = NH_4^+ + OH^-$	1.8×10^{-5}	$10^{-4.7}$
Methyl ammonium hydroxide	$CH_3NH_3OH = CH_3NH_3^+ + OH^-$	5×10^{-4}	$10^{-3.3}$
Dimethyl ammonium hydroxide	$(CH_3)_2NH_2OH = (CH_3)_2NH_2^+ + OH^-$	7.4×10^{-4}	$10^{-3.1}$
Trimethyl ammonium hydroxide	$(CH_3)_3NHOH = (CH_3)_3NH^+ + OH^-$	7.4×10^{-5}	$10^{-4.1}$
Ethyl ammonium hydroxide	$C_2H_5NH_3OH = C_2H_5NH_3^+ + OH^-$	5.6×10^{-4}	$10^{-3.3}$
Phenyl ammonium hydroxide	$C_6H_5NH_3OH = C_6H_5NH_3^+ + OH^-$	4.6×10^{-10}	$10^{-9.3}$
Hydrazine hydroxide	$H_2N \cdot NH_3OH = H_2N \cdot NH_3^+ + OH^-$	9.8×10^{-7}	10^{-6}
Zinc hydroxide	(1) $Zn(OH)_{2(s)} = Zn(OH)^+ + OH^-$	$K = 1, 2 \times 10^{-12}$ and $10^{-11.9}$	
	(2) $Zn(OH)^+ = Zn^{++} + OH^-$	$K = 4 \times 10^{-5}$ and $4 \times 10^{-4.4}$	

TABLE 23

SOLUBILITY PRODUCT CONSTANTS AT ROOM TEMPERATURE

Substance	Equilibrium	Solubility Product Constant	
Acetates			
Silver acetate	$CH_3COOAg_{(s)} = Ag^+ + CH_3COO^-$	4×10^{-3}	$10^{-2.4}$
Bromates			
Silver bromate	$AgBrO_{3(s)} = Ag^+ + BrO_3^-$	6×10^{-5}	$10^{-4.2}$
Bromides			
Cuprous bromide	$CuBr_{(s)} = Cu^+ + Br^-$	6×10^{-9}	$10^{-8.2}$
Lead bromide	$PbBr_{2(s)} = Pb^{++} + 2\,Br^-$	4.6×10^{-6}	$10^{-5.3}$
Mercurous bromide	$Hg_2Br_{2(s)} = Hg_2^{++} + 2Br^-$	1.3×10^{-22}	$10^{-21.9}$
Silver bromide	$AgBr_{(s)} = Ag^+ + Br^-$	5×10^{-13}	$10^{-12.3}$
Carbonates			
Barium carbonate	$BaCO_{3(s)} = Ba^{++} + CO_3^{--}$	1.6×10^{-9}	$10^{-8.8}$
Cadmium carbonate	$CdCO_{3(s)} = Cd^{++} + CO_3^{--}$	5.2×10^{-12}	$10^{-11.3}$
Calcium carbonate	$CaCO'_{3(s)} = Ca^{++} + CO_3^{--}$	6.9×10^{-9}	$10^{-8.2}$
Cobalt carbonate	$CoCO_{3(s)} = Co^{++} + CO_3^{--}$	8×10^{-13}	$10^{-12.1}$

Substance	Equilibrium	Solubility Product Constant	
Cupric carbonate	$CuCO_{3(s)} = Cu^{++} + CO_3^{--}$	2.5×10^{-10}	$10^{-9.6}$
Lead carbonate	$PbCO_{3(s)} = Pb^{++} + CO_3^{--}$	1.5×10^{-13}	$10^{-12.8}$
Magnesium carbonate	$MgCO_{3(s)} = Mg^{++} + CO_3^{--}$	4×10^{-5}	$10^{-4.4}$
Manganous carbonate	$MnCO_{3(s)} = Mn^{++} + CO_3^{--}$	9×10^{-11}	$10^{-10.1}$
Mercurous carbonate	$Hg_2CO_{3(s)} = Hg_2^{++} + CO_3^{--}$	9×10^{-17}	$10^{-16.1}$
Nickelous carbonate	$NiCO_{3(s)} = Ni^{++} + CO_3^{--}$	1.4×10^{-7}	$10^{-6.8}$
Silver carbonate	$Ag_2CO_{3(s)} = 2Ag^+ + CO_3^{--}$	8.2×10^{-12}	$10^{-11.1}$
Strontium carbonate	$SrCO_{3(s)} = Sr^{++} + CO_3^{--}$	7×10^{-10}	$10^{-9.2}$
Zinc carbonate	$ZnCO_{3(s)} = Zn^{++} + CO_3^{--}$	2×10^{-10}	$10^{-9.7}$
Chlorides			
Cuprous chloride	$CuCl_{(s)} = Cu^+ + Cl^-$	3.2×10^{-7}	$10^{-6.5}$
Lead chloride	$PbCl_{2(s)} = Pb^{++} + 2Cl^-$	1.6×10^{-5}	$10^{-4.8}$
Mercurous chloride	$Hg_2Cl_{2(s)} = Hg_2^{++} + 2Cl^-$	1.1×10^{-18}	$10^{-17.9}$
Silver chloride	$AgCl_{(s)} = Ag^+ + Cl^-$	2.8×10^{-10}	$10^{-9.6}$
Chromates			
Barium chromate	$BaCrO_{4(s)} = Ba^{++} + CrO_4^{--}$	8.5×10^{-11}	$10^{-10.}$
Calcium chromate	$CaCrO_{4(s)} = Ca^{++} + CrO_4^{--}$	7.1×10^{-4}	$10^{-3.2}$
Lead chromate	$PbCrO_{4(s)} = Pb^{++} + CrO_4^{--}$	2.0×10^{-16}	10^{-16}
Mercurous chromate	$Hg_2CrO_{4(s)} = Hg_2^{++} + CrO_4^{--}$	2×10^{-9}	$10^{-8.7?}$
Silver chromate	$Ag_2CrO_{4(s)} = 2Ag^+ + CrO_4^{--}$	1.9×10^{-12}	$10^{-11.7}$
Strontium chromate	$SrCrO_{4(s)} = Sr^{++} + CrO_4^{--}$	3.6×10^{-5}	$10^{-4.4}$
Cyanides			
Mercurous cyanide	$Hg_2(CN)_{2(s)} = Hg_2^{++} + 2CN^-$	5×10^{-40}	$10^{-39.3}$
Silver cyanide	$AgCN_{(s)} = Ag^+ + CN^-$	1.6×10^{-14}	$10^{-13.8}$
Fluorides			
Barium fluoride	$BaF_{2(s)} = Ba^{++} + 2F^-$	2.4×10^{-5}	$10^{-4.6}$
Calcium fluoride	$CaF_{2(s)} = Ca^{++} + 2F^-$	1.7×10^{-10}	$10^{-9.8}$
Lead fluoride	$PbF_{2(s)} = Pb^{++} + 2F^-$	4×10^{-8}	$10^{-7.4}$
Magnesium fluoride	$MgF_{2(s)} = Mg^{++} + 2F^-$	8×10^{-8}	$10^{-7.1}$
Strontium fluoride	$SrF_{2(s)} = Sr^{++} + 2F^-$	7.9×10^{-10}	$10^{-9.1}$
Hydroxides			
Aluminum hydroxide	$Al(OH)_{3(s)} = Al^{+++} + 3OH^-$	5×10^{-33}	$10^{-32.3}$
Cadmium hydroxide	$Cd(OH)_{2(s)} = Cd^{++} + 2OH^-$	2.0×10^{-14}	$10^{-13.7}$
Chromic hydroxide	$Cr(OH)_{3(s)} = Cr^{+++} + 3OH^-$	7×10^{-31}	$10^{-30.?}$
Chromous hydroxide	$Cr(OH)_{2(s)} = Cr^{++} + 2OH^-$	1×10^{-17}	10^{-17}
Cobaltic hydroxide	$Co(OH)_{3(s)} = Co^{+++} + 3OH^-$	1×10^{-43}	10^{-43}
Cobaltous hydroxide	$Co(OH)_{2(s)} = Co^{++} + 2OH^-$	2.5×10^{-16}	$10^{-15.6}$
Cupric hydroxide	$Cu(OH)_{2(s)} = Cu^{++} + 2OH^-$	1.6×10^{-19}	$10^{-18.8}$
Ferric hydroxide	$Fe(OH)_{3(s)} = Fe^{+++} + 3OH^-$	6×10^{-38}	$10^{-37.2}$
Ferrous hydroxide	$Fe(OH)_{2(s)} = Fe^{++} + 2OH^-$	2×10^{-15}	$10^{-14.7}$
Lead hydroxide	$Pb(OH)_{2(s)} = Pb^{++} + 2OH^-$	4×10^{-15}	$10^{-14.4}$
Magnesium hydroxide	$Mg(OH)_{2(s)} = Mg^{++} + 2OH^-$	8.9×10^{-12}	10^{-11}

SOLUBILITY PRODUCT CONSTANTS AT ROOM TEMPERATURE

Substance	Equilibrium	Solubility Product Constant	
Manganese hydroxide	$Mn(OH)_{2(s)} = Mn^{++} + 2OH^-$	2×10^{-13}	$10^{-12.7}$
Manganic hydroxide	$Mn(OH)_{3(s)} = Mn^{+++} + 3OH^-$	1×10^{-36}	10^{-36}
Mercuric hydroxide	$HgO_{(s)} + H_2O = Hg^{++} + 2OH^-$	3×10^{-26}	$10^{-25.5}$
Nickel hydroxide	$Ni(OH)_{2(s)} = Ni^{++} + 2OH^-$	1.6×10^{-16}	$10^{-15.8}$
Silver hydroxide	$\frac{1}{2}Ag_2O_{(s)} + \frac{1}{2}H_2O = Ag^+ + OH^-$	1×10^{-8}	$10^{-7.7}$
Stannous hydroxide	$Sn(OH)_{2(s)} = Sn^{++} + 2OH^-$	3×10^{-27}	$10^{-26.5}$
Zinc hydroxide	$Zn(OH)_{2(s)} = Zn^{++} + 2OH^-$	5×10^{-17}	$10^{-16.3}$
Iodates			
Barium iodate	$Ba(IO_3)_{2(s)} = Ba^{++} + 2IO_3^-$	1.3×10^{-9}	$10^{-8.9}$
Calcium iodate	$Ca(IO_3)_{2(s)} = Ca^{++} + 2IO_3^-$	1.7×10^{-6}	$10^{-5.8}$
Cupric iodate	$Cu(IO_3)_{2(s)} = Cu^{++} + 2IO_3^-$	1.4×10^{-7}	$10^{-6.9}$
Lead iodate	$Pb(IO_3)_{2(s)} = Pb^{++} + 2IO_3^-$	2.6×10^{-13}	$10^{-12.6}$
Mercuric iodate	$Hg(IO_3)_{2(s)} = Hg^{++} + 2IO_3^-$	3×10^{-13}	$10^{-12.5}$
Mercurous iodate	$Hg_2(IO_3)_{2(s)} = Hg_2^{++} + 2IO_3^-$	1.9×10^{-14}	$10^{-13.7}$
Silver iodate	$AgIO_{3(s)} = Ag^+ + IO_3^-$	3×10^{-8}	$10^{-7.5}$
Iodides			
Cuprous iodide	$CuI_{(s)} = Cu^+ + I^-$	1×10^{-12}	10^{-12}
Lead iodide	$PbI_{2(s)} = Pb^{++} + 2I^-$	8.3×10^{-9}	$10^{-8.1}$
Mercurous iodide	$Hg_2I_{2(s)} = Hg_2^{++} + 2I^-$	4×10^{-29}	$10^{-28.4}$
Silver iodide	$AgI_{(s)} = Ag^+ + I^-$	8.5×10^{-17}	$10^{-16.1}$
Thallous iodide	$TlI_{(s)} = Tl^+ + I^-$	2.5×10^{-8}	$10^{-7.6}$
Oxalates			
Barium oxalate	$BaC_2O_{4(s)} = Ba^{++} + C_2O_4^{--}$	1.5×10^{-8}	$10^{-7.8}$
Cadmium oxalate	$CdC_2O_{4(s)} = Cd^{++} + C_2O_4^{--}$	1.5×10^{-8}	$10^{-7.8}$
Calcium oxalate	$CaC_2O_{4(s)} = Ca^{++} + C_2O_4^{--}$	1.3×10^{-9}	$10^{-8.8}$
Cupric oxalate	$CuC_2O_{4(s)} = Cu^{++} + C_2O_4^{--}$	3×10^{-8}	$10^{-7.5}$
Ferrous oxalate	$FeC_2O_{4(s)} = Fe^{++} + C_2O_4^{--}$	2×10^{-7}	$10^{-6.7}$
Lead oxalate	$PbC_2O_{4(s)} = Pb^{++} + C_2O_4^{--}$	8.3×10^{-12}	$10^{-11.1}$
Magnesium oxalate	$MgC_2O_{4(s)} = Mg^{++} + C_2O_4^{--}$	8.6×10^{-5}	$10^{-4.1}$
Manganic oxalate	$Mn_2(C_2O_4)_{3(s)} = 2Mn^{+++} + 3C_2O_4^{--}$	7×10^{-20}	$10^{-19.2}$
Manganous oxalate	$MnC_2O_{4(s)} = Mn^{++} + C_2O_4^{--}$	1×10^{-15}	10^{-15}
Mercurous oxalate	$Hg_2C_2O_{4(s)} = Hg_2^{++} + C_2O_4^{--}$	1×10^{-13}	10^{-13}
Silver oxalate	$Ag_2C_2O_{4(s)} = 2Ag^+ + C_2O_4^{--}$	1×10^{-11}	10^{-11}
Strontium oxalate	$SrC_2O_{4(s)} = Sr^{++} + C_2O_4^{--}$	5.6×10^{-8}	$10^{-7.2}$
Zinc oxalate	$ZnC_2O_{4(s)} = Zn^{++} + C_2O_4^{--}$	1.5×10^{-9}	$10^{-8.8}$
Sulfates			
Barium sulfate	$BaSO_{4(s)} = Ba^{++} + SO_4^{--}$	1.5×10^{-9}	$10^{-8.8}$
Calcium sulfate	$CaSO_{4(s)} = Ca^{++} + SO_4^{--}$	2.4×10^{-5}	$10^{-4.7}$
Lead sulfate	$PbSO_{4(s)} = Pb^{++} + SO_4^{--}$	1.3×10^{-8}	$10^{-7.8}$
Strontium sulfate	$SrSO_{4(s)} = Sr^{++} + SO_4^{--}$	7.6×10^{-7}	$10^{-6.1}$

Substance	Equilibrium	Solubility Product Constant	
Sulfides			
Bismuth sulfide	$Bi_2S_{3(s)} = 2Bi^{+++} + 3S^{--}$	1×10^{-70}	10^{-70}
Cadmium sulfide	$CdS_{(s)} = Cd^{++} + S^{--}$	6×10^{-27}	$10^{-26.2}$
Cobalt sulfide	$CoS_{(s)} = Co^{++} + S^{--}$	5×10^{-22}	$10^{-21.3}$
Cupric sulfide	$CuS_{(s)} = Cu^{++} + S^{--}$	4×10^{-36}	$10^{-35.4}$
Ferrous sulfide	$FeS_{(s)} = Fe^{++} + S^{--}$	4×10^{-17}	$10^{-16.4}$
Lead sulfide	$PbS_{(s)} = Pb^{++} + S^{--}$	4×10^{-26}	$10^{-25.4}$
Manganous sulfide	$MnS_{(s)} = Mn^{++} + S^{--}$	8×10^{-14}	$10^{-13.1}$
Mercuric sulfide	$HgS_{(s)} = Hg^{++} + S^{--}$	1×10^{-50}	10^{-50}
Mercurous sulfide	$Hg_2S_{(s)} = Hg_2^{++} + S^{--}$	1×10^{-45}	10^{-45}
Nickelous sulfide	$NiS_{(s)} = Ni^{++} + S^{--}$	1×10^{-22}	10^{-22}
Silver sulfide	$Ag_2S_{(s)} = 2Ag^+ + S^{--}$	1×10^{-50}	10^{-50}
Thallous sulfide	$Tl_2S_{(s)} = 2Tl^+ + S^{--}$	1×10^{-22}	10^{-22}
Zinc sulfide	$ZnS_{(s)} = Zn^{++} + S^{--}$	1×10^{-20}	10^{-20}
Thiocyanates			
Cuprous thiocyanate	$CuCNS_{(s)} = Cu^+ + CNS^-$	4×10^{-14}	$10^{-13.4}$
Mercurous thiocyanate	$Hg_2(CNS)_{2(s)} = Hg_2^{++} + 2CNS^-$	3×10^{-20}	$10^{-19.5}$
Silver thiocyanate	$AgCNS_{(s)} = Ag^+ + CNS^-$	1×10^{-12}	10^{-12}

TABLE 24

DISSOCIATION CONSTANTS OF COMPLEX IONS

Equilibrium		Dissociation Constant	
AlF_6^{---}	$= Al^{+++} + 6F^-$	1.5×10^{-20}	$10^{-19.8}$
AlF_5^{--}	$= Al^{+++} + 5F^-$	4.3×10^{-20}	$10^{-19.4}$
AlF_4^-	$= Al^{+++} + 4F^-$	2×10^{-18}	$10^{-17.7}$
$Cd(NH_3)_4^{++}$	$= Cd^{++} + 4NH_3$	1×10^{-7}	10^{-7}
$Cd(CN)_4^{--}$	$= Cd^{++} + 4CN^-$	1×10^{-19}	10^{-19}
CdI_4^{--}	$= Cd^{++} + 4I^-$	5×10^{-7}	$10^{-6.3}$
$CdCl_3^-$	$= Cd^{++} + 3Cl^-$	4×10^{-3}	$10^{-2.4}$
$Cr(CNS)_3$	$= Cr^{+++} + 3CNS^-$	1.6×10^{-6}	$10^{-5.7}$
$Co(NH_3)_6^{++}$	$= Co^{++} + 6NH_3$	1.25×10^{-5}	$10^{-4.8}$
$Co(NH_3)_6^{+++}$	$= Co^{+++} + 6NH_3$	2.2×10^{-34}	$10^{-33.7}$
$Co(NH_3)_5H_2O^{+++}$	$= Co^{+++} + 5NH_3 + H_2O$	1.6×10^{-35}	$10^{-34.8}$
$Co(NH_3)_5Cl^{++}$	$= Co^{+++} + 5NH_3 + Cl^-$	1×10^{-38}	10^{-38}
$Cu(CN)_2^-$	$= Cu^+ + 2CN^-$	1×10^{-16}	10^{-16}
$Cu(NH_3)^+$	$= Cu^+ + NH_3$	7×10^{-7}	$10^{-6.2}$
$Cu(NH_3)_2^+$	$= Cu^+ + 2NH_3$	1.4×10^{-11}	$10^{-10.8}$
$Cu(CN)_4^{---}$	$= Cu^+ + 4CN^-$	2×10^{-27}	$10^{-26.7}$
$Cu(NH_3)_4^{++}$	$= Cu^{++} + 4NH_3$	5×10^{-15}	$10^{-14.3}$
$Cu(C_2O_4)_2^{--}$	$= Cu^{++} + 2C_2O_4^{--}$	5×10^{-11}	$10^{-10.3}$
$Fe(CN)_6^{----}$	$= Fe^{++} + 6CN^-$	1×10^{-35}	10^{-35}
$Fe(CN)_6^{---}$	$= Fe^{+++} + 6CN^-$	1×10^{-42}	10^{-42}
FeF_5^{--}	$= Fe^{+++} + 5F^-$	5×10^{-16}	$10^{-15.3}$
$FeCNS^{++}$	$= Fe^{+++} + CNS^-$	1×10^{-3}	10^{-3}
$Fe(CNS)_3$	$= Fe^{+++} + 3CNS^-$	3×10^{-6}	$10^{-5.5}$
$Fe(CNS)_6^{---}$	$= Fe^{+++} + 6CNS^-$	8×10^{-10}	$10^{-9.1}$
$PbCl_3^-$	$= Pb^{++} + 3Cl^-$	4.2×10^{-2}	$10^{-1.4}$
PbI_3^-	$= Pb^{++} + 3I^-$	3.6×10^{-6}	$10^{-5.4}$
$Mn(C_2O_4)^+$	$= Mn^{+++} + C_2O_4^{--}$	1×10^{-10}	10^{-10}
$Mn(C_2O_4)_2^-$	$= Mn^{+++} + 2C_2O_4^{--}$	2.5×10^{-17}	$10^{-16.6}$
$Mn(C_2O_4)_3^{---}$	$= Mn^{+++} + 3C_2O_4^{--}$	7×10^{-20}	$10^{-19.2}$
$Hg(CN)_4^{--}$	$= Hg^{++} + 4CN^-$	4×10^{-42}	$10^{-41.4}$
HgI_4^{--}	$= Hg^{++} + 4I^-$	5×10^{-31}	$10^{-30.3}$
$HgBr_4^{--}$	$= Hg^{++} + 4Br^-$	2.3×10^{-22}	$10^{-21.7}$
$HgCl_4^{--}$	$= Hg^{++} + 4Cl^-$	1×10^{-16}	10^{-16}
$Hg(CNS)_4^{--}$	$= Hg^{++} + 4CNS^-$	5×10^{-20}	$10^{-19.3}$
$Ni(NH_3)_4^{++}$	$= Ni^{++} + 4NH_3$	1×10^{-8}	10^{-8}
$Ni(NH_3)_6^{++}$	$= Ni^{++} + 6NH_3$	1.8×10^{-9}	$10^{-8.7}$
$Ni(CN)_4^{--}$	$= Ni^{++} + 4CN^-$	1×10^{-22}	10^{-22}
$Ag(SO_3)_2^{---}$	$= Ag^+ + 2SO_3^{--}$	2×10^{-9}	$10^{-8.7}$
$Ag(NH_3)_2^+$	$= Ag^+ + 2NH_3$	6×10^{-8}	$10^{-7.2}$
$Ag(S_2O_3)_2^{---}$	$= Ag^+ + 2S_2O_3^{--}$	6×10^{-14}	$10^{-13.2}$
$Ag(CN)_2^-$	$= Ag^+ + 2CN^-$	1.8×10^{-19}	$10^{-18.7}$
SnF_6^{--}	$= Sn^{++++} + 6F^-$	1×10^{-18}	10^{-18}
$Zn(NH_3)_4^{++}$	$= Zn^{++} + 4NH_3$	3.4×10^{-10}	$10^{-9.5}$
$Zn(CN)_4^{--}$	$= Zn^{++} + 4CN^-$	1×10^{-18}	10^{-18}

INDEX

INDEX

TABLES OF LOGARITHMS

ANSWERS TO PROBLEMS

FOUR–PLACE LOGARITHMS OF NUMBERS

LOGARITHMS

No.	0	1	2	3	4	5	6	7	8	9	1	2	3	4	5	6	7	8	9
10	0000	0043	0086	0128	0170	0212	0253	0294	0334	0374	4	8	12	17	21	25	29	33	37
11	0414	0453	0492	0531	0569	0607	0645	0682	0719	0755	4	8	11	15	19	23	26	30	34
12	0792	0828	0864	0899	0934	0969	1004	1038	1072	1106	3	7	10	14	17	21	24	28	31
13	1139	1173	1206	1239	1271	1303	1335	1367	1399	1430	3	6	10	13	16	19	23	26	29
14	1461	1492	1523	1553	1584	1614	1644	1673	1703	1732	3	6	9	12	15	18	21	24	27
15	1761	1790	1818	1847	1875	1903	1931	1959	1987	2014	3	6	8	11	14	17	20	22	25
16	2041	2068	2095	2122	2148	2175	2201	2227	2253	2279	3	5	8	11	13	16	18	21	24
17	2304	2330	2355	2380	2405	2430	2455	2480	2504	2529	2	5	7	10	12	15	17	20	22
18	2553	2577	2601	2625	2648	2672	2695	2718	2742	2765	2	5	7	9	12	14	16	19	21
19	2788	2810	2833	2856	2878	2900	2923	2945	2967	2989	2	4	7	9	11	13	16	18	20
20	3010	3032	3054	3075	3096	3118	3139	3160	3181	3201	2	4	6	8	10	13	15	17	19
21	3222	3243	3263	3284	3304	3324	3345	3365	3385	3404	2	4	6	8	11	12	14	16	18
22	3424	3444	3464	3483	3502	3522	3541	3560	3579	3598	2	4	6	8	10	12	14	15	17
23	3617	3636	3655	3674	3692	3711	3729	3747	3766	3784	2	4	6	7	9	11	13	15	17
24	3802	3820	3838	3856	3874	3892	3909	3927	3945	3962	2	4	5	7	9	11	12	14	16
25	3979	3997	4014	4031	4048	4065	4082	4099	4116	4133	2	3	5	7	9	10	12	14	15
26	4150	4166	4183	4200	4216	4232	4249	4265	4281	4298	2	3	5	7	8	10	11	13	15
27	4314	4330	4346	4362	4378	4393	4409	4425	4440	4456	2	3	5	6	8	9	11	13	14
28	4472	4487	4502	4518	4533	4548	4564	4579	4594	4609	2	3	5	6	8	9	11	12	14
29	4624	4639	4654	4669	4683	4698	4713	4728	4742	4757	1	3	4	6	7	9	10	12	13
30	4771	4786	4800	4814	4829	4843	4857	4871	4886	4900	1	3	4	6	7	9	10	11	13
31	4914	4928	4942	4955	4969	4983	4997	5011	5024	5038	1	3	4	6	7	8	10	11	12
32	5051	5065	5079	5092	5105	5119	5132	5145	5159	5172	1	3	4	5	7	8	9	11	12
33	5185	5198	5211	5224	5237	5250	5263	5276	5289	5302	1	3	4	5	6	8	9	10	12
34	5315	5328	5340	5353	5366	5378	5391	5403	5416	5428	1	3	4	5	6	8	9	10	11
35	5441	5453	5465	5478	5490	5502	5514	5527	5539	5551	1	2	4	5	6	7	9	10	11
36	5563	5575	5587	5599	5611	5623	5635	5647	5658	5670	1	2	4	5	6	7	8	10	11
37	5682	5694	5705	5717	5729	5740	5752	5763	5775	5786	1	2	3	5	6	7	8	9	10
38	5798	5809	5821	5832	5843	5855	5866	5877	5888	5899	1	2	3	5	6	7	8	9	10
39	5911	5922	5933	5944	5955	5966	5977	5988	5999	6010	1	2	3	4	5	7	8	9	10
40	6021	6031	6042	6053	6064	6075	6085	6096	6107	6117	1	2	3	4	5	6	8	9	10
41	6128	6138	6149	6160	6170	6180	6191	6201	6212	6222	1	2	3	4	5	6	7	8	9
42	6232	6243	6253	6263	6274	6284	6294	6304	6314	6325	1	2	3	4	5	6	7	8	9
43	6335	6345	6355	6365	6375	6386	6395	6405	6415	6425	1	2	3	4	5	6	7	8	9
44	6435	6444	6454	6464	6474	6484	6493	6503	6513	6522	1	2	3	4	5	6	7	8	9
45	6532	6542	6551	6561	6571	6580	6590	6599	6609	6618	1	2	3	4	5	6	7	8	9
46	6628	6637	6646	6656	6665	6675	6684	6693	6702	6712	1	2	3	4	5	6	7	7	8
47	6721	6730	6739	6749	6758	6767	6776	6785	6794	6803	1	2	3	4	5	5	6	7	8
48	6812	6821	6830	6839	6848	6857	6866	6875	6884	6893	1	2	3	4	4	5	6	7	8
49	6902	6911	6920	6928	6937	6946	6955	6964	6972	6981	1	2	3	4	4	5	6	7	8
50	6990	6998	7007	7016	7024	7033	7042	7050	7059	7067	1	2	3	3	4	5	6	7	8
51	7076	7084	7093	7101	7110	7118	7126	7135	7143	7152	1	2	3	3	4	5	6	7	8
52	7160	7168	7177	7185	7193	7202	7210	7218	7226	7235	1	2	2	3	4	5	6	7	7
53	7243	7251	7259	7267	7275	7284	7292	7300	7308	7316	1	2	2	3	4	5	6	6	7
54	7324	7332	7340	7348	7356	7364	7372	7380	7388	7396	1	2	2	3	4	5	6	6	7
	0	1	2	3	4	5	6	7	8	9	1	2	3	4	5	6	7	8	9

FOUR–PLACE LOGARITHMS OF NUMBERS

LOGARITHMS

No.	0	1	2	3	4	5	6	7	8	9	1	2	3	4	5	6	7	8	9
55	7404	7412	7419	7427	7435	7443	7451	7459	7466	7474	1	2	2	3	4	5	5	6	7
56	7482	7490	7497	7505	7513	7520	7528	7536	7543	7551	1	2	2	3	4	5	5	6	7
57	7559	7566	7574	7582	7589	7597	7604	7612	7619	7627	1	2	2	3	4	5	5	6	7
58	7634	7642	7649	7657	7664	7672	7679	7686	7694	7701	1	1	2	3	4	4	5	6	7
59	7709	7716	7723	7731	7738	7745	7752	7760	7767	7774	1	1	2	3	4	4	5	6	7
60	7782	7789	7796	7803	7810	7818	7825	7832	7839	7846	1	1	2	3	4	4	5	6	6
61	7853	7860	7868	7875	7882	7889	7896	7903	7910	7917	1	1	2	3	4	4	5	6	6
62	7924	7931	7938	7945	7952	7959	7966	7973	7980	7987	1	1	2	3	3	4	5	6	6
63	7993	8000	8007	8014	8021	8028	8035	8041	8048	8055	1	1	2	3	3	4	5	5	6
64	8062	8069	8075	8082	8089	8096	8102	8109	8116	8122	1	1	2	3	3	4	5	5	6
65	8129	8136	8142	8149	8156	8162	8169	8176	8182	8189	1	1	2	3	3	4	5	5	6
66	8195	8202	8209	8215	8222	8228	8235	8241	8248	8254	1	1	2	3	3	4	5	5	6
67	8261	8267	8274	8280	8287	8293	8299	8306	8312	8319	1	1	2	3	3	4	5	5	6
68	8325	8331	8338	8344	8351	8357	8363	8370	8376	8382	1	1	2	3	3	4	4	5	6
69	8388	8395	8401	8407	8414	8420	8426	8432	8439	8445	1	1	2	2	3	4	4	5	6
70	8451	8457	8463	8470	8476	8482	8488	8494	8500	8506	1	1	2	2	3	4	4	5	6
71	8513	8519	8525	8531	8537	8543	8549	8555	8561	8567	1	1	2	2	3	4	4	5	5
72	8573	8579	8585	8591	8597	8603	8609	8615	8621	8627	1	1	2	2	3	4	4	5	5
73	8633	8639	8645	8651	8657	8663	8669	8675	8681	8686	1	1	2	2	3	4	4	5	5
74	8692	8698	8704	8710	8716	8722	8727	8733	8739	8745	1	1	2	2	3	4	4	5	5
75	8751	8756	8762	8768	8774	8779	8785	8791	8797	8802	1	1	2	2	3	3	4	5	5
76	8808	8814	8820	8825	8831	8837	8842	8848	8854	8859	1	1	2	2	3	3	4	5	5
77	8865	8871	8876	8882	8887	8893	8899	8904	8910	8915	1	1	2	2	3	3	4	4	5
78	8921	8927	8932	8938	8943	8949	8954	8960	8965	8971	1	1	2	2	3	3	4	4	5
79	8976	8982	8987	8993	8998	9004	9009	9015	9020	9025	1	1	2	2	3	3	4	4	5
80	9031	9036	9042	9047	9053	9058	9063	9069	9074	9079	1	1	2	2	3	3	4	4	5
81	9085	9090	9096	9101	9106	9112	9117	9122	9128	9133	1	1	2	2	3	3	4	4	5
82	9138	9143	9149	9154	9159	9165	9170	9175	9180	9186	1	1	2	2	3	3	4	4	5
83	9191	9196	9201	9206	9212	9217	9222	9227	9232	9238	1	1	2	2	3	3	4	4	5
84	9243	9248	9253	9258	9263	9269	9274	9279	9284	9289	1	1	2	2	3	3	4	4	5
85	9294	9299	9304	9309	9315	9320	9325	9330	9335	9340	1	1	2	2	3	3	4	4	5
86	9345	9350	9355	9360	9365	9370	9375	9380	9385	9390	1	1	2	2	3	3	4	4	5
87	9395	9400	9405	9410	9415	9420	9425	9430	9435	9440	0	1	1	2	2	3	3	4	4
88	9445	9450	9455	9460	9465	9469	9474	9479	9484	9489	0	1	1	2	2	3	3	4	4
89	9494	9499	9504	9509	9513	9518	9523	9528	9533	9538	0	1	1	2	2	3	3	4	4
90	9542	9547	9552	9557	9562	9566	9571	9576	9581	9586	0	1	1	2	2	3	3	4	4
91	9590	9595	9600	9605	9609	9614	9619	9624	9628	9633	0	1	1	2	2	3	3	4	4
92	9638	9643	9647	9652	9657	9661	9666	9671	9675	9680	0	1	1	2	2	3	3	4	4
93	9685	9689	9694	9699	9703	9708	9713	9717	9722	9727	0	1	1	2	2	3	3	4	4
94	9731	9736	9741	9745	9750	9754	9759	9763	9768	9773	0	1	1	2	2	3	3	4	4
95	9777	9782	9786	9791	9795	9800	9805	9809	9814	9818	0	1	1	2	2	3	3	4	4
96	9823	9827	9832	9836	9841	9845	9850	9854	9859	9863	0	1	1	2	2	3	3	4	4
97	9868	9872	9877	9881	9886	9890	9894	9899	9903	9908	0	1	1	2	2	3	3	4	4
98	9912	9917	9921	9926	9930	9934	9939	9943	9948	9952	0	1	1	2	2	3	3	4	4
99	9956	9961	9965	9969	9974	9978	9983	9987	9991	9996	0	1	1	2	2	3	3	3	4
	0	1	2	3	4	5	6	7	8	9	1	2	3	4	5	6	7	8	9

ANSWERS TO PROBLEMS

CHAPTER 1. Pages 28–33.

(6) 1.37 M.

(7) 0.1 mole.

(8) 0.392 g.

(9) .0565 M.

(10) (a) 0.1 mole; (b) 0.1 M; (c) 0.2 M.

(11) (a) 3.15 g.; (b) 245.2 g.; (c) 5.30 g.; (d) 0.204 g.; (e) 13.0 g.

(12) (a) 1709 ml.; (b) 1176 ml.; (c) 368 ml.; (d) 310 ml.; (e) 40 ml.

(13) (a) 20 ml.; (b) 475 ml.; (c) 54 ml.; (d) 140 ml.; (e) 0.4 ml.

(14) 75 ml. 0.1 M $AgNO_3$ and 175 ml. water.

(15) 75 ml.

(16) 37.5 ml.

(17) 10 ml.

(18) 7.5 ml.

(19) (a) 17.4 M; (b) 6.15 M; (c) 13.15 M; (d) 4.72 M.

(20) 152 cm.

(21) (a) 92.8%; (b) 86.6%; (c) 89.6%; (d) 90.7%.

(22) 6.4 g.

(23) Fe_2O_3.

(24) 478.4 g.

(25) 6.6 g.

(26) 1398 lbs.

(27) 2 atoms; Cu_2S.

(28) Cr_2O_3.

(29) 19.9.

(30) 11.0 M.

(31) 9.1 ml.

(32) 58.9 ml.

(33) 200 ml. each of $AgNO_3$, $Pb(NO_3)_2$ and $Hg_2(NO_3)_2$ solutions.

(34) (a) $\rho_1 v_1^2/M = \rho_2 v_2^2/M$; $v_1^2/v_2^2 = \rho_2/\rho_1$; or $v_1/v_2 = \sqrt{\rho_2/\rho_1}$

$\rho_2/\rho_1 = 750/760 \times 273/311 = 0.866$

$v_1/v_2 = 0.93$; v_2 equals 215 miles per hour.

(b) $\rho_1 v^2/M_1 = \rho_2 v^2/M_2$ or $M_2/M_1 = \rho_2/\rho_1 = 0.866$

$M_2 = 86,600$ pounds.

(35) Smaller load on a humid day. The molecular weight of water

vapor is less than that of either oxygen or nitrogen. ρ is therefore smaller.

CHAPTER 3. Pages 67–69.

(2) 256 times faster.

(4) 16 times faster.

(11) 105.

(12) $K = 0.4$; (1) $d = 3$; (2) $d = 1.5$; (3) $a = 1.5$; (4) $a = 6$; (5) $b = 8$; (6) $b = 16$; (7) $d = 24$; (8) $d = 96$.

(13) (1) $\dfrac{(H^+)(CN^-)}{(HCN)} = K$; (2) $\dfrac{(NH_4^+)(OH^-)}{(NH_4OH)} = K$;

(3) $\dfrac{(H^+)^2(S^{--})}{(H_2S)} = K$; (4) $\dfrac{(Fe^{++})^2(Hg^{++})^2}{(Hg_2^{++})(Fe^{+++})^2} = K$;

(5) $\dfrac{(CO)(H_2O)}{(CO_2)(H_2)} = K$; (6) $\dfrac{(NO)^2(O_2)}{(NO_2)^2} = K$;

(7) $\dfrac{(NH_3)^2}{(N_2)(H_2)^3} = K$.

(17) Absorbed.

(18) More soluble.

CHAPTER 4. Pages 98–101.

(7) (a) 5; (b) 9; (c) 1; (d) 7.38; (e) 2.1.

(8) (a) $1.36 \times 10^{-3} M$; (b) $4.3 \times 10^{-4} M$; (c) $4.3 \times 10^{-3} M$; (d) $4.5 \times 10^{-6} M$; (e) $1.91 \times 10^{-3} M$; (f) $2 \times 10^{-3} M$; (g) $1.4 \times 10^{-4} M$; (h) $1 \times 10^{-2} M$; (i) $1.27 \times 10^{-6} M$; (j) $5.5 \times 10^{-5} M$.

(9) (a) $4.2 \times 10^{-3} M$; (b) $1.3 \times 10^{-3} M$; (c) $4.2 \times 10^{-4} M$; (d) $1.3 \times 10^{-4} M$; (e) $8.5 \times 10^{-4} M$; (f) $2.2 \times 10^{-3} M$; (g) $1.2 \times 10^{-2} M$; (h) $7.5 \times 10^{-3} M$; (i) $9.6 \times 10^{-7} M$.

(10) (a) 1.85×10^{-5}; (b) 1.84×10^{-5}; (c) 1.80×10^{-5}; (d) 1.80×10^{-5}; (e) 4.6×10^{-4}; (f) 4.2×10^{-10}; (g) 4.2×10^{-10}

(11) $8 \times 10^{-4} M$ each.

(12) $(H^+) = 2.5 \times 10^{-5} M$; $(Ac^-) = 2.4 \times 10^{-2} M$.

(13) (a) .068; (b) .0002; (c) .019; (d) .03; (e) .08.

(14) .074 M.

(15) $5.7 \times 10^{-4} M$.

(16) 0.72 M.

(17) 0.18 mole.

(18) $8.5 \times 10^{-6} M$.

(19) $1.2 \times 10^{-5} M$.

(20) (a) 1×10^{-5}; (b) $3.2 \times 10^{-4} M$; (c) .032; (d) $1 \times 10^{-5} M$.

(21) .011 M.

(22) .04 M.

(23) $5.5 \times 10^{-6} M$.

(24) $1.9 \times 10^{-6} M$.

(25) $9 \times 10^{-6} M$.

(26) .02 M.

(27) $2.6 \times 10^{-5} M$.

(28) $2.9 \times 10^{-5} M$.

(29) (a) 1; (b) 1.56; (c) 2.87; (d) 4.75.

(30) Condition necessary for correct answer is that

$$\frac{(Ac^-)}{(HAc)} = 0.185$$

(31) (a) One-half; (b) .05 M; (c) .05 M; (d) $1.8 \times 10^{-5} M$.

(32) First addition of NaOH: (a) one-tenth;   (b) .01 M;
(c) .09 M; (d) $1.67 \times 10^{-4} M$; (e) 3.78.

(33) (a) 10^{-4}; (b) 10^{-6}; (c) 10^{-7}; (d) 10^{-9}; (e) 10^{-10}.

CHAPTER 5. Pages 121–125.

(3) $1.67 \times 10^{-7} M$.

(14) (a) 2.8×10^{-10}; (b) 5×10^{-13}; (c) 8.5×10^{-17}; (d) 1.5×10^{-9};
(e) 1.83×10^{-12}; (f) 6.9×10^{-9}; (g) 7.9×10^{-10}.

(15) (a) 7.6×10^{-4} g. per 100 ml.;   (b) 7.9×10^{-4} g. per 100 ml.;
(c) 2.59×10^{-3} g. per 100 ml.; (d) 2.3×10^{-9} g. per 100 ml.;
(e) 0.104 g. per 100 ml.; (f) 1.6×10^{-2} g. per 100 ml.;
(g) 1.9×10^{-5} g. per 100 ml.;
(h) 1.69×10^{-6} g. per 100 ml.

(16) 2.1×10^{-9} mole per liter. 6.8×10^{-8} g. per 200 ml.

(17) 7.24×10^{-5} g. per 100 ml.

(18) (a) 0.30 g.; (b) 4×10^{-11} mole.

(19) (a) 2.8×10^{-9} mole; (b) 1.4×10^{-9} mole.

(20) (a) $5 \times 10^{-12} M$; (b) $4.3 \times 10^{-6} M$; (c) 8.5×10^{-14}.

(21) (a) $(Pb^{++}) = 1.25 \times 10^{-3} M$, $(I^-) = 2.5 \times 10^{-3} M$;
(c) 8×10^{-9}.

(22) (a) $3.6 \times 10^{-5} M$; (b) 4.6×10^{-3} g.

(23) 4.5×10^{-3} g. per 200 ml.

(24) $1 \times 10^{-4} M$.

(25) 1.16×10^{-4} g.

(26) 2.8×10^{-5}.

(27) $1 \times 10^{-3}\ M$; $1.8 \times 10^{-6}\ M$.

(28) (a) 3.8×10^{-7} g.; (b) 9.0×10^{-6} g.

(29) (a) 2.8×10^{-9} mole;   (b) 1.67×10^{-5} mole;
       (c) 1.67×10^{-5} mole;   (d) 2.8×10^{-9} mole;
       (e) 1.25×10^{-5} mole.

(30) 560.

(31) (a) $8.5 \times 10^{-16}\ M$;   (b) $2.8 \times 10^{-9}\ M$;   (c) AgI;
       (d) $3.0 \times 10^{-8}\ M$;   (e) $3 \times 10^{-5}\%$;   (f) 3.3×10^{6};
       (g) $5.6 \times 10^{-9}\ M$; $1.5 \times 10^{-8}\ M$;   (h) 3.3×10^{6}.

(32) (a) $8.5 \times 10^{-15}\ M$;   (b) $9.1 \times 10^{-4}\ M$;   (c) AgI;
       (d) $9.3 \times 10^{-14}\ M$;   (e) 1.1×10^{11};   (f) $1.29 \times 10^{-3}\ M$;
       (g) $6.6 \times 10^{-14}\ M$;   (h) 7.6×10^{10};

       (i) $\dfrac{(Pb^{++})^{\frac{1}{2}}}{(Ag^{+})} = 1.07 \times 10^{12}$;

       (j) Due to the fact that $\dfrac{(Pb^{++})^{\frac{1}{2}}}{(Ag^{+})}$ rather than $\dfrac{(Pb^{++})}{(Ag^{+})}$ is constant.

(33) 0.13 mole.

(34) .083 mole.

(35) 2.14 g. per 50 ml.

(36) 70.5 g.

(37) 22 moles per liter — impossible.

CHAPTER 6. Pages 143–146.

 (8) $5 \times 10^{-5}\ M$; No.

 (9) $(S^{--}) = 1.3 \times 10^{-13}\ M$; $(H^{+}) = 7.1 \times 10^{-5}\ M$.

(10) $(H^{+}) = 6.9 \times 10^{-4}\ M$.

(11) (a) $2.05 \times 10^{-4}\ M$;   (b) $6.5 \times 10^{-5}\ M$;   (c) $3.2 \times 10^{-5}\ M$;
       (d) $4.9 \times 10^{-6}\ M$; (e) $.016\ M$; (f) $.024\ M$; (g) $4.6 \times 10^{-2}\ M$.

(12) (a) $1.3 \times 10^{-13}\ M$;   (b) $1.3 \times 10^{-15}\ M$;   (c) $1.3 \times 10^{-17}\ M$;
       (d) $1.3 \times 10^{-19}\ M$;   (e) $1.3 \times 10^{-21}\ M$.

(14) (a) $0.3\ M$; (b) $1.44 \times 10^{-20}\ M$; (c) Yes; (d) No.

(15) $(Cd^{++}) = 6 \times 10^{-8}\ M$.

(16) 3.6×10^{-7} mole Pb^{++} ion per 100 ml.

(17) (a) $5 \times 10^{-33}\ M$;   (b) $1.7 \times 10^{-22}\ M$;   (c) $1.3 \times 10^{-17}\ M$;
       (d) $4 \times 10^{-47}\ M$;   (e) $1.3 \times 10^{-23}\ M$.

(18) $(H^{+}) < 2.4 \times 10^{-3}\ M$.

(19) $(S^{--}) = 7 \times 10^{-16}\ M$.

(20) (a) $1.6 \times 10^{-2}\ M$; (b) $1.6 \times 10^{-2}\ M$; (c) $6.2 \times 10^{-8}\ M$;
  (d) about $4 \times 10^{-18}\ M$.

(21) 7.2×10^{-16} mole Cu^{++} per 200 ml.; 1.1×10^{-6} mole Cd^{++}
  per 200 ml.

(22) $(H^+) = 1.1 \times 10^{-2}\ M$.

(23) $(H^+) = 5.7 \times 10^5\ M$, impossible.

(24) $(H^+) = 1.26 \times 10^{-2}\ M$.

CHAPTER 7. Pages 187–189.

(15) (a) 5.5×10^{-10}; (b) 5.4×10^{-10}; (c) 2×10^{-11};
  (d) 1.5×10^{-10}; (e) 2.5×10^{-5}; (f) 1×10^{-4};
  (g) 2.2×10^{-11}; (h) 4.8×10^{-11}; (i) 1.3×10^{-11};
  (j) 7×10^{-10}.

(16) (*A*) *0.1 M solutions:*
  (a) $7.4 \times 10^{-6}\ M$; (b) $1.3 \times 10^{-9}\ M$; (c) $1.4 \times 10^{-6}\ M$;
  (d) $2.6 \times 10^{-9}\ M$; (e) $6.3 \times 10^{-12}\ M$; (f) $3.2 \times 10^{-12}\ M$;
  (g) $4.8 \times 10^{-9}\ M$; (h) $4.6 \times 10^{-9}\ M$; (i) $1.1 \times 10^{-6}\ M$;
  (j) $1.2 \times 10^{-9}\ M$.
  (*B*) *.01 M solutions:*
  (a) $2.3 \times 10^{-6}\ M$; (b) $4.3 \times 10^{-9}\ M$; (c) $4.5 \times 10^{-7}\ M$;
  (d) $8.1 \times 10^{-9}\ M$; (e) $2 \times 10^{-11}\ M$; (f) $1 \times 10^{-11}\ M$;
  (g) $1.5 \times 10^{-8}\ M$; (h) $1.4 \times 10^{-8}\ M$; (i) $3.6 \times 10^{-7}\ M$;
  (j) $3.8 \times 10^{-9}\ M$.

(17) (*A*) *0.1 M solutions:*
  (a) 5.13; (b) 8.89; **(c)** 5.85; (d) 8.58; (e) 11.19;
  (f) 11.50; (g) 8.17; (h) 8.34; (i) 2.96; (j) 8.92.
  (*B*) *.01 M solutions:*
  (a) 5.64; (b) 8.38; (c) 6.35; (d) 8.09; (e) 10.70;
  (f) 11.0; (g) 7.68; (h) 7.85; (i) 2.44; (j) 8.42.

(18) (*A*) *0.1 M solutions:*
  (a) 7.4×10^{-5}; (b) 7.3×10^{-5}; (c) 1.4×10^{-5};
  (d) 1.2×10^{-4}; (e) 1.6×10^{-2}; (f) 3.2×10^{-2};
  (g) 1.5×10^{-5}; (h) 2.2×10^{-5}; (i) 2×10^{-5};
  (j) 8.5×10^{-5}.
  (*B*) *.01 M solutions:*
  (a) 2.3×10^{-4}; (b) 2.3×10^{-4}; (c) 4.4×10^{-5};
  (d) 3.8×10^{-4}; (e) 5.2×10^{-2}; (f) 0.1;
  (g) 4.7×10^{-5}; (h) 7×10^{-5}; (i) 6.3×10^{-5};
  (j) 2.7×10^{-4}.

(19) 15.2 g.

(20) 10.7 g.

(21) .08 mole.

(22) $1.85 \times 10^{-5} M$.

(23) $2.3 \times 10^{-5} M$.

(24) 4×10^{-10}.

(25) Impossible — 525 M.

(26) (a) 2.1×10^{-4}; (b) 2.2×10^{-12}; (c) 4.6×10^{-2}.

(27) 0.33 M.

(28) The value of $(Fe^{++})(S^{--})$ divided by the value of $(Fe^{++})(OH^-)^2$ gives $\dfrac{(S^{--})}{(OH^-)^2} = 2 \times 10^{-2}$. For the FeS to precipitate first, the value of this ratio must exceed the above. For $Fe(OH)_2$ to precipitate first, the value of this ratio in the solution must be less than the above. For any solution of Na_2S this ratio can be shown to be equal to 13. Therefore, the FeS precipitates first.

(29) (a) $5.3 \times 10^{-6} M$;   (b) $1 \times 10^{-7} M$;   (c) .018 M;
     (d) $4.3 \times 10^{-9} M$;   (e) $1.6 \times 10^{-13} M$.

(30) $(CO_3^{--}) = 1.1 \times 10^{-4} M$; $(OH^-) = 2.2 \times 10^{-6} M$.

(31) $MgCO_3$. For $MgCO_3$ to precipitate first, the ratio $\dfrac{(CO_3^{--})}{(OH^-)^2}$ must be greater than 4.5×10^6. In this solution, the ratio has a value of 2.2×10^8.

(32) (A) *Neglecting Hydrolysis:* (a) $7.8 \times 10^{-14} M$; (b) $2 \times 10^{-18} M$; (c) $2 \times 10^{-13} M$; (d) $1.3 \times 10^{-17} M$; (e) $2.2 \times 10^{-11} M$.

     (B) *With Hydrolysis:* (a) $6.8 \times 10^{-11} M$; (b) $1.8 \times 10^{-15} M$; (c) $1.8 \times 10^{-10} M$; (d) $2.5 \times 10^{-15} M$; (e) $1.9 \times 10^{-8} M$.

(33) $\dfrac{(Ac^-)}{(HAc)} = 1.85$.

(34) $1.6 \times 10^{-6} M$.

(35) $\dfrac{(HPO_4^{--})}{(H_2PO_4^-)} =$ (a) .062; (b) 0.62; (c) 6.2.

CHAPTER 8. Pages 213–214.

(9) AgCl precipitates.

(10) Yes.

(11) $2.6 \times 10^{-10} M$.

(12) For $Ag(CN)_2^-$, $(Ag^+) = 3.6 \times 10^{-7} M$.
     For $Ag(NH_3)_2^+$, $(Ag^+) = 9.4 \times 10^{-9} M$.

(13) No.

(14) No.

(15) 1.97 g. per 100 ml.

(16) $9.1 \times 10^{-4} M$.

(17) $6.9 \times 10^{-7} M$.

(18) $1.32 \times 10^{-4} M$.

(19) $1.7 \times 10^{-3} M$.

(20) (a) $Cd(NH_3)_4Cl_2$ solution; (b) 250.

(21) $(Cu^+) = 1.9 \times 10^{-19} M$; $(Cd^{++}) = 9.6 \times 10^{-12} M$.

(22) (a) $Ag(CN)_2^-$ ion first formed; later AgCl precipitates;
     (b) $.05 M$; (c) $(Cl^-) = 0.1 M$; $(Ag^+) = 2.8 \times 10^{-9} M$;
     $(CN^-) = 1.8 \times 10^{-6} M$.

CHAPTER 9. Pages 229–230.

(14) .034 mole.

(15) $(Zn^{++}) = 2.3 \times 10^{-6} M$; $(ZnO_2^{--}) = 2 \times 10^{-12} M$;
     $(H^+) = 2.2 \times 10^{-9} M$; $(OH^-) = 4.6 \times 10^{-6} M$.

(16) $(Zn^{++}) = 5 \times 10^{-13} M$; $(ZnO_2^{--}) = 1 \times 10^{-5} M$.

(17) $(Pb^{++}) = 4 \times 10^{-13} M$; $(HPbO_2^-) = 2 \times 10^{-3} M$;
     $(H^+) = 1 \times 10^{-13} M$.

(18) No.

(19) $(OH^-) = 2.5 \times 10^{-4} M$.

(21) $(Cu^{++}) = 1.6 \times 10^{-17} M$; $(HCuO_2^-) = 1.5 \times 10^{-3} M$;
     $(CuO_2^{--}) = 1.2 \times 10^{-3} M$.

MATHEMATICAL OPERATIONS. Pages 349–352.

(1) (a) 10^6; (b) 4×10^5; (c) 5×10^4; (d) 9×10^3;
    (e) 6×10^2; (f) 7×10^1; (g) 1.45×10^6; (h) 9.46×10^5;
    (i) 5.9×10^4; (j) 9.627×10^3; (k) 4.5×10^2;
    (l) 5.632×10^5; (m) 10^{-2}; (n) 3.2×10^{-3}; (o) 7×10^{-6};
    (p) 1.07×10^{-3}; (q) 9×10^{-10}; (r) 6.78×10^{-6};
    (s) 1.03×10^{-1}; (u) 1×10^{-1}; (v) 4.5×10^{-4};
    (w) 6×10^{-6}.

(2) (a) 1.26×10^9; (b) 5×10^3; (c) 6.06×10^{17};
    (d) 2.8×10^{-6}; (e) 5×10^{-4}; (f) 10^{-1}; (g) 7×10^4;
    (h) 3×10^8; (i) 6.25; (j) 1.8×10^{-7}; (k) 5×10^2.

(3) (a) 5×10; (b) 10^7; (c) $3.2 \times 10 = 32$; (d) 3×10^{-1};
    (e) 4.5×10^{-5}; (f) $2 \times 10 = 20$; (g) 5×10^9;
    (h) 6×10^{-12}; (i) 2×10^{-12}; (j) 5×10^{-1}; (k) 3.2×10^{-1};
    (l) 5×10^{13}; (m) 2×10^{-8}; (n) 5×10^{-2}.

(4) (a) 1885; (b) 16.5; (c) 16.45; (d) 3×10^{-4}; (e) $X = 10^{-4}$.

(5) (a) 3.33372; (b) 2.5315; (c) .0149; (d) $\bar{6}.826$ (or -5.174);
(e) 1.8277; (f) $\bar{1}.5877$ (or $-.4123$); (g) $\bar{3}.6$ (or -2.4);
(h) 2.602.

(6) (a) 4726; (b) 273.0; (c) 1.939; (d) .2226; (e) .0002905;
(f) .0001861; (g) .004337; (h) .5302.

(7) (a) $V = 310$; (b) $N = 3.56 \times 10^{22}$; (c) $M = 367$;
(d) $X = 3.1 \times 10^{-4}$.

(8) (a) 6.45×10^{10}; (b) 1.30×10^{-7}; (c) 1.73×10^{-9};
(d) 5.3×10^{14}; (e) 5.7×10^{14}.

(9) (a) 2×10^{-3}; (b) 4×10^{-6}; (c) 6×10^{4}; (d) 5×10^{-3};
(e) 1.58×10^{-2}; (f) 83.32; (g) 1.578×10^{-3}; (h) 1.20×10^{-7}.

(10) (a) (imaginary); (b) $+1.52 - 1.67$;
(c) $18.5 \times 10^{-4}, -19.5 \times 10^{-4}$; (d) $\pm 1.34 \times 10^{-3}$.

(11) (a) 4; (b) 11.70; (c) 5.46; (d) 7; (e) 4.59; (f) .871.

(12) (a) 10^{-7}; (b) 4×10^{-9}; (c) 5.0×10^{-6}; (d) 1.35×10^{-7};
(e) 5.62×10^{-10}; (f) 3.47×10^{-3}.

(13) (a) $P = \dfrac{K}{V}$; (b) $V = KT$; (c) $P = KT$; (d) $S = \dfrac{K}{\sqrt{m}}$;

(e) $F = \dfrac{K(m_1 \times m_2)}{d^2}$.

(14) (a) g. cm.$^{-3}$; (b) sec.$^{-1}$; (c) g. cm.^{2} sec.$^{-3}$.

(15) (g. cm.^{2} sec.$^{-3}$) does not equal (g. cm.^{2} sec.$^{-2}$).